Caribbean

Seashells

A guide to the Marine Mollusks of Puerto Rico and other West Indian Islands, Bermuda and the Lower Florida Keys

by

GERMAINE L. WARMKE, M. S.
INSTITUTE OF MARINE BIOLOGY,
UNIVERSITY OF PUERTO RICO

R. TUCKER ABBOTT, Ph.D.
PILSBRY CHAIR OF MALACOLOGY
ACADEMY OF NATURAL SCIENCES OF PHILADELPHIA

DOVER PUBLICATIONS, INC.
NEW YORK

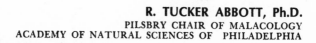

Published in Canada by General Publishing Company, Ltd., 30 Lesmill Road, Don Mills, Toronto, Ontario.
Published in the United Kingdom by Constable and Company, Ltd., 10 Orange Street, London WC 2.

This Dover edition, first published in 1975, is an unabridged republication of the fourth printing of the work originally published in 1961. It is reprinted by special arrangement with the original publisher, Livingston Publishing Company, 18 Hampstead Circle, Wynnewood, Pennsylvania 19096.

International Standard Book Number: 0-486-21359-5
Library of Congress Catalog Card Number: 74-20443

Manufactured in the United States of America
Dover Publications, Inc.
180 Varick Street
New York, N.Y. 10014

Foreword

Since the appearance of *American Seashells** in 1954, it has become increasingly evident that a West Indian supplement was much needed to satisfy the growing interest in tropical American marine shells. No area within a few hours of the United States has attracted so many naturalists and shell collectors as has the Caribbean. Yet, no manual existed that could fulfill the need for ready identification of West Indian shells or serve as a shell-travellers' guide for the many thousands now venturing into the Antilles, Bermuda and the Bahamas.

Quite independently, the authors of this book sought to fill this need, and before long, joined forces to bring this handbook into being. The combination of effort could not have been more ideal — one of us was very familiar with molluscan habitats and local conditions in the field and had ready access to photographic facilities, while the other had study collections and a great conchological library at hand, as well as experience in guiding the production of a new book.

The emphasis in this book is, of course, on the marine mollusks of Puerto Rico, for the senior author has spent a large part of the last ten years in collecting and dredging in the vicinity of the Institute of Marine

---

American Seashells by R. Tucker Abbott, 2nd (1974) ed., Van Nostrand Reinhold Co., $49.50.

Biology at Mayagüez. Because Puerto Rico stands at the zoological cross-roads of the West Indies, its fauna is a mixture of most of the elements of the tropical Western Atlantic — hence, this is as much a book about Caribbean shells as it is a near-complete census of the marine mollusks of Puerto Rico.

Acknowledgments

We wish to thank a number of persons who greatly aided us in collecting specimens and in preparing this book. For technical, malacological assistance: Dr. Myra Keen of Stanford University, Dr. William J. Clench and Dr. Ruth D. Turner of the Museum of Comparative Zoölogy at Harvard College, Dr. Harald A. Rehder of the United States National Museum, Mr. Gilbert Grau of California, and Dr. Robert Robertson of the Academy of Natural Sciences of Philadelphia. For assistance in field work and in obtaining unusual specimens: Dr. Juan A. and Eneida Rivero, the late Dr. N. T. Mattox, Al and Margaret Hayes, Kayo and Amy Phares, Jorge Rivera López, Donald Erdman, Ted and Lois Arnow, and a host of other shell enthusiasts. For manuscript, art and photographic help we are indebted to Dr. Harry E. Warmke, Joseph Morsello (color photography), Sally D. Kaicher (habitat drawings), Grenville F. Wilcox (maps), Virginia Orr, Laura Ellen Roark and Christine Boyce.

Our special gratitude is due the Institute of Marine Biology of the University of Puerto Rico which has officially encouraged and supported this and other scientific publications of importance to Puerto Rico and the natural sciences.

Note to the Dover Edition

Since it has not been feasible to revise the text for this reprint edition, the reader is asked to bear in mind that the information in Chapters I and II pertaining to such matters as the political situation, the availability and prices of books and periodicals, the addresses and stocks of shops and miscellaneous suppliers, transportation schedules and prices, and so forth, dates from about 1960. Although many of the references are still basically valid, persons planning to visit the Caribbean area will want to supplement this information with up-to-date data from one or more of the following sources:

Caribbean Travel Association
20 East 46th Street
New York City 10017
Telephone: (212) 682-0435

Antigua Barbuda Information Office
101 Park Avenue
New York City 10017
Telephone: (212) 683-1075

Aruba Information Center
576 Fifth Avenue
New York City 10036
Telephone: (212) 246-3030

Bahama Islands Tourist Office
30 Rockefeller Plaza
New York City 10020
Telephone: (212) 757-1611

Barbados Tourist Board
800 Second Avenue
New York City 10017
Telephone: (212) 986-6516

Bermuda Government Official Travel
Information Office
610 Fifth Avenue
New York City 10020
Telephone: (212) 246-6053

Curacao Tourist Board
604 Madison Avenue
New York City 10022
Telephone: (212) 265-0230

Dominican Republic Tourist and
Information Center
64 West 50th Street
New York City 10022
Telephone: (212) 581-2116

Haiti Government Tourist Bureau
30 Rockefeller Plaza
New York City 10020
Telephone: (212) PL 7-3517

Jamaica Information and
Booking Center
420 Madison Avenue
New York City 10017
Telephone: (212) 688-5686

Trinidad and Tobago Tourist Board
400 Madison Avenue
New York City 10017
Telephone: (212) 838-7750

Virgin Islands Government
Tourist Office
16 West 49th Street
New York City 10020
Telephone: (212) JU 2-4520

Contents

List of Plates

PLATE

PLATE

(all illustrated specimens are from Puerto Rico)

A Caribbean Library

TRAVEL GUIDES

Butler, Paul: *Butler's Caribbean and Central America,* D. Van Nostrand Co., Inc., 1960

Clark, Sydney: *All the Best in the Caribbean,* Dodd, Mead and Co.. Inc., 1959

Fodor, Eugene, editor: *Fodor's Guide to the Caribbean, the Bahamas, and Bermuda,* David McKay Co., Inc., 1962

Hancock, Ralph: *Puerto Rico—A Travel Guide,* D. Van Nostrand Co.. Inc., 1962

Martin, Lawrence and Sylvia: *Standard Guide to the Caribbean,* Funk and Wagnalls Co., 1962

Marvel, Evalyn: *Guide to Puerto Rico and the Virgin Islands,* Crown Publishers, 1961

Smith, Bradley: *Escape to the West Indies,* Alfred A. Knopf, Inc., 1961

Wilhelm, John: *John Wilhelm's Guide to the Caribbean,* McGraw-Hill Book Co., 1960

NATURAL HISTORY REFERENCE BOOKS

Allen, Robert: *Birds of the Caribbean,* Viking Press, Inc., 1961

Bond, James: *Birds of the West Indies,* Houghton Mifflin Co., 1961

Frey, Hans: *Dictionary of Tropical Fishes,* T. F. H. Publications, 1961

Hargreaves, Dorothy and Bob: *Tropical Blossoms of the Caribbean,* Hargreave Industrial Co., 1960

Herklots, G.A.C.: *Birds of Trinidad and Tobago,* Wm. Collins Sons & Co., Ltd., 1961

Junge and Mees: *Avifauna of Trinidad and Tobago,* E. J. Brill, Leyden, The Netherlands

Little, E. L. Jr., and Wadsworth, F. H.: *Common Trees of Puerto Rico and the Virgin Islands,* (in preparation)

McCandless, James B., M.D.: *A Field Guide to the Birds of Puerto Rico,* Mayagüez, Puerto Rico, 1958

Menninger, Edwin A.: *Flowering Trees of the World for Tropics and Warm Climates,* The Hearthside Press, 1961

Pertchik, B. and H.: *Flowering Trees of the Caribbean,* Holt, Rinehart and Winston, Inc., 1959

Seaman, George: *Amphibians of the Virgin Islands,* St. Croix, U.S.V.I.

Taylor, Lady: *Introduction to the Birds of Jamaica,* MacMillan and Co., Ltd., 1955.

Women's Garden Clubs of Havana: *Flowering Plants from Cuban Gardens,* Criterion Books, Inc., 1958

The list above is not intended to be complete. The serious biologist will find many other publications (some out of print) in the library. Bird students will find the Field Check Lists published by the Florida Audubon Society of great help. They may be obtained for 5¢ each from P.O. Box 825, Maitland, Florida. Cards have been published for Trinidad and Tobago, Hispaniola, Jamaica, Puerto Rico, and (on one card) Aruba, Curacao, and Bonaire. A card for the American Virgin Islands may be ordered from G. A. Seaman, Christiansted, St. Croix, U.S.V.I.

CARIBBEAN

SEASHELLS

TEXT FIG. 1. A rocky shoreline in Puerto Rico with Periwinkles and Nerites above the water line and Chitons, Keyhole Limpets and Purpura submerged in the tidepool.

CHAPTER I

Guide to Shelling
in the Caribbean

A conchological revolution is taking place in one of the richest shell-collecting areas in the world. The recent influx of tourists into the West Indies has improved tenfold the transportation facilities, lodgings and living conditions throughout the Caribbean. Only a decade ago, many remote islands and isolated reefs were accessible only to those shell collectors who were willing to pitch a tent, eat out of tin cans and undertake uncomfortable schooner or bus rides. Today, planes fly into almost every island that is large enough to have a runway. Modern, air-conditioned inns and motels are located on every island that can lay claim to attractive beaches, good fishing or pleasant scenery. In an increasing number of places it is possible to rent drive-yourself cars and diving gear, and even hire shell guides.

Because most of the Puerto Rican marine shells are also found elsewhere in the Caribbean, this book will serve the exploring conchologist in any area of the tropical Western Atlantic — from Bermuda to Panama; from Yucatan, Mexico, to Trinidad and Brazil. Yet, each group of islands has its own endemic forms of shells, an intriguing zoological fact which lures the shell collectors into island-hopping explorations.

This guide is not intended to be complete, at least in this first edition, but from it travelling conchologists will be able to plan their Caribbean collecting trips with a little more intelligence than might be possible by consulting the standard tourist guides. Conchologists and naturalists are not mainly concerned with dance-floor facilities, historic shrines or rules of proper dinner dress.

Conchological excursions into the Caribbean may be undertaken under a variety of conditions (smooth or rough), varying lengths of time

3

(a weekend flight to Bimini or Puerto Rico or a year of island-hopping), and by any type of collector (novice or expert; 18- or 80-year old). Even part-time collecting, if the best ports are chosen, can be combined successfully with a pleasure cruise. Whatever kind of shelling trip you plan, there are certain basic, and obvious, rules to be followed. First, consult a travel agency or recently returning travellers about the latest living and political conditions. Secondly, plan your collecting trip within the limits of your budget, your collecting equipment, and the available facilities for cleaning and caring for your collection. Improper preparation, no matter how simple your plans, can turn a potentially successful collecting trip into a chaos of smelly shells, abandoned collections and short tempers.

The increasing popularity of the West Indies has been reflected in a constantly growing number of reliable travel books. Many of these are revised frequently, some annually. A partial list of these reference books will be found on page 329.

Some modern guides in various branches of natural history are making their appearance and, as travel increases in the Caribbean area, it is expected that more books will appear. A few of these titles are also listed on page 329.

THE SHELL COLLECTOR IN THE CARIBBEAN

On the whole, the islands of the Caribbean are healthful and the waters safe for collecting and skin diving. In Bermuda, Nassau and the leading cities of the other islands, health conditions and drinking water are as safe as in Miami, Florida. But for trips to outlying islands or stay-overs in smaller towns, it is recommended that you have typhoid shots in addition to the *required* smallpox vaccination. In some islands it is not safe to drink unboiled water or milk. Remember, you will be in the tropics where too much fruit and rum can cause diarrhea. Those intending to dredge should take seasickness pills recommended by a physician. A small first-aid kit and sunburn lotion inevitably come in useful to the over-zealous collector. Mosquito lotion (such as "OFF" or "6-12") and sunglasses should be taken.

Never collect or swim barefooted, nor collect at night or on an off-shore reef without a companion. Pamper your feet; wear socks under your sneakers or canvass shoes if your feet have not been toughened, for there is nothing that will bring collecting to an absolute halt quicker than painful or infected blisters. Obituaries of divers using compressed air equipment usually read: "He went diving alone", "He trained himself to use the gear", or "He teased a shark once too often." If you have not taken a training course in this type of diving, stick to a face mask and shallow water. There are no known venomous mollusks in the Caribbean, and all are edible, although not all necessarily palatable. The

Long-spined Purple Sea-urchin is poisonous to the touch, and skin-breaks from the shorter-spined species, as well as corals, can sometimes result in secondary infection if the wounds are not immediately washed, sterilized and bandaged. The Portuguese Man-o'-war (the "jellyfish" with the purple float) and a very few sponges and corals can cause painful, but not dangerous nor long-lasting stings. Medical facilities and good physicians are available on all of the main and many of the small islands.

An inexpensive and illustrated booklet entitled "Sea Pests" by C. Phillips and W. H. Brady (1953) may be obtained by writing to The Marine Laboratory, University of Miami, Florida.

COLLECTING EQUIPMENT

Those who fly to their main destination are naturally limited in the amount of collecting gear they can take with them. This can be solved in three ways: shipping in advance; obtaining equipment and supplies in the islands; or taking especially light, folding gear. In the first instance, arrangements should be made many weeks in advance with the manager of your lodgings and with a shipping firm. In an emergency, gear can be expensively air-freighted. Pails, jars, screens, rope, crowbars, shipping crates, packing material, etc. can be purchased at main cities, although not as cheaply as in the United States. Among the recommended items to take with you on the plane are swim suits, sneakers (preferably "broken in"), a tried-and-found-true face mask (snorkel optional), mosquito lotion, notebook, labels, charts, pencils, a few cloth collecting bags (about 7 by 18 inches and with draw-strings), and a copy of "How to Collect Shells" (obtainable for $2.00 from the "Secretary, American Malacological Union, Box 318, Marinette, Wisconsin"). Some collectors have built folding dredge frames and folding glass-bottomed buckets to take on the plane. Upon arrival, the former will need extra iron weights and the latter a putty or plastic sealer.

TIMING YOUR TRIP

The so-called "cool, breezy" season for tourists is usually the poorest for shell collecting. That zephyr, extolled in travel pamphlets, can make the water too rough for collecting, except on the lee side of an island. May to September is usually best, despite the chance of rain. There is usually ample radio warning of hurricanes which are apt to occur from July to late September, but between these infrequent storms the weather is usually calm. Most species breed in the summer, and at that time many congregate in colonies to lay their eggs.

It is best to limit your collecting to one island and to set up headquarters at one place where cleaning facilities are good. Little real success can be had in a strange region within a week. It may take one to two days to get settled and arrange for transportation or guides; another few days to locate the best collecting grounds; at least two days to clean up, pack and, if necessary, arrange for mailing or shipping home your loot. A two week's stay will give you a fair sampling of the shells in the area; four to six weeks, with a week of dredging, will net you about 60% of the species (from 100 to 300). If you have an opportunity to re-visit the same island another year, try to choose another part of the year, since some species are seasonally abundant.

Cleaning and Packing

Unless you have your own boat or will be in one spot for several weeks or months, the greatest problem is cleaning your live-collected specimens. Boiling the live shells in water for five or ten minutes and extracting the "meat" with a bent pin or curved probe is the simplest method. The fancier the hotel, the less likely you are to get sympathetic assistance or facilities for boiling and laying out your shells to dry in the sun. Wrap your dried shells (*with their proper locality labels*) in newspaper and pack them in cardboard cartons. If you mail them, indicate that they are "seashells for study; no commercial value." It is against U. S. Federal laws to send or bring home live snails. Larger shipments may be crated and shipped via surface vessel.

Numerous, small, live shells, especially those obtained from the dredge and screens, may be preserved in 70 percent alcohol (sugar alcohol made in the West Indies is usually cheap), allowed to soak for a few days, then dried in the sun and finally wrapped in newspaper. They may also be transferred while still wet into plastic bags. Drain out most of the alcohol, heat-seal the end, and wrap in newspaper. Do not use formalin unless you add a buffer, such as a tablespoon of borax to each quart. In an emergency, live snails may be killed in pure table salt or crude sea salt, mailed in plastic bags, and cleaned later. Remember to keep the locality data inside every package!

BERMUDA

Statistics — On the east side of the Gulf Stream, off North Carolina, and about 700 miles southeast of New York. 28 miles in length; 9 principal islands. British Crown Colony. Moderately expensive. Health conditions excellent. Best shelling from June to late September. Access by air (3 hours) or ship (40 hours). Consult: "Beautiful Bermuda" by Euphemia Y. Bell and Associates, 10th or later editions, 1947, 736 pages.

Bermuda has a very interesting shell fauna, although, because of its cool winter-time water, it cannot compare in richness with that of the

West Indies. About 400 species occur around the islands, and there are several dozen endemic species and subspecies of land mollusks. The scallop, *Pecten ziczac*, is unusually large and common in Little Sound; the rare "albino" form is not uncommon. Collecting is generally poor in Hamilton Harbour, but some gravelly beaches on the south side have colorful *Asaphis deflorata*, and the mangrove areas at the "Foot-of-the-lane" have abundant *Nitidella*. Collecting is better on the small islands, such as Agar's Island where there used to be a biological station. Nearby Fairyland, reached by taxi or bus, is fairly good at low tide. The North Shore is good only for the rock-dwellers, but Bailey's Bay is excellent for dredging. Castle Harbour is moderately good along the shores of Tucker's Town and the Causeway. Deep dredging from a larger boat off Castle and Nonsuch Islands is good, but the sea is apt to be rough. Along the South Shore there are several profitable, sheltered bays. Hungry Bay, not far from Hamilton, is sometimes good. Devonshire Bay is good. Pink Beach is fair for beach drift, but the unusual, tiny, pink *Synaptoco-chlea picta* is abundant! Somerset is one of the best shelling areas. If you headquarter at the excellent Cambridge Beaches on Mangrove Bay, you can reach a variety of habitats. The clam, *Heterodonax bimaculata*, living in the sand beaches on the west side of King's Point is huge and exceedingly beautiful. The reef shallows several miles west of Somerset, reached only by boat, are good for scuba diving. The peculiar Bermuda form of *Strombus gigas* is abundant and, occasionally, *Charonia variegata* and huge *Pinna* are found.

There are two good shell shops, both operated by Mr. Ted Nielsen who is most cooperative. One is on East Broadway Street in Hamilton, the other on South Shore Road in Paget. Jeanne and Park Breck (phone 2391) are experienced skin divers who will take you diving for shells at a reasonable price. The Bermuda Government Aquarium at the Flatts has a shell exhibit, and collecting nearby is fairly good if you can get out to Gibbet or to Trunk Island. The Bermuda Biological Station is located near the Swing Bridge, opposite Kindley Air Field, in St. George's Parish. Conchologists will get useful information here.

BAHAMA ISLANDS

Statistics — Located east of Florida and north of Cuba and consisting of about 20 inhabited and 2,000 minor islands. British Possession. Moderately expensive to inexpensive. Health conditions excellent. Best shell collecting in the summer and around the larger islands. Access by air from Miami or ship from New York or Miami. Charter boats numerous.

The Bahamas have a fairly rich Caribbean shell fauna, few endemic species, and a sprinkling of Florida species. The shallows of the Great

Bahama Bank are poor, but the littoral areas of New Providence (Nassau), Eleuthera and Grand Bahama Island are moderately rich. Many attractive species, such as *Tellina radiata,* the small *Lucina* and *Trivia,* are very abundant. Many small, choice species, such as *Typhis fordi,* can be collected at low tide at night north of Hog Island, opposite Nassau. The larger shells, such as *Xancus, Cassis* and *Strombus* are now only common at the "out islands." Motor transportation around New Providence is comfortable and relatively inexpensive. At Grants Town, New Providence, there is an interesting Shell Factory operated by Mrs. Babs Holt, owner of the Cockle Shell Shop on Bay Street, Nassau.

Bahama Airways, Mackey Airlines and BOAC out of Miami or Fort Lauderdale go to Nassau, Eleuthera, Bimini and Grand Bahama, all of which have accommodations and rather good shell collecting, especially at night at low tide. Many smaller islands could be explored by charter boats and new conchological areas undoubtedly uncovered. A 42-foot cabin cruiser costs about $300.00 per week, plus fuel and food (1959), but other less expensive charters can be arranged by writing the Nassau Yacht Haven on Bay Street. Charters for 15 to 20 people at about $200 per ten days can be obtained in Florida. Be sure you choose a group that is primarily interested in collecting and skin diving, and not in sightseeing or fishing.

Collecting on the outer shores of Great and Little Abaco and their associated cays is reported to be excellent. The north coast of Grand Bahama Island and the west sides of Andros and Abaco Islands are very poor because of the white silt. West End, Eight Mile Rock, and Hawksbill Creek, Grand Bahama Island, are reported to be from excellent to fair.

CUBA

Statistics — Directly south of Florida and the largest of the Greater Antilles (760 miles in length). A Spanish-speaking republic, but English is spoken by many Cubans. Havana and Varadero expensive; other smaller cities reasonable and reasonably healthy. Year-round collecting; summer best. Access by air or boat. Island transportation: air best; train and bus usually rugged. You can take your own car or hire a Hertz ($50 per week plus gasoline at 32 cents per gallon). Avoid visits during political unrest.

The land mollusks are the most numerous (2000 species) and the most colorful in the New World. The land-shell collector in Cuba will find many endemic species of such genera as *Liguus* and *Polymita.* The best spots are the Eastern tip of the island for *Polymita* and the famous Viñales valley for many of the most beautiful operculates. The Museum Poey at the University of Havana has a very complete series of identified Cuban mollusks.

Cuba has a rich and varied marine shell fauna. The east end is richest, but many other areas, such as Cienfuegos and Cochinos Bay (south side) and Matanzas Harbor (north coast) are good, especially for dredging. The collecting is reported to be better along the coast east, rather than west, of Cienfuegos, especially one mile east of the lighthouse at Punta de los Colorados where *Conus, Cypraea, Cittarium* and *Columbella* are abundant. The beaches at Varadero are poor, but the inner bays are good. Santiago de Cuba, Oriente Province (2 hours by plane from Havana) has a new motel, the Rancho Club, which is excellent and inexpensive. The shell collecting, especially dredging and skin diving, is excellent. U. S. Navy personnel will find collecting in the Guantánamo Bay area excellent. In the bay, in the grass flats, are *Cassis, Strombus, Vasum* and huge *Murex*. Cuesco, Windmill and Cable Beaches on the south shore are excellent, with the rare *Conus granulatus* sometimes cast ashore. *Conus daucus* is moderately common.

The Isle of Pines is normally a favorite American visiting spot. It is healthful and has several good motels and hotels. The beaches in the north are poor which discourages tourists but favors conchologists. Local transportation is best done by boat. The shell fauna has never been investigated but rumors are that many pleasant surprises are in store for the explorer. North Americans have been very welcome here. Access by air from Havana. Freight from Tampa. Take mosquito lotion to ward off sand flies.

JAMAICA

Statistics — Largest and most mountainous of the British West Indies. 90 miles south of Cuba. 146 miles long and 51 miles wide. Climate healthy; accommodations and transportation modern. Access by many steamship and air lines. Collecting year-round, but probably best in summer. Beach collecting best in the winter, windier months.

Jamaica has a rich shell fauna, and it is believed that over 1000 species will eventually be found in her waters. Collecting areas are spotty and no survey has been made for the more productive ones. The south shore is in general poor, except for the Kingston Harbor area. In fact, nice *Strombus pugilis* may be had in front of the Myrtle Bank Hotel (expensive). Port Antonio on the north shore is reportedly an excellent collecting locality. Skin divers have found *Strombus gallus* moderately common in the past. Montego Bay is expensive and the collecting moderately good, although many nearby areas remain to be explored. Fern Gully is a famous scenic retreat, a botanist's dream, and has interesting varieties of operculate land shells (take vials with 70 percent alcohol). Boat charters are possible and diving guides available. If staying any length of time, contact fishpot fishermen who will save the rare shells that accidentally get into the pots or are carried in by hermit crabs. The west end of Jamaica is reported to be a fairly good collecting area. The land snail fauna of the island is very rich.

In Kingston, the Institute of Jamaica has an exhibit and study collection of shells, and its staff can give you information on local collecting conditions. If planning a long and serious collecting trip, first write to the director, C. Bernard Lewis, who can smooth your way. In return for help, courtesy suggests that you deposit a share of your conchological spoils with this excellent scientific institute which is trying to develop collections with very limited staff.

GRAND CAYMAN ISLAND

Statistics — A 22-mile-long island located south of western Cuba and 180 miles northwest of Jamaica. British. Moderately expensive. Transportation and boat charter good. Access by air. Freighter service from Tampa. Also flights to Little Cayman and Cayman Brac to the east.

About 300 species of seashells are known from Grand Cayman. Reef collecting at the east end is good. Dredging in Frank Sound and the outer reaches of North Sound result in about 20 to 40 species, mostly small. Inner North Sound is poor except for abundant *Astraea phoebia* (small, delicately spined form), smooth cockles and *Marginella*. West Bay and its beaches are poor except after storms. The smooth *leucozonalis* form of *Leucozonia nassa* is abundant on the shore benches at low tide. The scallop, *Chlamys imbricata,* is very common under reef rocks in shallow water. For a detailed account, with maps and illustrations of shells, write the Academy of Natural Sciences of Philadelphia, 19th and the Parkway, Philadelphia 3, Pennsylvania, for "The Marine Mollusks of Grand Cayman Island" (monograph no. 11, $4.00).

Cayman Brac is reported to have good shelling, but it is conchologically *terra incognita,* so far as marine mollusks are concerned. The modern, 14-room Buccaneer's Inn is $9 double in the summer. Worth investigating, and any academy or museum in the United States specializing in mollusks would "flip" at receiving a good set of shells from here. This also applies to Little Cayman Island but there are no lodging facilities to our knowledge.

A trip to Little Cayman is easily arranged from Cayman Brac only 5 miles away. The channel between is rough. Little Cayman is almost completely surrounded by reefs and the collecting ought to be very interesting. Endemic species of the land snail, *Cerion*, on each island are attractive and locally abundant.

HAITI

Statistics — A French-speaking Republic occupying the western third of

Hispaniola Island; faces Cuba, and bordered on the east by the Dominican Republic. Hotels are clean in Port-au-Prince. Local transportation fair. Living conditions poor elsewhere and milk and water must be boiled, except at recommended hotels. Malaria present in some areas. Cars may be rented; boats sometimes chartered. Access by air or ship. Collecting year-round, but the winter months are windy and it is rainy from April through June and late September through November. If you do not mind heat, July and August are best.

The shell fauna of Haiti is not well-known, but from small collections made 60 years ago, it is evident that it is rich. The species found along the south and north shores are probably coral reef associates, while those in Port-au-Prince and La Gonave Island are a combination of mud and reef species. Boats can be chartered very reasonably at the Casino Pier in Port-au-Prince for a day's collecting around Sand Cay's coral reefs. From the air, the north coast around Cap Haitien and Chouchou Bay looks like an ideal reef collecting area, but the winds during the winter months would make collecting difficult. A full-fledged expedition to Haiti would, at this time, require careful, advanced planning.

DOMINICAN REPUBLIC

Statistics — A Spanish-speaking Republic occupying the eastern two-thirds of Hispaniola Island. Santo Domingo, the capital, is modern and healthy; outlying towns less so. Transportation good. Cars may be rented from Hertz; air service to the north and east. Summer is the best time for shell collecting, but in winter the south shore is relatively calm. Access by air and ship.

The shell fauna is rich in the Dominican Republic and offers great opportunities, since good roads, air service and an increasing number of clean lodgings are available to American tourists. Dredging would probably be very profitable off Monte Cristi, Puerto Plata and Sosua on the north coast. The south shore has not been properly investigated for shells. The rare *Terebra taurinus* is not uncommon in some areas. Bivalve collecting is good, especially for the large, keeled *Mactra alata*.

Marine shell collecting is rich, with a great variety of species, at Santa Barbara de Samana on the north shore of Samana Bay, northeast Hispaniola. This coast consists of a series of small, crescent-shaped bays and rocky headlands, offering a wide variety of habitats. Collecting is poor at Sanchez because of the Yuna River, but probably improves greatly 5 miles from the town. Small boats are available in the area of Samana Bay.

The very rare *Conus centurio* has been dredged in 30 feet of water in the small harbor of Puerto Plata on the north coast.

VIRGIN ISLANDS

Statistics —
   American Virgin Islands: To the east of Puerto Rico, and consisting
   of St. Thomas, St. John and St. Croix. All easy to get around;
   healthy conditions; boats available. St. John is least spoiled, part of
   it being a National Park. Jeeps and guides available. Access by air
   and ship. Collecting year-round, but probably somewhat better in
   the summer.
   British Virgin Islands: To the northeast of the American Virgin
   Islands, and consisting of Tortola, Virgin Gorda, Anegada, and
   other small islands. Drinking water must be boiled. Access by boats
   only. Poor island transportation. Collecting fair to good.

Collecting is good at St. Croix which is almost completely surrounded
by coral reefs. Beach pickings are best on the north shore from Ham
Bluff to Shoy Point. Over 600 species have been reported from this island.
A useful account of the occurrences and habitats of many of these species
is found in "A Check List of the Marine Shells of St. Croix" published
privately in 1959 by G. W. Nowell-Usticke, Christiansted, St. Croix
(nomenclature unreliable).

Collecting on St. Thomas and St. John is as good as that on St. Croix,
and both have a few species not found at the latter island. The delightful Water Isle Hotel in St. Thomas is run by ardent shell enthusiasts
and has cleaning and collecting facilities.

Remote Anegada Island in the British Virgins has a small but interesting shell fauna. *Cyphoma* abundant; *Astraea, Vasum* and *Nitidella*
specimens unusually large.

ST. KITTS and NEVIS ISLANDS

Statistics — Southeast of the Virgin Islands and 45 miles west of Antigua
   in the Leeward Islands of the Lesser Antilles. Two, small, volcanic
   islands, two miles apart. A British Colony. Healthy conditions;
   ample tourist facilities. Access by air and steamship.

These two islands, and Anguilla 60 miles to the northwest, are conchologically poorly known and are greatly in need of investigation.
There are no real tourist facilities on Anguilla.

ANTIGUA

Statistics — In the Leeward Islands north of Guadeloupe. 108 square
   miles in area. British Colony. Healthy conditions. Good tourist
   facilities, both inexpensive and very expensive. Transportation good.
   Boats available. Access by several air and steamship lines. Collecting
   best in the summer.

Dredging and skin diving reported to be good. The shell fauna is moderately rich. The very unusual *Globivasum globulus* is found from the low tide mark to a depth of 20 feet on rocky bottom at the entrances of Falmouth and English Harbors. A good census of the marine shells of this island has not been made as yet.

BARBADOS

Statistics — In the Lesser Antilles about 100 miles east of the main chain of the Windward Islands. A small limestone island, about 20 miles in length and with 60 miles of beaches and limestone cliffs. A unit territory of the West Indies Federation with a very healthy climate, good roads and with cars and small boats available. Access by several steamship and air lines. Collecting year-round, but best in summer.

The shell fauna of limestone Barbados is fairly rich, although lacking in some species found on the volcanic islands. The coral reef fauna is quite rich. Skin diving and dredging is good on the calm west side where most of the beaches are located. The east faces the open Atlantic where waves are 4 to 10 times as high as those on the west coast. The rocky shores are characterized by a pinkish band just above the surf zone. This is due to a coralline alga. The common rock-dwellers are *Fissurella, Purpura, Thais, Leucozonia, Acmaea, Nerita*, etc. Bath-sheba and Conset Bay on the east side are good places for *Astraea caelata, Cittarium pica, Planaxis nucleus* and *Tegula excavata*. Deeper-water species occasionally are washed ashore on the east side after storms, but on the whole the west coast is more productive. For a detailed account of the fauna of Barbadian rocky shores, see J.B. Lewis, Canadian Journal of Zoology, vol. 38, pp. 391-435 (April 1960).

A new biological station, the Bellairs Research Institute of McGill University, is located on the west side at St. James.

GUADELOUPE

Statistics — A French Territory of two adjoining islands located in the Leeward Islands north of Dominica. Passport required if staying more than 8 days. Living conditions and tourist facilities fair. Roads fair; cars may be rented; boats available.

Early French naturalists reported several hundred interesting species from Guadeloupe. It is undoubtedly very rich, but skin diving and dredging would have to supplement shore collecting. The very rare and handsome *Morum dennisoni* Reeve is found here. Marine charts look enticing. A new hotel is planned for the near future.

MARTINIQUE

Statistics — An insular French Department, 45 miles in length, and part of the Windward Island group of the Lesser Antilles. Passport required (except for short cruise visits), but no visa unless you intend to stay more than 3 months. The venomous fer-de-lance snake is present, but rare. Living conditions fair, but rapidly improving. Boil drinking water. Car and boat rentals possible. Collecting year-round.

This is a famous collecting locality in the old conchological literature, and a present-day exploration of the island would doubtlessly bring to light many interesting and rare species. Dredging would, indeed, be very rewarding. The best beaches are along the south coast but the collecting is poor, except after a storm.

TRINIDAD and TOBAGO

Statistics — Trinidad, 50 miles long, lies just off the northeast coast of Venezuela; pleasanter Tobago, 26 miles long, is 21 miles northeast of Trinidad and reached by air or coastal steamer. Both are British and have good living conditions and transportation facilities.

Both islands have a fairly rich shell fauna. Tobago, where famous Buccoo Reef is located, offers good collecting. Shelling guides are available, but the area is being over-collected. *Voluta musica* is uncommon on some reefs of both islands. The west side of Trinidad is poor for shells because of the muddy Gulf of Paria. Summer, although hot, is the best time for collecting.

CURAÇAO, ARUBA and BONAIRE

Statistics — Three small islands lying off the Venezuelan coast and belonging to the Netherlands. The natives speak Papiamento (Negro-Spanish), Dutch is the official language but both English and Spanish are spoken by many. Conditions healthy with modern hotels (expensive and inexpensive) and good transportation on Curaçao and Aruba. Access by air and/or steamship. Collecting year-round, but skin diving is only possible at the southwestern shores.

Although the marine fauna of these islands is largely West Indian, there are many interesting species either endemic or unusually common. *Conus dominicanus, Conus armillatus, Conus granulatus* and *Voluta musica* are moderately common. *Latirus eppi, Latirus distinctus* and *Cypraea surinamensis* are reported from Curaçao; *Conus bermudensis, Oliva fusiformis* and *Ancilla glabrata* are to be found on Aruba. Dredging and skin diving would be extremely profitable. The Caribbean Marine-Biological Institute is located on Curaçao. It has published a well-illustrated, English account of the shallow-water gastropods of the Netherlands Antilles (by H. E. Coomans, Studies Fauna Curaçao, vol. 8, No. 31, pp. 42-111, 16 pls., 1958). The author records about 200 species, but, as he points out, no serious, widespread collecting has yet been undertaken, and the total census of marine mollusks doubtlessly reach more than seven hundred.

COZUMEL and ISLA MUJERES, MEXICO

Statistics — Isla Mujeres is a small island on the Yucatan coast, 200 miles east of Merida. A 7-hour bus ride to Puerto Juarez; a freighter makes 4 trips a day. One inn on the island; inexpensive. A venture for young people.

Cozumel, off the east coast of Yucatan has tourist facilities and is reached by air from Miami or New Orleans.

The marine mollusks of these two islands are virtually unknown, and a knowledge of them would be of great assistance to conchology. The yellow sand beaches of Cozumel are shell-less, but the shallow reef area at the north end, shown on marine charts, looks promising. Arrangements would have to be made for a local boat rental and a fisherman guide, and collecting would be possible only during the calm summer months. A little knowledge of Spanish would be useful.

TEXT FIG. 2. The coral reef flats support a host of tropical snails and bivalves.

CHAPTER II

Shell Collecting
in Puerto Rico

Although Puerto Rico is only 130 miles long and 35 miles wide, its strategic position in the center of the Antillean Chain makes it one of the most interesting and certainly one of the richest islands for marine mollusks. Only a few hours by air from New York and Miami, its accessibility and pleasant climate make it an increasingly popular mecca for shell collectors and coral-reef explorers.

While the modern history of Puerto Rico begins with Christopher Columbus in 1493 and with its first governor, Ponce de León, in 1508, the mollusk history of the island did not properly begin until Don Juan Gundlach, in 1883, made his report on 212 marine species. The list rose to 535 species when William H. Dall and Charles T. Simpson published an account for the United States Fish Commission in 1901. In 1951, Richard A. McLean issued an illustrated account of the marine bivalves of Puerto Rico and the Virgin Islands.

This first edition of *Caribbean Seashells* now brings the total number of Puerto Rican marine mollusks to 858 — 202 of them bivalves, 437 gastropods, the few remaining from the smaller classes. It is conservatively estimated that another three or four hundred species will be added as diligent collecting continues over the years.

BEACHES

Puerto Rico offers great diversity in shell-collecting areas, each with its own particular type of shells. The island has about 300 miles of beautiful beaches, most of which are excellent for swimming, but as a rule rather poor for shells. This is mainly because the wave-dashed sand beaches are inhospitable to the average mollusk. Among the few beach-dwellers are the attractive Wedge Clams or *Donax* shells, small Auger snails (*Terebra*) and the tiny *Olivella* and Moon snails (*Polinices*).

17

TEXT FIG. 3. Mangrove roots are the favorite holdfast for Periwinkles, Mussels, and Oysters.

If one has the good fortune to visit a sand beach after a violent storm, the coastline may be heavily strewn with a wide variety of freshly killed mollusks that normally inhabit the offshore reefs and deeper waters. Scallops, Cones, Venus clams, Frog Shells of the genus *Cymatium*, and long *Turritella* Auger Shells may be present by the hundreds of thousands. Within a day or so, the tides and waves will have recaptured most of these shells. The autumn and winter months are generally best for beachcombing. But the novice collector should not be misled by the relatively poor representation of wave-worn shells on the beach. The secret is to collect where the mollusk shells live.

ROCKY SHORES

The exposed rocks of the hard shoreline offer a readily accessible collecting area for several dozen species of mollusks. Care must be taken by the collector not to stumble on the sharp rocks or be drenched by an unusually large wave. Low tide and calm days are the safest times to collect. Tidepools, crevices and algae-covered rocks support a host of periwinkles, several species of *Nerita,* including the famous Bleeding Tooth shell, and several kinds of eight-valved chitons. The whitish Beaded Periwinkles are found on the upper levels where the waves rarely wet the rocks. The limpets live near the low tide mark where the bottom is flatter and covered with algal growths. *Thais* and *Purpura* rock shells are usually so well camouflaged by seaweed growths that they are apt to be overlooked.

SHALLOW-WATER COLLECTING

For the collector who enjoys getting his feet wet, there is a wealth of material to be found just a few feet below the surface of the sea. By overturning rocks and poking into crevices, a large number of *Astraea, Latirus, Cittarium, Tegula, Turbo* and *Thais* will be found. The *Barbatia* Ark clams, oysters, the *Anomia* Jingle Shells and *Chama* Jewel Boxes customarily attach themselves to the underside of large slabs. By sieving the sand under loose rocks and by brushing detritus off the underside of corals, an unusually large number of minute shells of many genera can be obtained. The most conspicuous species on the grass bottoms of Puerto Rican bays is the Tulip Shell, *Fasciolaria tulipa*. Raking or running a hand sieve through the weeds will bring to light many *Cerithium, Tricolia* and tiny *Rissoina*. Mud and sandy-mud shallows support a host of interesting clams, some of which lie near the surface while others dig several inches below the surface.

REEF COLLECTING

The vast majority of the larger and more attractive species are found in the vicinity of the shallow-water, coral reefs. A glass-bottomed bucket, face mask or SCUBA diving outfit will open a fascinating new world to those who have not observed many of the living mollusk animals in their native habitat. Snails and clams are shy and generally shun bright sunlight, so it becomes necessary to overturn rock slabs and dig into the sand to find your shell treasures. Night collecting, when the sea is calm and the water not too deep, is very profitable. A strong flashlight or coleman lantern will bring into view many Olive and Cowrie shells which never appear during the daylight hours. Exercise common safety rules and avoid brushing against the poisonous spines of the giant purple sea-urchin. In sandy areas, look for tell-tale trails on the bottom which will reveal the presence of travelling mollusks. Crack open coral blocks with a hammer or iron bar for the Date Mussels and other boring clams.

If you are interested in skin diving or snorkeling, trips from San Juan, Fajardo, or La Parguera are offered at reasonable rates. See "Que Pasa in Puerto Rico", the free official visitors' guide to Puerto Rico, for more detailed information.

Mangrove Areas

The mangroves have a variety of mollusks living on their roots. High above the water on the trunks and branches is the best place to find the Periwinkle, *Littorina angulifera*. At the water line, oysters cling to the roots for support. In company with oysters, one can find the beautiful *Murex brevifrons*. *Chama, Pteria, Brachidontes,* and many other species of bivalves also are found on roots of the mangroves.

Below the water line the mangrove roots are usually covered with various kinds of fine, green algae, making them a favorite home for a multitude of small mollusks. Dr. Robert Robertson told us how to wash these algae-covered roots in a bucket of water to recover a wealth of small forms. By vigorous washing, the sand and tiny shells settle to the bottom of the pail.

The average person tends to be repelled by oozy mud flats, but to the avid shell collector this is just one more interesting area for collecting. High up at the edge of salt marshes such forms as *Melampus, Tralia,* and *Truncatella* are quite common and easy to collect. Many small gastropods in such genera as *Batillaria, Cerithiopsis, Neritina,* and *Bulla* are commonly found in the shallow waters near the mangroves.

Dredging

An important aid to the collector is dredging. Contrary to the general impression, it is not necessary to own a yacht and an expensive dredge. One can collect from a small outboard motor boat equipped with a hand-operated dredge. For beginners, we recommend two articles on the subject, "Dredging for Every One" by Tom Burch and "Four to Four Hundred Feet Beneath the Sea Dredging in Florida Waters" by Jeanne S. Schwengel. Both articles are reprinted in a booklet "How to Collect Shells" published by the American Malacological Union. The booklet also gives helpful hints on diving for shells and obtaining shells from fish stomachs.

Dredging is a fascinating activity and filled with great suspense and anticipation. The dredge we most often used is homemade and is manually operated. It is made of a strong iron frame, 36" x 12" x 18", covered with heavy ¼-inch mesh galvanized hardware cloth and a layer of copper window screen. The dredge has two strong leading edges which are bent to dig into the bottom. It is well to have a substantial piece of chain attached directly to the dredge, so that its weight will keep the dredge in a horizontal position and the scraping edge in contact with the bottom.

In collecting from a small boat, we simply dump the dredged loads a little at a time on to an 18" x 18" tray which has two layers of fine-mesh screen at the bottom. Mud and sand are washed through and the larger rocks, grass, sea urchins, etc. removed by hand from the top of the screen. Of course, if one has a large boat available, dredging is easier. In this case a winch can be used to pull up the dredge. For sorting large amounts of the material, we have a stand which has spaces for 3 screens supported by wooden frames. The top screen has ½" wire mesh, the middle one ¼" mesh and the bottom one is made of nylon screen similar to that used for window screens. The dredged material is dumped on to the upper screen, and a hose is used to help wash away the mud and sand.

MONA, VIEQUES, AND CULEBRA

There are three larger islands off Puerto Rico, which are well worth the collector's attention if he has time to visit them. These are Mona Island, some 40 miles off the western end of Puerto Rico, and Culebra and Vieques, off the eastern end of Puerto Rico. Such interesting shells as *Conus granulatus* Linné (Glory-of-the-Atlantic Cone), *Conus ranunculus*, and *Tellina radiata* are found in the clear waters of Mona. Many of the species reported by Dall and Simpson (1901) were from Ensenada Honda, Culebra. The northeast coast of Culebra also has a good shelling beach. Vieques is excellent for skin diving. There is regular ferry-boat service from Fajardo to Vieques and Culebra, but the visitor will have to make his own arrangements to visit Mona.

HOW TO GET AROUND THE ISLAND

If you are a United States citizen, there is no need for a passport or visa when you come to Puerto Rico because the island is a U. S. possession.

There are several companies which offer cars for rent (drive-yourself) at rates comparable to those in the continental U. S. These are available at the airport and at most of the larger hotels. Fast and inexpensive transportation is provided by the Puerto Rico Motor Coach Company which offers daily scheduled service between San Juan and Mayagüez with stops at Arecibo, Ramey, and Aguadilla. The "públicos" (taxis which take a full load of passengers on regular routes) also provide reasonable transportation and reach every section of the island. Caribair operates four plane flights daily between San Juan and Mayagüez, and between San Juan and Ponce.

The Office of Information of the Economic Development Administration publishes (in English) an interesting monthly booklet called "Que Pasa in Puerto Rico". Be sure to obtain a copy; it has suggestions about hotels, restaurants, transportation, shopping, guided tours, and almost anything else of interest about the island. It can be obtained free of charge from the Department of Tourism in San Juan or the Office of Information, Economic Development Administration, Box 2672, San Juan, Puerto Rico, or in the lobby of almost any hotel. A map of the island is most useful when travelling. The Tourism bureau or most gasoline service stations will be happy to provide you with these.

Useful Spanish words and sentences for the shell collector:

1. beach	playa		15. after	después
2. bathing beach	playa de baño		16. good	bueno
			17. place	sitio
3. shell, shells	caracol, caracoles		18. to rent	alquilar
4. boat	bote		19. taxi	público, taxi
5. rowboat	bote de remos		20. now	ahora
6. where	dónde		21. later	más tarde
7. when	cuando		22. today	hoy
8. reef	arrecife		23. tomorrow	mañana
9. coral reef	arrecife de coral		24. more or less	más o menos
10. please	por favor		25. round trip	ida y vuelta
11. thank you	gracias		26. too much	demasiado
12. far	lejos		27. how much	cuanto
13. near	cerca		28. stop	pare
14. before	antes		29. stop here	párese aquí
			30. to buy	comprar

Useful sentences:

1. Where is the beach?
   ¿Dónde está la playa?
2. Is it far from here?
   ¿Está lejos de aqui?
3. I want to go to the beach.
   Yo quiero ir a la playa.
4. Where can I rent a boat?
   ¿Dónde puedo alquilar un
   bote?
5. How far is it?
   ¿A qué distancia está?
6. How far to the coral reef?
   ¿A qué distancia está el
   arrecife de coral?
7. Where can I find sea shells?
   ¿Dónde puedo encontrar cara-
   coles marinos?
8. Wait for me.
   Espérame.
9. Come back in one hour.
   Regrese dentro de una hora.
10. Is that a good place to collect
    shells?
    ¿Es ese un buen sitio para
    coleccionar caracoles?
11. Ask the children if they would
    like to look for shells for me.
    Dígale a los niños que si quier-
    en buscar caracoles para mí.
12. I wish to have a driver to take
    me to the beach and help me
    to collect shells.
    Me gustaría consequir un cho-
    fer que me lleve a la playa y
    me ayude a coleccionar cara-
    coles.

INSTITUTE OF MARINE BIOLOGY

The Institute of Marine Biology was formally established in 1954. It is a part of the University of Puerto Rico and is associated with the College of Agriculture and Mechanic Arts at Mayagüez, at the extreme west end of the island. Each year a 6-week summer course on some phase of marine biology is given. In addition, the Institute offers opportunities to qualified scientists to carry on research in tropical marine biology and oceanography. The Institute is now building a study collection of the marine algae, corals, sponges, fishes and shells of Puerto Rico. A museum is planned to display these to the public and to enable persons to identify the material they find while on the island. The office buildings are on the college grounds at Mayagüez. The marine laboratory which is an hour's drive from Mayagüez is located on the small island of Magueyes, a few yards opposite La Parguera.

TEXT FIG. 4. The muddy marsh areas abound with tiny Horn Shells, Nerites and Melampus snails. A *Cerion* land snail is attached to the overhanging twig.

CHAPTER III

Studying Shells

One of the satisfying aspects of shell collecting is the many pleasant hours spent in arranging and identifying your new-found specimens. A jumble of carelessly housed shells becomes a nuisance and soon will be neglected or lost. While several other more general books on conchology deal thoroughly with the subject of arranging and methods of identification, we are including in this guide book such an account and a short glossary of conchological terms.

CLEANING AND PRESERVING SHELLS

Small live specimens, $1/4$ inch or less in size, offer no problem as they can be dropped into 70% grain alcohol where they may remain indefinitely or be removed after a day or two and dried. Clams and other bivalves should be placed in fresh water for a few hours until the shell valves gape. Then the soft parts may be removed and the shells washed and dried.

There are several ways of cleaning gastropods. The easiest and quickest method is to put them in tap water, bring to a slow boil, then remove from the fire and let cool slowly to prevent cracking of the shell. The animal is then carefully twisted out in a corkscrew motion. If the animal has retracted far into the shell, the larger ones, such as *Strombus, Fasciolaria* and *Murex,* usually can be reached with a bent wire clothes hanger, crochet hook, or tweezers. Once you can get a good hold on the animal with your fingers, continue to apply a gentle, twisting pressure until it finally slips free. The operculum should be saved and placed in the aperture of its own shell; a plug of cotton will prevent it from falling out.

Some people prefer to bury their shells near ant nests and let the ants do the cleaning job. Others prefer to rot the animals out in water. For the large *Strombus, Charonia* and *Cassis* there is still another method. The live shell is placed in the shade, aperture up. When the animal is out far enough, make a lasso and put it around the foot, just back of the operculum. Suspend the shell from a tree. Gradually the shell drops away from the internal parts by the shell's own weight.

If the animal breaks inside the shell, vigorous rinsing will usually remove the remaining fragments; if not, let it stand partially filled with water, and after a few days, rinsing may be all that is necessary. A few drops of formaldehyde placed in the shell may also help to eliminate bad odors.

For cleaning the outside of the shell, a small fingernail brush is very useful. If the shell is heavily encrusted, a stiff wire brush will bring surprising results. Some people use hydrochloric acid for removal of the heavier growth; however, this should be used with great care and caution. Hydrochloric acid is a strong acid and will dissolve the shell as well as the overgrowths — and your fingers also — if you are not careful. It is always well to save at least a few of the shells with the periostracum intact because the "skin" is as much a part of the shell as the operculum. Again we recommend the booklet "How to Collect Shells" for much valuable information on the cleaning and preserving of all kinds of mollusks.

Your Collection

The value of your collection is proportional to the data you assemble. Keeping accurate locality data with specimens is most essential if you intend either to exchange shells or to donate them to a museum or institution at some future date. An example of good data would be:

> No. 178
> *Conus mus* Hwass
> Under rocks, 1 mile east of
> Rincón Lighthouse, Puerto Rico.
> Mary Keiser, coll. May 15, 1961

Notes concerning the depth of the water, type of bottom, and relative abundance are also interesting and useful.

GLOSSARY OF CONCHOLOGICAL TERMS

Throughout the identification part of this book there appear many words of a technical nature. Although all of them may be found in a standard, unabridged dictionary, they sometimes have a connotation which is restricted to the field of malacology. We have attempted to keep these words to a minimum, but some are so basic and useful in the description of a shell that we are including here a brief glossary of terms. The accompanying illustrations will help the novice with such terms as spire, ribs, aperture and columella.

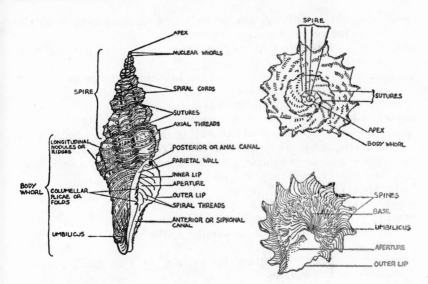

TEXT FIG. 5. Parts of the gastropod shell.

acute — sharp; a spire with an angle of less than 90 degrees.

adductor muscles — (in a bivalve) muscles which hold the valves together.

anal — pertaining to or near the anus or posterior opening of the alimentary canal.

anterior — in front of; the forward end.

aperture — an opening; the "mouth" of a shell.

apex — the top of the spire of a snail shell.

apical — pertaining to the apex.

appressed — lying flat or close against.

axial — (in snail shells) in the same direction of the axis, i.e. from apex to the base, as in axial ribs which are parallel to the edge of the outer lip.

base — the bottom of; in snail shells: the end opposite the apex; in clam shells: the basal margin opposite the upper or hinge margin.

beak — (of a clam shell) the earliest part formed.

bivalve — a pelecypod, usually with two shelly valves, such as a clam, oyster, mussel or scallop.

body whorl — the last and usually largest turn or whorl of a snail shell.

byssus — a clump of thread-like, chitinous filaments secreted by the foot of a mussel or other bivalve which serves as an anchor.

calcareous — shelly; of hard calcium carbonate.

callus — a swelling or deposit of calcareous or enamel-like material.

canal — a tubular prolongation; in snails: the siphonal canal is at the base of the shell and contains the siphon.

cancellate — criss-crossing lines of sculpture, usually at right angles to each other.

cardinal teeth — the main or largest teeth in a bivalve hinge located just below the beaks or umbones.

carnivorous — feeding on living animal matter.

cephalopod — a squid, Nautilus or octopus.

chondrophore — a pit or spoon-like shelf in the hinge of a bivalve, such as *Mactra,* and into which fits a chitinous cushion or resilium.

columella — a pillar or column around which the whorls of a snail form their spiral circuit.

compressed — flattened or "squashed".

concave — hollow or dished, as opposed to convex.

concentric — as in circles or lines of sculpture, one within the other, having a common center or parallel to the edge of the shell of a bivalve.

crenulate — notched or having the margin cut into small, rounded scallops or undulations.

denticles — small, pointed, tooth-like projections.

denticulate — toothed.

dextral — turning clock-wise or to the right; "right-handed".

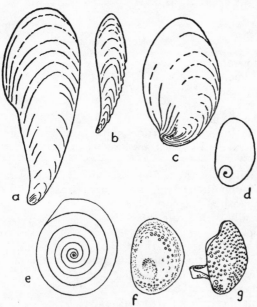

TEXT FIG. 6. Various types of opercula. a, ungulate and corneous *(Vasum muricatum)*; b, sickle-shaped and corneous *(Strombus pugilis)*; c, concentric with subcentral nucleus *(Murex brevifrons)*; d, paucispiral and corneous *(Littorina ziczac)*; e, multispiral and corneous *(Cittarium pica)*; f, calcareous *(Astraea tecta)*; g, papillose, paucispiral and calcareous *(Nerita fulgurans)*.

divaricate — branching apart.

dorsal — belonging to the dorsum or back; opposite to ventral.

elongate — lengthened; longer than wide.

epidermis — skin of the soft part of a mollusk. See periostracum.

equilateral — (in bivalves) the anterior and posterior end of equal size.

equivalve — (in bivalves) each valve equal in size and shape.

escutcheon — (in bivalves) a long, somewhat depressed area on the dorsal area just posterior to the beaks.

fathom — a measure of water depth equal to six feet.

flamulations — small flame-shaped spots of color.

gastropod — a univalve, snail, conch, periwinkle, etc.

gastroverm — a member of the class Monoplacophora; limpet-shaped, segmented, snail-like mollusks living in deep water.

gaping — (as in bivalves) having the valves not meet, so as to leave a hole or gape.

gibbose or gibbous — swollen.

glabrous — smooth.

glazed — having a shiny surface or shiny deposit.

globular — globe- or sphere-shaped, like a ball.

granulated — having a rough surface of grain-like elevations.

habitat — the kind of place where an organism normally lives.

herbivorous — feeding on vegetable matter.

hinge — (in a bivalve) the elongate, shelly, dorsal ridge, usually with teeth, where the valves are joined or interlocked.

hyaline — glassy and semi-transparent.

inequilateral — (in bivalves) one end of the clam shell not the same size or shape as the other.

inequivalve — (in bivalves) one valve larger or more convex than the other.

iridescent — reflecting the colors of the rainbow.

lamella — a thin plate or ridge; (plural: lamellae).

lanceolate — long and spearhead-shaped.

lateral — to the side of the mid-line of the body.

lateral teeth — (in bivalves) small teeth either anterior or posterior to the main cardinal teeth in the hinge.

ligament — a band of tough, brown, elastic material which unites the dorsal margins of a clam, usually posterior to the beaks; sometimes externally visible, rarely internal.

lira (plural: lirae) — small, long ridges of sculpturing, usually in the aperture of a snail shell.

littoral — pertaining to the shore.

longitudinal — direction of the longest diameter; in snails, spoken of as axial (as in axial ribs).

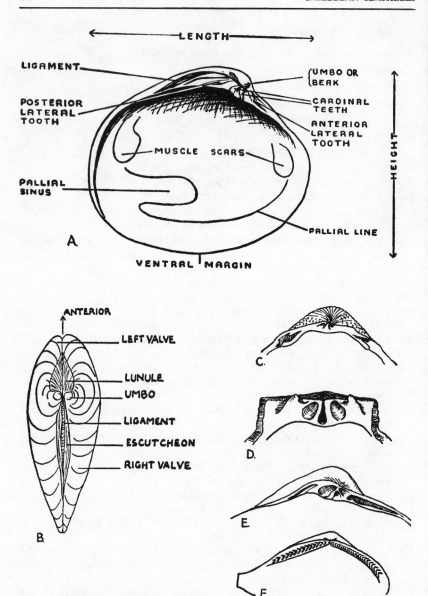

TEXT FIG. 7. Parts of the bivalve shell. a, interior; b, top view; c, *Cardium* hinge; d, *Spondylus* hinge; e, *Mactra* hinge; f, *Nuculana* hinge.

lunule — a heart-shaped area in front of the beaks of a bivalve.

maculated — irregularly spotted.

mantle — a fleshy layer or cape which secretes the shell of a mollusk.

median — middle.

millimeter — one tenth of a centimeter (metric system); one inch is equivalent to 25.37 mm.

mucus — a sticky, slimy, watery secretion; adjective: mucous.

nacre — iridescent layer of shell, sometimes called "mother-of-pearl".

nacreous — pearly.

nodose — with knob-like projections.

nodule — a small, knob-like hump or projection.

nodulose — with small knobs.

nuclear whorls — (in snail shell) the first whorls formed in the apex; those whorls formed in the egg or veliger stage.

nucleus — center.

operculum — cover or lid; in snails, a shelly or horny plate attached to the foot and used to close the aperture of the shell; plural: opercula.

orbicular — circular and flattish.

outer lip — the apertural margin of the last part of the body whorl of a snail shell.

ovate — egg-shaped in outline.

pallial line — (on the inside of some clam shells) a linear scar marking the attachment of the margin of the fleshy mantle to the shell.

pallial sinus — a notch or embayment in the pallial line caused by the attachment of the siphon's retractile muscles. It may be deep, shallow or absent, depending upon the species.

parietal wall — (in a snail shell) the area on the whorl near the columella and opposite the outer lip; sometimes called the inner lip.

pelecypod — a bivalve, clam, mussel, oyster, scallop, etc.

penultimate whorl — the next to the last whorl, or the one before the body whorl.

periphery — (of a whorl) the summit of the outline or margin, sometimes bearing a series of knobs.

plait — a fold.

plankton — life floating or drifting in the sea.

planorboid — shaped like a *Planorbis* snail or having the whole coil in the same plane.

plica — a fold; plural: plicae.

plicate — folded or with plaits or plicae.

plication — a fold or longitudinal, low rib.

porcellaneous — having the quality of porcelain; hard and shiny.

pustules — small, pimple-like elevations.

pyriform — pear-shaped.

quadrate — square or squarish in outline.

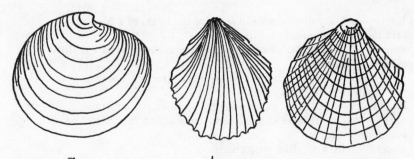

a.   b.   c.

TEXT FIG. 8. Types of sculpture found on the bivalve shell. a, concentric; b,
radial; c, cancellate.

radial — (in bivalves) lines of color or sculpture fanning out from the
beaks to the margins of the valve.

recurved — bent downwards.

reflected — bent backwards; reflexed.

reticulate — crossed like network.

revolving — (of cords or grooves on a snail shell) turning with the
whorls, or spirally.

rostrate — produced into a narrow beak-like projection.

rufose — reddish.

ruga — an irregular fold in the surface sculpture; plural: rugae.

rugose — rough.

sculpture — a pattern of raised or depressed markings on the shell's
surface.

sensu stricto — in the restricted sense; e.g., the subgenus *Strombus* itself,
and not any of the other subgenera in *Strombus*.
Abbreviation: s.s.

sinistral — (of a snail shell) turning anti-clockwise; "left-handed".

shoulder — (of a whorl) the top or largest part of the outline of a
whorl.

siphon — a tubular structure through which water enters and/or leaves
the mollusk's mantle cavity.

spiral — revolving; as lines going in the direction of the turning of the
whorls.

spire — the upper part of a snail shell from the apex to the body whorl,
but not including the latter.

stria — a fine line; plural: striae.

striated — marked with rows of fine grooves or threads, usually microscopic in size.

suture — a spiral line or groove where one whorl touches the other.

synonym — having the same meaning; or being a later name for the
same species.

teeth — (in a bivalve) the shelly protuberances on the dorsal margin of a valve which fit into corresponding sockets of the opposite valve.

translucent — allowing light to pass through, but not transparent.

trigonal — somewhat triangular in shape.

truncate — having the end cut off squarely.

tubercules — small, raised projections.

umbilicus — a small hole or depression in the base of the body whorl of a snail shell.

umbo — (plural: umbones) the early part of a clam's valve.

undulate — having a wavy surface.

univalve — a snail shell; gastropod.

valve — one of the shelly halves of a clam shell.

varix — a prominent raised rib on the surface of a snail shell, caused by a periodic thickening of the lip during rest periods in the shell's growth; plural: varices.

ventral — the lower side, opposite the dorsal area.

ventricose — swollen.

vitreous — glassy.

whorl — a complete turn or volution of a snail shell.

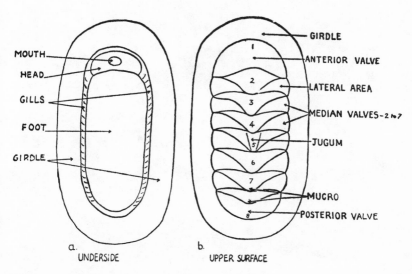

Text fig. 9. Parts of the chiton shell.

CHAPTER IV

Periwinkles, Conchs and Other Snails

Class *GASTROPODA*

Subclass *PROSOBRANCHIA*
Order *ARCHAEOGASTROPODA*
Superfamily *PLEUROTOMARIACEA*

Family *SCISSURELLIDAE*
GENUS *Schismope* Jeffreys, 1856

Schismope cingulata O. G. Costa, 1861

Belt Slit-shell
Text fig. 10

Mediterranean and Caribbean.

About 1 mm. in size, thin, fragile. Fresh specimens are cream to tan in color. Spire low, aperture large. Sculptured by very delicate reticulation. Young specimens with a long, narrow slit on periphery of body whorl, resembling *Scissurella*. The slit is closed in adult specimens.

TEXT FIG. 10. *Schismope cingulata* O. G. Costa. a, shell 1 mm. in size; b, under side of shell with animal extended.

A

B

A common shallow-water species found living on algae clinging to mangrove roots.

Family FISSURELLIDAE
Subfamily EMARGINULINAE
GENUS *Emarginula* Lamarck, 1801

Emarginula phrixodes Dall, 1927   Ruffled Rimula
                                                            Plate 5 c

Eastern U. S. and the West Indies.

¼ to ⅓ inch in length, 50 to 75% as high. Color white. Apical whorls half way down the posterior slope; slit at base of anterior slope. Sculpture consists of radial ribs and concentric cords. The two are about equally pronounced, so the shell appears to be made up of a series of square pits. A beautiful deep-water shell. To date, we have only found one specimen in beach drift at Rincón, Puerto Rico.

Emarginula pumila A. Adams, 1851   Pygmy Emarginula
                                                            Plate 5 a

Southeast Florida, Bermuda, the West Indies to Brazil.

⅓ to ½ inch in length, thin but strong. Extremely variable in shape. Color white to yellow. Base oval to squarish with a narrow, short slit at the anterior end. Sculpture consists of radial ribs and irregular concentric cords. Easily separated from *E. phrixodes* Dall because it is usually larger, flatter and has stronger radial sculpture. Dredged from shallow water to 90 fathoms. *Subemarginula rollandii* Pilsbry, 1891 is a synonym. Reported by Dall and Simpson under the latter name. Dead shells are common in beach sand.

GENUS *Hemitoma* Swainson, 1840
Subgenus *Hemitoma* Swainson, 1840

Hemitoma octoradiata Gmelin, 1791   Eight-ribbed Limpet
                                                            Plate 5 f

Southeast Florida and the West Indies.

¾ to 1 inch in length, with a notch on the anterior margin. Color white, gray, or cream. Sculpture consisting of 8 evenly spaced, nodulous, radiating ribs with smaller riblets between. Base oval, with the ribs often projecting beyond the base. Apex inclined backward and to the right. In dead specimens the apex is often worn down to a white callus. The animal is striking in appearance. It is yellowish with a greenish cast; the foot, mantle, proboscis, and tentacles are all outlined in bright-purplish red. In addition to this, a little from the base of the foot, there is a single horizontal row of arrow-shaped red markings. Very common under rocks. This is probably what Gundlach (1883) referred to as *Subemarginula notata* Linné. *H. rubida* Verrill, 1950 is a synonym.

Hemitoma emarginata Blainville, 1825   Emarginate Limpet
Plate 5 b

Florida Keys and Greater Antilles.

¾ to 1 inch in length, elevated, with a small notch on the anterior margin. Color white to gray. Differs from *H. octoradiata* in having pronounced reticulate sculpture and compound ribs. Rare in 40 to 80 feet in Mayagüez Harbor. *Emarginula ostheimerae* Abbott, 1958 is a young form of this species.

Subfamily *DIODORINAE*
GENUS *Diodora* Gray, 1821
Subgenus *Diodora* Gray, 1821

Diodora listeri Orbigny, 1853   Lister's Keyhole Limpet
Plate 5 j

South half of Florida and the West Indies.

1¼ and 1¾ inches in length, solid, elevated. Color white, cream, or gray; sometimes with black, gray, or brown rays. Sculpture consists of alternating large and small radiating ribs. Crossed by concentric cords which form square pits over the surface of the shell. The orifice is keyhole in shape and black on the outside. Base ovate; margin crenulated with paired teeth. Animal cream-colored, brown and opaque-white speckled. One of the most common intertidal limpets of Puerto Rico.

Diodora cayenensis Lamarck, 1822   Cayenne Keyhole Limpet
Plate 5 k

Southeast U. S. to Brazil.

1 to 2 inches in length, elevated and narrower anteriorly. It resembles *Diodora sayi,* but when closely examined the two can easily be separated. *D. cayenensis* has every fourth rib noticeably larger, its orifice is key-hole shaped, and its apex is not as near the anterior end as in *D. sayi.* The color is extremely variable. *Diodora alternata* Say is this species. It is fairly common on intertidal rocks in Puerto Rico.

Diodora sayi Dall, 1899   Say's Limpet

Southeast Florida, Greater Antilles to Brazil.

1 inch in length, moderately heavy. Apex directed forward, anterior slope short, straight, or concave. Posterior slope long and convex. Sculpture consists of numerous fine, close-set, radiating ribs that are crossed by many concentric threads. Color white or cream or faintly rayed with olive; surface dull. Quite common on rocks in southwest Puerto Rico.

Diodora dysoni Reeve, 1850   Dyson's Keyhole Limpet
Plate 5 e

Florida, the Bahamas and West Indies to Brazil.

½ to ¾ inch in length; color white or cream with 8 solid, broken, or black-dotted rays. Apex slightly in front of center and characterized by a blunt knob situated behind the posterior wall of the orifice. The orifice is small, almost triangular and usually bounded anteriorly and laterally by a black line. Moderately common in Puerto Rico.

Diodora minuta Lamarck, 1822   Dwarf Keyhole Limpet
                                                                  Plate 5 g
        Southeast Florida and the West Indies.

½ inch in length, thin, depressed. Apex situated at the anterior third of the shell. Front slope slightly concave, back slope convex. Orifice narrow and trilobate. Sculpture consists of numerous radiating ribs, crossed by concentric threads that produce a beaded surface. Color white with many ribs partly or entirely black, forming radiating triangles. Spaces between ribs always white. Lives on intertidal rocks.

Diodora variegata Sowerby, 1862   Variegated Keyhole Limpet
                                                                  Plate 5 d
        Bahama Islands to the northern Lesser Antilles.

Similar to *D. minuta,* but when pigment is present, the color is solid and appears on both the ribs and the spaces between. *D. variegata* also shows a reticulated pattern, rather than fairly strong radiating ribs crossed by fine concentric threads. Fairly common in Puerto Rico.

Diodora viridula Lamarck, 1822   Green Keyhole Limpet
                                                                  Plate 5 i
        Florida, south through the Antilles and Gulf of Mexico to Trinidad.

About 1 inch in length, characterized by white radial ribs and green intermediate ribs. Orifice long, narrow, trilobate, and stained with black. It can be found attached to rocks in the lower intertidal zone. Moderately common in Puerto Rico.

Diodora arcuata Sowerby, 1862   Arcuate Limpet
                                                                  Plate 5 h
        Florida, Bahamas, West Indies south to Trinidad.

About ⅜ inch in length. Base elliptical, raised slightly at the center, so that the shell rests on its ends. This species resembles *D. variegata* but differs in being higher, the orifice smaller and situated more anteriorly. The sculpture is scaly in *D. arcuata,* and beaded or reticulated in *D. variegata.* Color of rays tan or light brown. This normally rare shallow-water species is fairly common in Puerto Rico.

GENUS *Lucapinella* Pilsbry, 1890

Lucapinella limatula Reeve, 1850   File Fleshy Limpet
                                                                  Plate 6 d
        Southeastern U. S. to the West Indies.

¾ inch in length, depressed. Color whitish with weak pink or brown discoloring. Sculpture consists of irregular radial ribs, crossed by laminae which form small imbricated scales where they intercept the radial ribs. Base ovate. Orifice large and almost at the center of the shell. Dredged from 6 to 80 fathoms. Reported from Mayagüez and Cataño, Puerto Rico.

GENUS *Lucapina* Sowerby, 1835

Lucapina suffusa Reeve, 1850 — Cancellate Fleshy Limpet
Plate 6 f

South half of Florida and the West Indies.

1 to 1½ inches in length, low, and oblong in outline. Orifice large, oval, and generally stained bluish black. Color a delicate mauve to pinkish. Sculpture consists of numerous radiating ribs crossed by concentric threads. Found under rocks, uncommon. Animal usually orange in color. Previously listed as *L. cancellata* Sowerby.

Lucapina sowerbii Sowerby, 1835 — Sowerby's Fleshy Limpet
Plate 6 a

Southeast Florida and the West Indies to Brazil.

¾ inch in length. Much like *L. suffusa*, but smaller, and with the orifice unstained. Color white to buff with 7 to 9 small splotched rays of pale brown. The sculpture consists of about 60 alternating, large and small radiating ribs crossed by 9 to 13 concentric threads. Found under rocks at low-tide zone. When alive, the mantle extends over the edge of the shell. Animal cream colored, finely speckled with light-brown. Not common. Previously listed as *L. adspersa* Philippi, 1845.

Subfamily FISSURELLINAE
GENUS *Fissurella* Bruguière, 1789
Subgenus *Cremides* H. and A. Adams, 1854

Fissurella nodosa Born, 1778 — Knobby Keyhole Limpet
Plate 6 g

Lower Florida Keys and the West Indies.

1 to 1½ inches in length, with 20 to 22 strongly nodulated, radiating ribs. Color white to brown; interior white. Margin strongly crenulated. Orifice long and contracted in the middle. Common on the rocks between tide lines.

Fissurella barbadensis Gmelin, 1791 — Barbados Keyhole Limpet
Plate 6 l

Southeast Florida, Bermuda and the West Indies.

1 to 1½ inches in length, with irregular radiating ribs. Orifice almost round, inside border of orifice green with a reddish-brown line. Color variable, from grayish white to brownish pink, blotched with purple-brown. Interior marked with concentric bands of green and white. It lives on rocks at low-tide level. The most abundant limpet in Puerto Rico.

Fissurella rosea Gmelin, 1791   Rosy Keyhole Limpet

Southeast Florida and the West Indies to Brazil.

1 inch in length. Similar to *F. barbadensis* but thinner, flatter, and narrower at the anterior end. Orifice green, more oval, and bordered by pink. Fairly common in beach drift. This may be only a form of *barbadensis.*

Fissurella angusta Gmelin, 1791   Pointed Keyhole Limpet
                                                   Plate 6 j

Lower Florida Keys, Bahamas, and south to British Guiana.

¾ to 1 inch in length. Sculpture consists of 9 or 10 slightly nodulous ribs projecting a little beyond the basal margin. Similar to *F. barbadensis* but flatter, pointed anteriorly, and the internal callus is light-brown to reddish. Frequently covered with calcareous algae. An intertidal species. Not common in Puerto Rico.

Subgenus *Clypidella* Swainson, 1840

Fissurella fascicularis Lamarck, 1822   Wobbly Keyhole Limpet
                                                   Plate 6 h

Southeast Florida and the West Indies.

¾ to 1¼ inches in length. Color dark-pink, with the spaces between the ribs white. Interior white, tinged with pink. The outline is broadly oval, with both ends of the shell elevated. Orifice keyhole in shape and located slightly towards the anterior end. Border crenulated. Common in Puerto Rico.

Subgenus *Fissurella* Bruguière, 1789

Fissurella nimbosa Linné, 1758   Rayed Keyhole Limpet
                                                   Plate 6 k

Puerto Rico south to the northern coast of South America.

About 2 inches in length, heavy, elevated, conical, and narrower anteriorly. Base ovate. Orifice large and oblong. Sculpture consists of numerous smooth ribs; these are crossed by fine growth lines. Ground color buff with rays of purplish red, dark-brown, or green to black; interior pale-green. Not found on the west coast of Puerto Rico, but common on the east and south coasts. On the north coast it appears to be limited to the area east of Palo Seco.

Superfamily *PATELLACEA*
Family *ACMAEIDAE*
GENUS *Acmaea* Eschscholtz, 1830
Subgenus *Collisella* Dall, 1871

Acmaea antillarum Sowerby, 1831   Antillean Limpet
                                                   Plate 6 e

South half of Florida and the West Indies.

¾ to 1 inch long, oval, depressed, and rather thin. Color variable: exterior with few or many reddish brown radial rays on a white background. Interior glossy white with a brown callus in the central part; border commonly marked with numerous brownish radial lines. Formerly known as *A. candeana* Orbigny. Animal cream colored with a green cast towards the apex of the shell. Edge of mantle with single row of opaque-white granules. Abundant on rocks in Puerto Rico.

Acmaea pustulata Helbling, 1779   Spotted Limpet
Plate 6 c

Southeast Florida, the West Indies, and Bermuda.

½ to 1 inch in length, oval, flat to moderately elevated. Exterior white; usually flecked with red- or orange-brown. Interior glossy white with a white, yellow, or orange callus. Shell moderately thick, sculptured with numerous axial ribs which are crossed by fine concentric threads. Animal cream colored, heavily speckled with browns, becoming dark-green towards apex of shell. Tentacles bright-green. Edge of mantle with groups of opaque white and brown granules. Common on rocks in Puerto Rico.

Acmaea pustulata form *pulcherrima* Guilding

It would appear that when this species settles upon the long, flat leaves of the turtlegrass, *Thalassia*, it becomes thinner, smoother, more brightly colored and flatter in shape. The outline of the base of the shell may be oblong in order that the shell's edge not extend over the edge of the blade of turtlegrass. It was reported from Puerto Real and Aguadilla by Dall and Simpson.

Acmaea jamaicensis Gmelin, 1791   Jamaica Limpet

Southeast Florida and the West Indies.

½ inch in maximum diameter, high, conic; base circular-ovate. Both ends lower than center. 15 to 20 rather large, white radial ribs on a black background. Interior white, occasionally with black-spotted edge and a thickened central callus which is light-brown to black. We have found only one specimen of this species in Puerto Rico, and it was completely white.

Acmaea leucopleura Gmelin, 1791   Dwarf Suck-On Limpet
Plate 6 b

Southeast Florida and the West Indies.

About ½ inch in diameter, flat to moderately high, with several alternating black and white rays. The black rays divide into two near the edge of the shell. Interior white; callus sometimes brown or black. Animal cream to white in color with light-pink proboscis and tentacles.

Reasonably common on the south coast of Puerto Rico. Lives on the shell of live *Cittarium* [Livona] snails.

Acmaea cubensis Reeve, 1855   Cuban Limpet

Bahamas and West Indies.

½ inch or less in maximum diameter, high, conic. Surface with numerous narrow rays of white and black or brown. Rays often obsolete, giving the shell a blotched effect. This shell is similar to *A. leucopleura*, but it is higher and surface rays are more numerous and not so consistent. The callus is usually dark-brown and covers most of the inside of the shell. Most common on the northwest coast of Puerto Rico. This may be only a form of *A. leucopleura*.

Superfamily *TROCHACEA*
Family *TROCHIDAE* (Top-shells)
GENUS *Euchelus* Philippi, 1847

Euchelus guttarosea Dall, 1889   Red-spotted Euchelus
Plate 7 a

Florida to the West Indies.

About ¼ inch; whorls rounded; color white or white with red or reddish-brown dots. Nuclear whorls smooth; remaining whorls coarsely reticulated with nodules at the intersections. No umbilicus; aperture rounded, 6 or 8 teeth within, and nacreous. Reasonably common from shallow dredgings in Puerto Rico.

GENUS *Solariella* Wood, 1842

Solariella amabilis Jeffreys, 1865

Florida, Gulf of Mexico, and West Indies.

About ¼ inch in length, pyramidal, pearly, somewhat iridescent, with 2 spiral ridges on the upper part of the last 3 or 4 whorls. The suture is deep and narrow, and below it on the sloping shoulder are numerous axial ridges. Aperture small, nearly round; the last whorl is but slightly joined to the penultimate whorl; umbilicus rather large, funnel-shaped. Reported from Mayagüez by Dall and Simpson.

GENUS *Microgaza* Dall, 1881

Microgaza rotella Dall, 1889   Dall's Dwarf Gaza

Southeast U. S. to the West Indies.

¼ inch in diameter, spire flat, whorls about 5. Shell beautifully iridescent throughout and is sometimes marked with zigzag brown flames. Surface smooth except for a spiral row of small nodules just below the suture. Umbilicus fairly wide, very deep, bounded at its edge by a sharp, crenulated ridge. A deep-water species, reported from Aguadilla and Mayagüez by Dall and Simpson.

GENUS *Synaptocochlea* Pilsbry, 1890

Synaptocochlea picta Orbigny, 1842   Painted False Stomatella
Plate 7 b

Florida, Bermuda, and the West Indies.

Between ⅛ and ¼ inch in size; ear shaped. Color variegated white and reddish purple or reddish brown. Sculptured with many fine granulose spiral threads. Columella white; aperture large, outside color showing through. Dead shells found in drift sand. "Albino" forms have been called *inconcinna* Pilsbry, 1921 and *lactea* Usticke, 1959. A black form was named *nigrita* Rehder, 1939.

GENUS *Pseudostomatella* Thiele, 1921

Pseudostomatella coccinea A. Adams, 1850   Scarlet False Stomatella
Plate 7 h

Greater Antilles.

About ⅛ inch in size. Color bright-red with some white blotches; upper whorls marked with alternating brown and white radiating bands. Surface sculptured with many spiral threads and numerous microscopic radial lines. Whorls shouldered. Umbilicate. Aperture large. Rare; to date we have found only 2 specimens of this beautiful little shell. *P. c. rubroflammulata* Pilsbry is probably a color form of this species.

Pseudostomatella erythrocoma Dall, 1889   Dall's False Stomatella
Plate 7 - 1

West Indies.

4 to 6 mm. in diameter at the base; depressed conic; with 4 or 5 rounded whorls. Color yellowish, variegated with rose pink and opaque white. Radiating sculpture of occasionally irregular lines of growth; spiral sculpture of fine, close, raised threads. Sculpture strongest on earlier whorls. Umbilicus small but well-marked. Aperture rounded, pearly within, joined by a thin callus on the body whorl; lip thin. Common from shallow-water dredgings in western Puerto Rico.

GENUS *Cittarium* Philippi, 1847

Cittarium pica Linné, 1758   West Indian Top-shell
Plate 7 m

Southeast Florida and the West Indies.

2 to 4 inches in length, conical, heavy. Color grayish white with purplish black zigzag splotches. Aperture round, large and pearly within; umbilicus wide and deep. Operculum horny, circular, and multispiral.

Called "burgao" by the natives and used as a food. Very common on and under coral rocks in Puerto Rico. *Livona* Gray, 1847 is this genus.

GENUS *Tegula* Lesson, 1832

Tegula fasciata Born, 1778   Smooth Atlantic Tegula
Plate 7 d

Southeast Florida and the West Indies.

½ to ¾ inch in width. Whorls rounded, surface smooth. Color light or dark reddish brown, finely mottled with red and white, sometimes with a lighter colored band on the periphery. Umbilicus deep, round and smooth. Two white teeth at base of columella; callus white. Operculum horny and multispiral. Moderately common under rocks at low tide in Puerto Rico. *T. hotessieriana* Orbigny 1842 is probably the young of this species. *T. substriata* Pilsbry is this species.

Tegula lividomaculata C. B. Adams, 1845   West Indian Tegula
Plate 7 f

Key West and the West Indies.

¾ inch in width and about ½ inch in length. Surface sculptured with small spiral cords; it lacks the oblique lines of growth found in *T. excavata.* Color of shell grayish to brownish white with small reddish and dark-brown mottlings. Umbilicus round, deep and furrowed. Columella with one large tooth and several smaller, indistinct ones below. Operculum brown, horny and multispiral. Common under rocks in Puerto Rico. *T. canaliculata* Orbigny (non Brocchi) is this species.

Tegula excavata Lamarck, 1822   Green-base Tegula
Plate 7 e

Caribbean.

½ to ¾ inch in length and width. Surface sculptured with spiral cords and oblique lines of growth. Base concave. Color light-brown, heavily mottled with black-brown markings, rarely bluish gray. Umbilicus deep, round, surrounded by pearly or iridescent green color. A moderately common rock-dwelling species in Puerto Rico.

GENUS *Calliostoma* Swainson, 1840

Calliostoma javanicum Lamarck, 1822   Chocolate-lined Top-shell
Plate 7 j

Lower Florida Keys and the West Indies.

¾ to 1 inch in height. Color yellow-orange with chocolate-brown spiral lines. Whorls flattened; sculptured with about 10 spiral, beaded threads alternating with dark-brown spiral lines. Umbilicus white, smooth-sided, deep. Spire angle about 70 degrees. Northwest Puerto Rico (rare). *C. zonamestum* A. Adams is probably a synonym.

Calliostoma jujubinum Gmelin, 1791   Jujube Top-shell
Plate 7 g

Lower Florida Keys, the Bahamas, and the West Indies.

½ to 1¼ inch in height. Spire angle about 50 degrees. Color cream, brown or reddish, often maculated with white. Whorls rounded at periphery; sculptured with numerous beaded spiral cords with finer beaded threads between. Umbilicus smooth-sided, narrow, and deep. Found dead on beaches at the west end of Puerto Rico.

Calliostoma jujubinum form *rawsoni* Dall, 1889

Similar to *C. jujubinum* but smaller, with a narrow umbilicus; columella thin with a very weak basal tooth. Shell more conical and much darker in color. Reported from Vieques by Dall and Simpson.

Calliostoma pulchrum C. B. Adams, 1850   Beautiful Top Shell

Southeast U. S., the Gulf of Mexico, and the West Indies.

⅜ inch in length, ¾ as wide. Characterized by a pair of strong spiral cords just above the suture. Spiral cords are white with distantly spaced red-brown dots. Rest of whorls pearly green with 6 or 7 beaded spiral threads. Sides of whorls straight. Columella almost upright; its inner side rounded, pearly. No umbilicus. Rare in Puerto Rico but not uncommon in the Virgin Islands.

Family TURBINIDAE
Subfamily LIOTIINAE
GENUS *Arene* H. and A. Adams, 1854

Arene cruentata Mühlfeld, 1829   Star Arene
Plate 8 e

Southeast Florida and the West Indies.

Between ¼ and ½ inch in diameter, turbinate. Color whitish with small, bright-red or reddish brown splotches on the upper part of the whorls. Whorls 4 to 6, angular, with the periphery bearing a series of about a dozen, strong, triangular spines which are hollow on their anterior edges; below is a smaller spiral row of minor spines. Suture channeled. Axial sculpture of microscopic, crowded, sharp threads. Aperture circular, pearly within. Umbilicus round, very deep, and bordered by 3 spiral, beaded cords. Operculum circular, multispiral. An uncommon shallow-water species in Puerto Rico. *A. vanhyningi* Rehder, 1939 is a smoothish form of this species.

Arene tricarinata Stearns, 1872   Three-corded Arene
Plate 7 i

Southeast U. S. to the West Indies.

About ⅛ inch in diameter, turbinate in shape. Color white or tan with brown or reddish speckling. Body whorl sculptured with 3 beaded spiral cords on the squarish periphery. The entire shell is covered by delicate microscopic axial threads. Suture minutely channeled and bounded below by a beaded spiral cord. Umbilicus round, deep, and bordered by 7 to 9 distinct beads. Common from shallow dredgings. *Liotia (Arene) gemma* Tuomey and Holmes is this species.

Genus Cyclostrema Marryat, 1818

Cyclostrema cancellatum Marryat, 1818   Cancellate Cyclostreme
Plate 7 c

Southeast Florida to the West Indies.

½ inch in diameter, flat-topped. Color dull-white. Surface cancellate by 15 to 17 low, axial ribs which are nodulous when crossing the 12 smaller spiral cords. Periphery angulate, with 3 spiral cords. Umbilicus deep. This is a relatively rare species which inhabits rocky bottoms. Kay Yates found a very good specimen of this beautiful little species on the beach, just north of Rincón Lighthouse — a new record for Puerto Rico.

Subfamily TURBININAE
Genus *Turbo* Linné, 1758
Subgenus *Marmarostoma* Swainson, 1829

Turbo castanea Gmelin, 1791   Chestnut Turban
Plate 7 k

Southeast U. S., Texas, and the West Indies.

1 inch in length, turbinate. Color gray, orange, or brown, commonly spotted with white. Sculpture consists of close set, revolving nodulous cords. Aperture rounded, white or pearly in fresh specimens. Operculum calcareous. Callus on columella heavy. Very common under rocks all around the island. *Turbo versicolor* Usticke, 1959 (non Gmelin, 1791), *muricatus* Usticke, 1959 (non Linné) and *T. crenulatus* Gmelin, 1791 are synonyms.

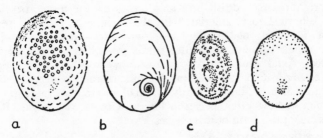

Text fig. 11. Various *Turbinidae* opercula. a, *Astraea caelata*, outer calcareous surface, pustulose; b, under surface of same showing where the foot muscle is attached; c, *A. tuber*, outer calcareous surface with a thick, arched, tapering ridge; d, *Turbo castanea*, outer calcareous surface, smoothish.

Subgenus *Taeniaturbo* Woodring, 1928

Turbo canaliculatus Hermann, 1781   Channeled Turban
Plate 7 n

Lower Florida Keys and the West Indies.

2 to 3 inches in length, turbinate. Color tan, spotted with white, orange, and dark brown. A deep, smooth channel runs just below the suture. Sculpture consists of 16 to 18 strong, spiral, smooth cords on body whorl. Umbilicus narrow. Formerly *T. spenglerianus* Gmelin, 1791. A deep-water species.

GENUS *Astraea* Röding, 1798
Subgenus *Lithopoma* Gray, 1850

Astraea caelata Gmelin, 1791   Carved Star-Shell
Plate 8 j

Southeast Florida and the West Indies.

2 to 3 inches in diameter, pyramidal. Color dirty-white or greenish, mottled with reddish brown. Sculpture consists of strong, revolving ridges crossed by oblique, hollow, scale-like spines. Base has a series of deep, revolving scaly ridges. Operculum oval, thick, white on the outside and finely pustulose. Moderately common in shallow water, especially on the "Cayos".

Astraea tuber Linné, 1758   Green Star-shell
Plate 8 h

Southeast Florida and the West Indies.

1 to 2 inches in diameter, rather elevated. Color green and white, mottled with brown. Sculpture consists of fine and coarse oblique ridges on the upper part of the whorls. Base somewhat rounded and comparatively smooth. Operculum brown on the inside; exterior with a thick, arched, tapering ridge (like a comma). A common shallow-water species, found with *A. caelata*.

Subgenus *Astralium* Link, 1807

Astraea phoebia Röding, 1798   Long-spined Star-shell
Plate 8 g

Southeast Florida and the West Indies.

2 to 2½ inches in diameter, low, nearly flat below. Characterized by the flat, triangular spines at the periphery of the whorls. Color white, yellowish, or light-brown; inside of aperture silvery pearl. Usually with umbilicus, but sometimes without. A very closely related species, *Astraea brevispina* Lamarck, has shorter and less conspicuous spines and a splotch of bright orange-red around the umbilical region. *A. phoebia* is

fairly abundant in Puerto Rico but *brevispina* has not been reported from this area as yet. Formerly *longispina* Lamarck.

Subgenus *Calcar* Montfort, 1810

Astraea tecta Solander, 1786   Imbricated Star-shell
                                                               Plate 8 i
Greater and Lesser Antilles.

1 inch in diameter, elevated, conical, color light-brown to ash-white. Characterized by its long, strong axial ribs which extend to the base of the shell. Base flattened, radiately striated, scalloped at the periphery. Not common in Puerto Rico. Alias *A. imbricata* Gmelin, 1791.

Family *PHASIANELLIDAE*
Subfamily *TRICOLIINAE*
GENUS *Tricolia* Risso, 1826

Tricolia affinis C. B. Adams, 1850   Polka-dot Pheasant
                                                               Plate 8 a
Lower Florida Keys and the West Indies.

¼ to ⅜ inch in length, moderately elongate, and smooth. Color rose or orange-brown, with numerous small red and white dots which are usually paired. Frequently with red zigzag axial bars and white streaks. Umbilicus slit-like. This species is larger than any of the other *Tricolia* found in the West Indies. Previously listed as *Phasianella umbilicata*. Found living on marine grass. Not uncommon all around Puerto Rico.

Tricolia adamsi Philippi, 1853   Adams' Pheasant
                                                               Plate 8 c
West Indies and the coast of Central America.

Less than 3/16 inch in length, fairly thin and subglobose. Color light-pink, spotted with red dots, except for white triangles below the suture. This species can be separated from *T. affinis* by smaller size and lower spire. In this species the small red dots are not constantly paired with white dots as they are in *T. affinis*. Less common than the other species of *Tricolia*.

Tricolia thalassicola Robertson, 1958   Thalassia Pheasant
                                                               Plate 8 d
Southeast U. S., West Indies to Brazil.

Just over ¼ inch in length, with rounded whorls. Color cream, with large, regularly-spaced, brown, orange, or olive-green spots. In addition there are 7 pairs of axial to oblique flames of color on the body whorl just below the suture and the periphery. Found living on turtlegrass (*Thalassia testudinum* Konig). Previously listed as *P. umbilicata*.

Tricolia bella M. Smith, 1937   Shouldered Pheasant
Plate 8 f

Southeast Florida, the West Indies to Brazil.

Less than ¼ inch in length, with shouldered whorls. Color variable, usually tan or white with pink, orange, red and brown dots or flames. Characterized by its sculpture of numerous, very small, beaded spiral cords. There is also a smooth form of this species, but we have not found it in Puerto Rico. Common from shallow-water dredgings. *T. pulchella* C. B. Adams is this species.

Tricolia tessellata Potiez and Michaud, 1838   Checkered Pheasant
Plate 8 b

West Indies.

Less than ¼ inch in length, similar to *T. affinis* but usually smaller and not as elongated; the spire is more blunt. Characterized by the narrow, spiral bands of orange or red that descend obliquely over the whorls. Some specimens are completely dark-brown. Found in association with *T. affinis* but much more common all around Puerto Rico.

Superfamily NERITACEA
Family NERITIDAE
Subfamily NERITINAE
GENUS *Nerita* Linné, 1758

Nerita peloronta Linné, 1758   Bleeding Tooth
Plate 9 g

Southeast Florida, Bermuda, and the West Indies.

¾ to 1½ inches in length, coarsely sculptured with spiral cords which are strongest on the early whorls. Color yellowish with red and black zigzag markings. Parietal area stained blood-red around the 2 or 3 white teeth. Operculum a beautiful orange and brown. Very abundant on the rocks between tide lines throughout the West Indies.

Nerita versicolor Gmelin, 1791   Four-toothed Nerite
Plate 9 k

Southern Florida, Bermuda and the West Indies.

¾ to 1 inch in length, coarsely sculptured with spiral cords throughout. Color white, variegated with red and black. Parietal area white to yellowish and with 4 strong teeth. Operculum brownish gray, finely papillose on the upper surface and smooth below. Very common on the ocean-swept rocks. *N. nigrocincta* Usticke, 1959 (not Röding, 1798) is a synonym.

Nerita tessellata Gmelin, 1791   Tessellated Nerite
Plate 9 h

Florida to Texas, Bermuda, and the West Indies.

¾ inch in length. Color white, checked with black; sometimes the entire shell is black with a few white markings. Sculpture consists of strong, spiral cords. Parietal area with 2 weak teeth in the center. Operculum pustulous, black. Very common on and under rocks between tides throughout the West Indies.

Nerita fulgurans Gmelin, 1791   Antillean Nerite
Plate 9 i

Southeast Florida, Bermuda, and the West Indies.

¾ to 1¼ inches in length, very similar to *N. tessellata,* but with a lighter colored, yellowish gray operculum. The mouth is relatively wide, the teeth are more prominent, and the parietal area tends to have a yellowish cast to it. This is a salt- to brackish-water inhabitant. Uncommon in Puerto Rico.

GENUS *Puperita* Gray, 1857
Subgenus *Puperita* Gray, 1857

Puperita pupa Linné, 1767   Zebra Nerita
Plate 9 a

Southeast Florida and the West Indies.

⅓ to ½ inch in length, smooth, white with zebra-like black stripes. Interior yellow-orange. Columella teeth very weak. Operculum light-yellow. Lives above high-water mark; common in tide pools. The allied species *P. tristis* Orbigny has not been reported from Puerto Rico.

GENUS *Neritina* Lamarck, 1816
Subgenus *Vitta* Mörch, 1852

Neritina virginea Linné, 1758   Virgin Nerite
Plate 9 f

Florida to Texas, Bermuda, and the West Indies.

¼ to ¾ inch in length, smooth and polished. Color patterns and shades show an endless variety, from white, yellow, red, purple, olive, and black with mottling, polka-dots, stripes, and zigzag markings. Parietal area white or yellow with many, small, irregular teeth. Operculum usually black and smooth. Very common on intertidal and brackish water mud flats in Puerto Rico and other Caribbean Islands.

Neritina meleagris Lamarck, 1822   Scaly Nerite
Plate 9 j

Central America and the Antilles to South America.

About ½ inch in length, smooth, glossy. Color brownish olive to bluish gray. The color pattern has the effect of imbricating scales with a white edge. This character helps to separate it from the other *Neritina*. Columella edge bears small, irregular teeth varying in size, from about 4 to 10 in number. A brackish- to salt-water species. Uncommon in Puerto Rico.

Neritina clenchi Russell, 1940　　　　　　　　　　Clench Nerite
Plate 9 c

Florida, Central America, and the Antilles.

¾ to 1 inch in length, smooth, glossy. Color patterns and shades resembling *N. virginea* in their variability. It can be separated from *virginea* by its large size and less globose form. The edge of the parietal area opposite parietal teeth is outlined with dark orange-yellow; in *N. virginea* it is outlined in black. Operculum opaque, calcareous, and black to pink. This species prefers fresh- or brackish-water. R. Coté collected numerous live specimens from Tortuguero Lagoon, located on the north coast of Puerto Rico.

Neritina piratica Russell, 1940　　　　　　　　　　Netted Nerite
Plate 9 b

Central America, Antilles to South America.

About ¾ inch in length, smoothish. Color brownish yellow or olive-green with black zigzag axial lines forming a reticulated network over the shell. Columella edge bears very small irregular teeth. A brackish-water species inhabiting swampy areas. Not common in Puerto Rico.

Neritina punctulata Lamarck, 1816　　　　　　　　Spotted Nerite
Plate 9 d

Central America and the Antilles.

¾ to 1 inch in length, and with a smooth, dull surface. Color usually purplish pink with many suboval whitish spots. The spots are outlined on the aperture end by a heavy black line. Spire very low and rounded. Parietal area smooth and flat. Columella area white, bearing no teeth or very faint irregular ones. This is a fresh-water species but dead shells are found on the beaches and for this reason it is included for comparison.

Neritina reclivata Say, 1822　　　　　　　　　　　Olive Nerite

Florida, Texas, and the West Indies to South America.

½ inch in length, globose, thin, glossy, commonly with the spire eroded away. Color brownish green, olive or brownish yellow with numerous axial lines of black, brown or lavender. Parietal area smooth, bluish white to yellowish and bearing a variable number of fine, irregular teeth on the columellar edge. Like the above species, this is a brackish- to fresh-water species which we include for comparison. Reported from Vieques by Dall and Simpson.

Subfamily SMARAGDIINAE
GENUS *Smaragdia* Issel, 1869
Subgenus *Smaragdia* Issel, 1869

Smaragdia viridis viridemaris Maury, 1917   Emerald Nerite
                                                                      Plate 9 e

Southeast Florida, the West Indies, and Bermuda.

¼ to ⅓ inch in length, smooth and shiny. Color bright-green or yellowish with a few small, white or purple markings. Parietal area white or light-green with 7 to 9 minute teeth. Operculum light-green, glossy and smooth, except for microscopic lines. Abundant in turtlegrass beds in shallow water. True *S. viridis viridis* Linné, 1758 comes from the Mediterranean. *S. v. merida* Dall, 1903, is a fossil from Florida and may be this subspecies. *S. v. weyssei* Russell, 1940 is the same.

Family PHENACOLEPADIDAE
GENUS *Phenacolepas* Pilsbry, 1891

Phenacolepas hamillei Fischer, 1856   Hamille's Limpet
                                                                      Plate 6 i

Florida Keys and the West Indies.

About ¼ inch in length, fragile, limpet-like (*Acmaea*) in shape. White or straw-colored. Apex recurved and to one side. Surface sculpture with numerous, fine, raised radiating lines and irregular concentric growth lines. Interior smooth and polished. Reasonably common from shallow dredgings in Puerto Rico.

Family COCCULINIDAE
GENUS *Cocculina* Dall, 1882

Cocculina portoricensis Dall and Simpson, 1901   Puerto Rico Cocculina

Puerto Rico.

Described from San Juan Harbor, in 310 fathoms. We have not found this species.

Order MESOGASTROPODA
Superfamily LITTORINACEA
Family LITTORINIDAE
GENUS *Littorina* Férussac, 1822
Subgenus *Melarhaphe* Menke, 1828

Littorina ziczac Gmelin, 1791   Zebra Periwinkle
                                                                      Plate 9 - 1

South half of Florida to Texas, the West Indies and Bermuda.

Female shells about 1 inch long and about half as wide; males about ½ inch in length and ½ inch in width. Shell moderately thick. Color gray, with oblique, wavy, or zigzag lines of brown or purplish brown. Aperture and columella various shades of brown. Operculum dark-brown (fig. 6d). Very abundant on the rocks at low tide. *L. interrupta* Philippi, 1856 and *lineata* Orbigny, 1842 are synonyms.

Littorina nebulosa Lamarck, 1822   Cloudy Periwinkle
Plate 9 p

West Indies.

½ to ¾ inch in length, moderately thick and dull. First 2 or 3 whorls worn smooth; spiral lines present on other whorls. Columella area long, wide, smooth, and without umbilicus. Color variable, bluish white or dirty yellow, commonly with reddish brown speckling, especially in young shells. Operculum pale mahogany-brown. A subspecies, *L. nebulosa tessellata* Philippi, has also been reported from Puerto Rico. It differs from the typical form in having a fairly regular checked pattern of brownish red on a grayish white background. *L. nebulosa* is not as common as the other littorines in Puerto Rico.

Subgenus *Littoraria* Gray, 1834

Littorina angulifera Lamarck, 1822   Angulate Periwinkle
Plate 9 s

South half of Florida, Bermuda and the West Indies.

1 to 1½ inches in length, thin but solid. Color yellowish to reddish brown with darker markings. Columella pale purplish in the central part; the edges are whitish. Sculpture consists of many fine, spiral grooves, except on the first 2 whorls, which are smooth. Operculum pale-brown. It is found well above high-tide mark. Usually attached to mangrove roots and trunks. A common species in Puerto Rico.

Subgenus *Neritrema* Récluz, 1869

Littorina meleagris Potiez and Michaud, 1838   Spotted Periwinkle
Plate 9 n

Southern Florida and the West Indies.

⅛ to ¼ inch in length, moderately thick, and with a very thin periostracum. Color light-to dark-brown with white spots, more or less in spiral rows. Fairly common on rocks in the intertidal zone. Previously listed as *L. guttata* Philippi, 1847.

Littorina mespillum Mühlfeld, 1824   Dwarf Periwinkle
Plate 9 m

Key West, Florida, and the Caribbean Area.

¼ inch in length with a low spire; periostracum brown and thin. Color white to brown, sometimes with rows of small round blackish spots. Columella and aperture glossy brown; umbilicus chink-like. Lives in splash pools from high-tide line to 6 or 7 feet above. Reported from San Juan by Gundlach. Rare in Puerto Rico.

GENUS *Nodilittorina* von Martens, 1897
Subgenus *Echinolittorina* Habe, 1956

Nodilittorina tuberculata Menke, 1828   Common Prickly-winkle
                                                                    Plate 9 r

South Florida, Bermuda and the West Indies.

½ to ¾ inch in length, rounded at the base. Several spiral rows of small, fairly sharp nodules are lined up axially one under the other. Color brownish gray. Columella flattened, often excavated and forming a shelf. Operculum paucispiral (see text fig. 12). Common on rocks near the high-tide line. Erroneously listed in most books at *Tectarius tuberculatus* Wood. Previously reported as *Tectarius trochiformis* Dillwyn, 1817 from Puerto Rico.

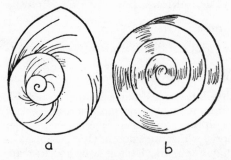

TEXT FIG. 12. Opercula of a, *Nodilittorina tuberculata*, paucispiral; b, *Echininus nodulosus*, multispiral.

a   b

GENUS *Echininus* Clench and Abbott, 1942
Subgenus *Tectininus* Clench and Abbott, 1942

Echininus nodulosus Pfeiffer, 1839   False Prickly-winkle
                                                                    Plate 9 o

Southeast Florida and the West Indies.

½ to 1 inch in length, squarish at the base. Superficially very similar to *Nodilittorina tuberculata* but has a multispiral operculum, columella not shelved. Found high on the rocks. Moderately common.

GENUS *Tectarius* Valenciennes, 1833
Subgenus *Cenchritis* von Martens, 1900

Tectarius muricatus Linné, 1758   Beaded Periwinkle
                                                                    Plate 9 q

Lower Florida Keys, Bermuda, and the West Indies.

½ to 1 inch in length, solid, with several rows of small, rounded white beads. Color light-brown in young specimens, adults ash-gray; interior light-brown. Operculum dark-brown, chitinous, and paucispiral. Very common on the rocks above high-tide line. Specimens have been found living 20 to 30 feet above high tide at Cabo Rojo Light in Puerto Rico.

Superfamily *RISSOACEA*
Family *HYDROBIIDAE*
GENUS *Truncatella* Risso, 1826

Truncatella pulchella Pfeiffer, 1839   Beautiful Truncatella
Plate 10 b

Southeast U. S. and the West Indies.

5.5 to 7.5 mm. in length, white to light-amber. 17 or more rather poorly developed axial costae. Outer lip simple, usually thin. Operculum paucispiral and corneous. Young specimens have the first 2 whorls smooth, with the remaining whorls moderately to rather fully costate. Reasonably common above tide line. Members of this genus are essentially land dwellers.

Truncatella pulchella   Double-lip Truncatella
     form *bilabiata* Pfeiffer, 1840   Plate 10 a

Florida and the West Indies.

Similar to *T. pulchella* but with well-developed costae and a duplex outer lip. Found in moist, shady areas above high-tide line. Not common. *Truncatella subcylindrica* Linné, 1767 previously reported from Puerto Rico, is European. See Johnsonia, vol. 2, no. 25.

Truncatella caribaeensis Reeve, 1842   Caribbean Truncatella
Plate 10 e

Caribbean.

7 to 9 mm. in length. Color white to light-orange. Similar to *pulchella,* but with well-developed axial costae and thickened outer lip. Found under boards and rocks above high-tide line. *T. succinea* C. B. Adams, 1845, is a synonym.

Subgenus *Tomlinitella* Clench and Turner, 1948

Truncatella scalaris Michaud, 1830   Shouldered Truncatella
Plate 10 c

Florida, the Bahamas, and south to the Lesser Antilles.

4.5 to 5.0 mm. in length, gray to orange in color. Sculpture consists of 8 to 11 prominent axial costae and microscopic spiral threads between them. Outer lip double. Operculum thin and corneous. Common above high tide on the south coast of Puerto Rico.

Truncatella scalaris clathrus Lowe, 1832   West Indian Truncatella
Plate 10 d

West Indies.
Differs from *T. scalaris* in having 13 to 16 costae instead of 8 to 11. Uncommon in Puerto Rico.

Family *RISSOIDAE*
Subfamily *RISSOINAE*
GENUS *Rissoina* Orbigny, 1840
Subgenus *Rissoina* Orbigny, 1840

Rissoina bryerea Montagu, 1803   Caribbean Risso
Plate 10 m

South Florida to the Lesser Antilles.

4.5 to 6 mm. in length, white, with 16 to 22 slightly slanting, strong, axial ribs per whorl. Spiral threads may be present on the base of the shell. Operculum yellow, paucispiral and corneous. One of the most common *Rissoina* species in Puerto Rico, from shallow dredgings. The word *Rissoina* is pronounced "riss-o-ee-na".

Rissoina fischeri Desjardin, 1949   Fischer's Risso
Plate 10 n

Cuba and Puerto Rico.

Similar in appearance to *R. bryerea* but with strongly convex whorls; suture deep. 10 to 15 curving axial ribs. Lip thin. Color translucent-white. Uncommon around the island of Puerto Rico.

Rissoina multicostata C. B. Adams, 1850   Many-Ribbed Risso
Plate 10 h

Southeast Florida and the West Indies.

6 to 7 mm. in length, white to cream. About 7 whorls, the first glossy and smooth; others sculptured with about 28 very regular ribs. Numerous spiral striae between the ribs; these striae are stronger at the base where they cross the longitudinal ribs. Found at the northwest end of Puerto Rico. Uncommon.

Subgenus *Schwartziella* Nevill, 1884

Rissoina chesneli Michaud, 1830   Chesnel's Risso

Southeast U. S. and the West Indies.

3 to 5 mm. in length, shiny white. Sculptured with 10 to 15 axial

ribs. Whorls 8, somewhat rounded, suture fairly deep. Strong tooth on the inner side of outer lip. Not common.

Subgenus *Zebinella* Mörch, 1876

Rissoina striatocostata Orbigny, 1842   Antillean Risso

Antilles.

7 to 8 mm. in length, with 8 to 10 almost flat whorls. Color white to yellow. The nuclear whorls (first 2 or 3) are glassy and without sculpture. Sculpture consists of numerous longitudinal and spiral threads; the longitudinal threads are fewer and more prominent on the earlier whorls. The spiral threads are strongest on the lowest part of the body whorl. Common all around Puerto Rico.

Rissoina decussata Montagu, 1803   Decussate Risso
                                                       Plate 10 o
North Carolina to the Lesser Antilles.

6 to 8 mm. in length, glossy-white, with 25 to 30 weak axial ribs which are finely and spirally striated. Closely resembling *R. striato-costata* but less slender; and with less pronounced sutures. Obtained from shallow dredgings.

Subgenus *Phosinella* Mörch, 1876

Rissoina cancellata Philippi, 1847   Cancellated Risso
                                                       Plate 10 - 1
Southeast Florida and the West Indies.

8 mm. in length, elongate; color white to tan. Surface strongly cancellated with 16 to 18 longitudinal ribs and 4 or 5 spiral ribs, which become more numerous on the base. Basal notch well-developed. Operculum light-brown, paucispiral and corneous. Common on beaches and in shallow dredgings all around Puerto Rico.

Subgenus *Morchiella* Nevill, 1881

Rissoina striosa C. B. Adams, 1850   Striate Risso
                                                       Plate 10 i
Southeast Florida and the West Indies.

5 to 10 mm., white to cream. Sculptured with transverse folds which are obsolete on the lower part of the middle whorls and on most of the last whorls. Spiral striae deeply impressed and crowded. Suture moderately impressed. Apex acute with glassy nuclear whorls. Fairly common in drift sand in Puerto Rico.

GENUS *Zebina* H. and A. Adams, 1854

Zebina browniana Orbigny, 1842   Smooth Risso
                                                          Plate 10 f
Carolina, Florida, and the West Indies.

4 to 5 mm. in length, smooth, with nearly flat whorls. Color white, sometimes with 2 or 3 pale-brown bands; highly polished. Apex acute, aperture rather small, outer lip thickened. Dead shells are common in drift sand on beach and in shallow dredgings. Formerly placed in the genus *Rissoina*.

GENUS *Microdochus* Rehder, 1943

Microdochus floridanus Rehder, 1943   Florida Microdochus
                                                          Plate 10 g
Florida and the West Indies.

About 2 mm in length, ovate-conic, thin, yellowish. Postnuclear whorls convex, finely spirally lirate. Umbilicus narrow but distinct, aperture ovate, outer lip simple. Rare from shallow dredgings.

GENUS *Alvania* Risso, 1826

Alvania auberiana Orbigny, 1842   West Indian Alvania
                                                          Plate 10 k
West Indies.

About 2 mm. in length, globose, slightly umbilicated. Color yellowish-white. Whorls 5, first 2 smooth, others sculptured with axial and spiral ribs. Axial and spiral sculpture of about the same intensity, except at the base of the body whorl where the longitudinal ribs disappear and only the spiral ones remain. Aperture subcircular. Uncommon.

Alvania gradata Orbigny, 1842   Shouldered Alvania
                                                          Text fig. 13 a
West Indies.

3 mm. in length, short and stout. Color white, sometimes light-orange. There is a deep channel between the whorls. Whorls 6, the first 2 usually smooth; the others sculptured with heavy longitudinal ribs, 12-14 on the body whorl. There are many wavy microscopic spiral striae between the ribs; these are also present below the spiral ridge at the base of the shell. Operculum mahogany-brown, paucispiral, and corneous. Reasonably common from shallow dredgings.

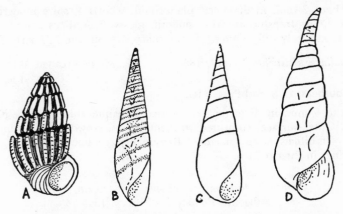

TEXT FIG. 13. Small univalves. a, *Alvania gradata*, 3 mm.; b, *Eulima bifasciata*, ¼ inch; c, *Balcis intermedia* Contraine, ¼ to ½ inch; d, *Stilifer subulatus* Broderip and Sowerby, ½ to ¾ inch.

Alvania aberrans C. B. Adams, 1850   Cerith-like Alvania
                                                  Plate 10 j
West Indies.

About 5 mm. in length, elongate, somewhat resembling a small *Cerithium*. Dull-white; sculpture cancellate. Aperture small, deeply notched anteriorly. Uncommon in beach drift.

Alvania portoricana Dall and Simpson, 1901   Puerto Rican Alvania
                                                  Plate 29 m
Puerto Rico.

3 mm. in length, thin, rather slender, bluish white. Feeble reticulate sculpture on 5 whorls. Dall and Simpson reported one specimen from Mayagüez in 25 fathoms. Rare.

Alvania epima Dall and Simpson, 1901   Epima Alvania

Puerto Rico.

2 mm. in length, subtranslucent, pinkish white. Surface reticulate. Described from Mayagüez, Puerto Rico; found in about 25 fathoms, sand bottom. Rare.

Family VITRINELLIDAE
GENUS *Vitrinella* C. B. Adams, 1850

Vitrinella helicoidea C. B. Adams, 1850   Helix Vitrinella

Southeast U. S. to the West Indies.

About 2 mm. in diameter, planorboid, whorls 4, spire moderately raised. Color translucent-white, smooth, glossy. Umbilicus round, very deep, moderately wide. Outer lip thin, sharp. Uncommon in Puerto Rico.

Vitrinella multistriata Verrill, 1884   Many-threaded Vitrinella
Text fig. 14 g
Southeast U. S. and Puerto Rico.

3 to 5 mm. in diameter, compressed. Opaque-white, with a glossy sheen. Outer surface sculptured with numerous, crowded, spiral incised lines. Umbilicus deep, narrow. Reasonably common from shallow dredgings in Puerto Rico.

GENUS *Cyclostremiscus* Pilsbry and Olsson, 1945
Subgenus *Ponocyclus* Pilsbry, 1953

Cyclostremiscus beaui Fischer, 1857   Beau's Vitrinella
Plate 11 b
Southeast U. S. to the West Indies.

About ⅓ to ½ inch in diameter, depressed. Color opaque-white. Whorls 4, rounded, sculptured with 5 or 6 smooth, spiral threads and numerous, much finer threads between. Umbilicus wide and deep. Uncommon in Puerto Rico.

Cyclostremiscus trilix Bush, 1897   Trilix Vitrinella
Text fig. 14 a
Southeast U. S. to the West Indies.

3-4 mm. in diameter, 4 flattened whorls. Opaque-white. Shell apparently smooth except for 3 spiral cords on the last whorl. Whorls concave on top. Umbilicus deep. Bush reports that the operculum is thin, horny, circular. This is a common species off Cape Hatteras, North Carolina, but rare in Puerto Rico. We have only 2 specimens in our collection.

GENUS *Teinostoma* H. and A. Adams, 1854

Teinostoma obtectum Pilsbry and McGinty, 1945   Plugged Teinostoma
Text fig. 14 b
Florida to the West Indies.

About 2 mm. in diameter, depressed. Color opaque-white. Smooth with a large umbilical callus. Found in drift sand and reasonably common in shallow dredgings.

Teinostoma clavium Pilsbry and McGinty, 1945   Key Teinostoma

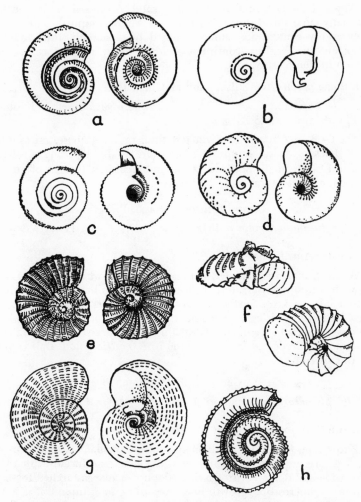

TEXT FIG. 14. Vitrinellidae found in Puerto Rico. a, *Cyclostremiscus trilix* Bush; b, *Teinostoma obtectum* Pilsbry and McGinty; c, *Episcynia inornata* Orbigny; d, *Cochliolepis parasitica* Stimpson; e, *Pleuromalaxis balesi* Pilsbry and McGinty; f, *Macromphalina sp?;* g, *Vitrinella multistriata* Verrill; h, *Spirolaxis exquisita* Dall and Simpson.

Florida and the West Indies.

Approximately 2 mm. in diameter, solid, depressed, white. Surface with many close spiral striae. Periphery of whorls rounded. The base is rather evenly convex, its center occupied by a smooth, thick, slightly convex umbilical callus, continuous with a heavy parietal callus. Not common in Puerto Rico.

Teinostoma parvicallum Pilsbry and McGinty, 1945

Tiny-calloused Teinostoma

Florida and Puerto Rico.

Shell 1.8 to 2.2 mm. in diameter, thin, rather globose, milky-translucent. Lacking spiral sculpture. There are 4 slightly convex whorls. Umbilical callus small, but closing the umbilicus at all stages of growth. Uncommon, shallow water to 50 fathoms.

GENUS *Episcynia* Mörch, 1875

Episcynia inornata Orbigny, 1842   Hairy Vitrinella
                                                      Text fig. 14 c
Greater Antilles.

About 2 mm. in diameter, depressed, vitreous-white, whorls 5, convex, with a minutely serrate peripheral keel. Umbilicus deep, bounded by an angle or keel. Surface nearly smooth under the periostracum, which bears spiral fringes of filaments above and below the periphery. The operculum and living animal of this species are still unknown. Not uncommon in dredgings from 30 to 100 ft. *E. multicarinata* Dall is probably this species.

GENUS *Cochliolepis* Stimpson, 1858

Cochliolepis parasitica Stimpson, 1858   Parasitic Vitrinella
                                                       Text fig. 14 d
South Carolina to the West Indies.

2 to 4 mm. in maximum diameter, thin, discoidal, flattened on top, with 3 whorls rapidly increasing in size. Color translucent-white. Umbilicus wide and deep. Peristome thin, the upper margin arched forward. Sculpture of microscopic growth lines. According to Stimpson, it is found living under the scales of the annelid worm, *Acoetes lupina,* in South Carolina. Our specimens were dredged from shallow water. Uncommon.

GENUS *Leptogyra* Bush, 1897

Leptogyra inconspicua Bush, 1897   Inconspicuous Leptogyra

Puerto Rico.

Reported from Mayagüez by Dall and Simpson.

Genus *Parviturboides* Pilsbry and McGinty, 1950

Parviturboides comptus Woodring, 1928   Miniature Turbo
Plate 11 c

Jamaica (fossil), Puerto Rico.

About 2 mm. in diameter, stout, thick, umbilicate. Color dull-white. Last whorl sculptured with about 7 strong spiral cords. The upper 2 are rather strongly nodulose where they are crossed by the low axial ribs. The intervals between the spiral cords are crossed by fine, closely and evenly-spaced axial threads. Aperture circular, outer and inner lips very thick. Outer lip denticulate. Reasonably common from shallow dredgings. This species was described as a fossil (*Fossarus comptus*) from Jamaica; there is no question that it is still living in Puerto Rico.

Genus *Pleuromalaxis* Pilsbry and McGinty, 1945

Pleuromalaxis balesi Pilsbry and McGinty, 1945   Bales' False Dial
Text fig. 14 e

Florida, Cuba, and Puerto Rico.

Less than 2 mm. in diameter, 3 to 4 whorls, semi-translucent white to tan. Sculptured with fine, spiral striae and strong, widely spaced radial ribs. Peripheral zone flattened or concave between 2 projecting nodulose keels. Rare in Puerto Rico.

Superfamily CERITHIACEA
Family TURRITELLIDAE
Genus *Turritella* Lamarck, 1799

Turritella variegata Linné, 1758   Variegated Turret shell
Plate 3 - 1; 11 h

West Indies.

3½ to 4½ inches in length. Color pale-brown and variegated with reddish brown and purplish brown. Aperture rounded to subquadrate. Operculum brown, horny, and multispiral. Whorls nearly flat, but having suture well marked by a slight shoulder above and below. Several specimens were collected at Cataño, P. R., which had some or all whorls distinctly rounded. Very common in shallow bays in Puerto Rico.

Turritella exoleta Linné, 1758   Eastern Turret shell
Plate 11 i

South half of Florida and the West Indies.

2 inches in length, elongated. Whorls ridged above and below and concave in the middle. Color yellowish white, obscurely flamed with orange-brown. Rare in Puerto Rico. Found in deep water.

GENUS *Vermicularia* Lamarck, 1799

Vermicularia knorri Deshayes, 1843   Knorr's Worm shell
                                                          Plate 12 c
Southeast U. S. to the West Indies.

Worm-like shell, early whorls evenly and closely coiled, white in color. The later whorls are detached, irregularly drawn out and orange-brown in color. Operculum horny, circular, concave and filling the aperture. Common in sponges. Dead shells are frequently washed ashore.

Vermicularia spirata Philippi, 1836   West Indian Worm shell

Southeast Florida and the West Indies.

Similar to *knorri,* but the early whorls are dark in color. Reported from Mayagüez by Dall and Simpson.

Family *ARCHITECTONICIDAE*
GENUS *Spirolaxis* Monterosato, 1913

Spirolaxis exquisita Dall and Simpson, 1901   Exquisite Spirolax
                                                          Text fig. 14 h
Jamaica (fossil), Cuba, and Puerto Rico.

3 mm. in diameter, with detached whorls; subquadrate in section, with a minutely serrate keel at each angle. Shell translucent-white, polished and smooth between the keels. Quoting Dall and Simpson, "This is one of the most exquisite little gems of the sea that can be imagined". A fairly deep water form (25 to 50 fathoms) obtained from dredgings at Mayagüez. Rare.

GENUS *Heliacus* Orbigny, 1842

Heliacus cylindricus Gmelin, 1791   Cylinder Sundial
                                                          Plate 11 a
Lower Florida Keys and the West Indies.

About ½ inch in diameter, conic, elevated. Color reddish brown to black, often spotted with white just above the suture and on the periphery. Whorls somewhat rounded, sculptured with minutely beaded, closely packed spiral cords. Umbilicus narrow, round, very deep, its border well crenulated. Fairly common at low tide. This is probably *cyclostomus* Menke, 1830.

Heliacus aethiops Menke, 1830

Reported from Puerto Rico by Menke and by Gundlach. This may be a form of *cylindricus.*

Heliacus bisulcatus Orbigny, 1845   Orbigny's Sundial
                                                       Plate 11 f
Southeast U. S. to the West Indies.

¼ to ½ inch in diameter, spire scarcely elevated. Color tan. Whorls flat, sculptured with revolving beaded cords; on the periphery there are two rows of larger beads. Sculpture of the base much like that above. Umbilicus wide and deep, border crenulated. Aperture nearly round, operculum solid conic, chitinous. Previously reported as *Solarium bisulcatum*. Dredged from 15 to 200 fathoms off Puerto Rico.

Heliacus infundibuliformis Gmelin, 1791   Channeled Sundial
                                                       Plate 11 d
West Indies.

⅝ inch in length, spire moderately flattened. Unicolor, light-brown to dark-brown. Whorls separated by a deep channel. Umbilicus wide, fairly deep and decreasing in size; border freely crenulated. Whorls rounded, sculptured by minutely beaded flattened spiral cords. Aperture rounded. Sometimes found on the beach in drift sand.

GENUS *Architectonica* Röding, 1798

Architectonica nobilis Röding, 1798   Common Sundial
                                                       Plate 11 g
Southeast U. S. to the West Indies.

1 to 2 inches in diameter, heavy. Color cream with orange-brown spots. Suture well-marked. Sculpture of 4 or 5 spiral cords which are usually beaded. Umbilicus deep, surrounded by a strongly crenulated spiral cord. Operculum brown and paucispiral. Moderately common in shallow dredgings. *A. granulata* Lamarck is this species.

GENUS *Philippia* Gray, 1847
Subgenus *Psilaxis* Woodring, 1928

Philippia krebsi Mörch, 1875   Krebs' Sundial
                                                       Plate 11 e
Southeast U. S. to the West Indies.

½ inch in diameter. Color tan with light-brown markings, especially prominent at periphery of shell and just below the suture. Glossy smooth on top, except for 2 microscopic spiral threads above the suture. Periphery and base smooth, umbilicus bordered by 2 beaded spiral rows. Operculum chitinous and multispiral. Moderately common from 16 to 63 fathoms.

Family VERMETIDAE
GENUS *Petaloconchus* H. C. Lea, 1843
Subgenus *Macrophragma* Carpenter, 1856

Petaloconchus irregularis Orbigny, 1842   Irregular Worm shell
                                                       Plate 12 h

South half of Florida and the West Indies.

Worm-like shells which are greatly coiled and live in closely packed colonies. Color brown, strongly wrinkled by heavy longitudinal and spiral cords. Common. Attached to rocks.

Petaloconchus erectus Dall, 1888   Erect Worm shell
                                                         Plate 12 a
Southeast Florida and the West Indies.

Similar to *P. irregularis* but with the last part of the tube rising vertically or nearly so. It is smaller, smoother and white or cream in color. Uncommon, attached to rocks and dead coral.

Petaloconchus mcgintyi Olsson and Harbison, 1953
                                              McGinty's Worm shell
                                                         Plate 12 e
Florida and Puerto Rico.

Worm-like, solitary, attached by the earliest whorls. Easily recognized by the long, erect terminal tube rising from the center. Color pinkish brown. Surface smoothish or wrinkled with growth lines and exceedingly faint, pustulose spiral threads. A common species on the coral reefs off La Parguera on the south coast of Puerto Rico and at Vieques. When first described, this species was temporarily placed in the genus *Lemintina*. *Lemintina* are without opercula. Our specimens have a chitinous, multispiral operculum.

Petaloconchus floridanus Olsson and Harbison, 1953
                                              Florida Worm shell
                                                         Plate 12 i
Florida to the West Indies.

Shell solitary or in clusters of few individuals, small or of medium size. Irregularly coiled, attached by one side along its whole length to some object; when mature, the coiling relaxes, the end often becoming free and drawn-out. Surface coarsely reticulate.

GENUS *Serpulorbis* Sasso, 1827

Serpulorbis decussata Gmelin, 1791   Decussate Worm shell
                                                         Plate 12 d
Southeast U. S. to the West Indies.

A large, heavy, worm-tube mollusk found attached to stones and other shells. The longitudinal ridges are quite prominent. Yellowish to brown. Common. The genus *Lemintina* Risso, 1826 is evidently based upon a worm and not a mollusk.

Serpulorbis riisei (Mörch, 1862)   Riise's Worm shell
                                                    Plate 12 f
West Indies.

Similar to *S. decussatus* but larger, with more pebbly sculpture. Light-brown above and dark-brown below. Common on the northwest coast of Puerto Rico.

Family *SILIQUARIIDAE*
GENUS *Siliquaria* Bruguière, 1789

Siliquaria anguillae (Mörch, 1861)   Slit Worm shell
                                                    Plate 12 g
West Indies.

Shell worm-like with whorls irregularly coiled, unattached throughout. Characterized by the elongated slit on the middle of the whorls. Early whorls white and smooth; later whorls spinose and stained brown. Reasonably common on the northwest coast of Puerto Rico.

Family *CAECIDAE*
GENUS *Caecum* Fleming, 1813
Subgenus *Caecum* Fleming, 1813

Caecum floridanum Stimpson, 1851   Florida Caecum
                                                    Text fig. 15 j
North Carolina to the West Indies.

3-5 mm. in length, white or cream. Sculptured with 20 to 30 strong rings, their intervals and edges finely crenulated by minute longitudinal threads. The last 3 or 4 rings are enlarged and more widely separated. Apical plug with a large pointed prong. Aperture circular, in life closed by a multispiral horny operculum. Very common shallow-water species in Puerto Rico.

Subgenus *Micranellum* Bartsch, 1920

Caecum pulchellum Stimpson, 1851   Beautiful Little Caecum
                                                    Text fig. 15 a
Eastern U. S. and the West Indies.

About 2 mm. in length, translucent and tan when alive, chalky-white when dead. Sculptured with 20 to 30 fine, rounded rings nearly equally spaced. Plug rounded. Operculum dark-brown, concave, and multispiral. The most abundant *Caecum* in Puerto Rico. Found living on grass in shallow water all around the island.

Subgenus *Elephantanellum* Bartsch, 1920

Caecum imbricatum Carpenter, 1858   Imbricate Caecum
                                                    Text fig. 15 g
Florida and the West Indies.

2 to 4 mm. in length, white, with about 14 longitudinal ribs. There are numerous flattish rings which are fairly large at the base and become smaller and more numerous towards the apex. Plug with a fairly long, pointed prong. *C. cooperi* S. Smith is a similar northern species. Fairly common in Puerto Rico.

Caecum insigne de Folin, 1867   Brown Caecum
Text fig. 15 f

Jamaica, Puerto Rico.

About 3 mm. in length and 1 mm. in width, tapering slightly towards the apex. Color white to brown, most specimens having some brown. Sculpture variable; there are 35 to 45 rings crossed by a multitude of longitudinal striae. Some beach-worn specimens are almost smooth. Apical plug with an elongate, oblique, pointed projection. Fairly common in beach drift.

Caecum plicatum Carpenter, 1858   Pleated Caecum
Text fig. 15 i

West Indies.

3 to 5 mm. in length, translucent-white. Sculpture consists of about 20 prominent longitudinal ribs and numerous microscopic circular lines between the ribs at the base only. Lip of aperture with 3 or 4 cancellate, swollen rings. Plug with a small horn-like projection. Reasonably common.

Caecum coronellum Dall, 1892   Coronate Caecum
Text fig. 15 h

Southeast U. S. and the West Indies.

3 to 4 mm. in length, opaque-white. Sculptured with numerous (about 30) slightly raised, equally spaced longitudinal ribs. Lip of aperture with 3 or 4 swollen, denticulate rings. Found living on grass and algae at base of mangrove roots.

Caecum clava de Folin, 1867   Nail Caecum
Text fig. 15 e

West Indies.

2 or 3 mm. in length, white, characterized by a bulge at base. Aperture constricted. Longitudinal ribs with a few rings at the extremities. Plug with a small projection. Obtained from shallow dredgings. Not common.

Subgenus *Fartulum* Carpenter, 1857

Caecum nebulosum Rehder, 1943   Mottled Caecum
Text fig. 15 d

Florida Keys and Puerto Rico.

2 to 3 mm. in length, glossy, white with light-brown and chalk-white

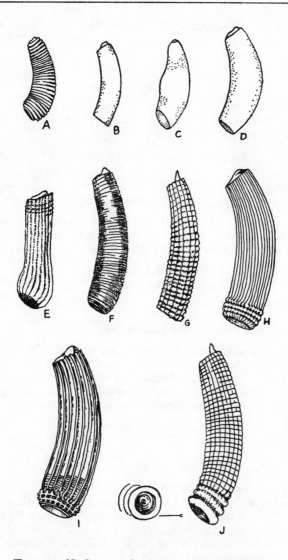

TEXT FIG. 15. Caecums from Puerto Rico. a, *Caecum
pulchellum* Stimpson, (2 mm); b, *C. antillarum* Carpenter (3 mm); c, *C. nitidum* Stimpson, (2 mm); d,
C. nebulosum Rehder, (3 mm); e, *C. clava* de Folin,
(2 to 3 mm); f, *C. insigne* de Folin, (3 mm); g, *C.
imbricatum* Carpenter, (2 to 4 mm); h, *C. coronellum* Dall, (3 to 4 mm); i, *C. plicatum* Carpenter, (3
to 5 mm); j, *C. floridanum*, (3 to 5 mm).

mottling. Smooth. Resembling *C. nitidum,* but larger, not swollen in the middle, and with a nonconstricted aperture. Reasonably common from shallow dredgings.

Caecum antillarum Carpenter, 1858   Antillean Caecum
                                                       Text fig. 15 b

West Indies.

About 3 mm. in length, fragile, glossy, white. Smooth, except for microscopic lines. Rare.

Subgenus *Meioceras* Carpenter, 1858

Caecum nitidum Stimpson, 1851   Little Horn Caecum
                                                       Text fig. 15 c

Southern half of Florida and the West Indies.

2 mm. in length, glossy, white to pale-brown with irregular chalk-white mottling. Smooth, swollen in the middle, and with an oblique, constricted aperture. Very common from shallow dredgings.

Family PLANAXIDAE
GENUS *Planaxis* Lamarck, 1822

Planaxis lineatus da Costa, 1778   Dwarf Atlantic Planaxis
                                                       Plate 13 f

Lower Florida Keys and the West Indies.

¼ inch long, solid. Color whitish-cream, with close, revolving brown bands; sometimes uniformly white. Sculpture consists of small spiral cords which are much more distinct on the upper whorls and base, obsolete elsewhere. Aperture oval, operculum corneous, light-brown. Periostracum thin and translucent. Common on intertidal rocks all around Puerto Rico.

Planaxis nucleus Bruguière, 1789   Black Atlantic Planaxis
                                                       Plate 13 a

Southeast Florida and the West Indies.

½ inch long, solid, polished and dark-brown. Sculptured throughout with rather widely-spaced grooves, which are well-marked below the suture, on the base and behind the outer lip, but are faint elsewhere. Outer lip thick, grooved within. Columella area dished; basal notch deep and well-marked. Periostracum gray-black, and smooth. A fairly common littoral species.

Family MODULIDAE
GENUS *Modulus* Gray, 1842

Modulus modulus Linné, 1758   Atlantic Modulus
                                                       Plate 11 j

Florida to Texas and the West Indies.

About ½ inch in length, solid, umbilicate. Color grayish-white flecked with brown. Sculpture consists of many revolving cords and a series of rather strong radiating ribs. Outer lip strongly ridged within; columella terminated by a prominent tooth-like projection. Operculum circular, reddish brown, multispiral. Common on seaweed in shallow water.

Modulus carchedonius Lamarck, 1822   Angled Modulus
                                                                   Plate 11 k

Greater Antilles south to the northern coast of South America.

Not as common as *M. modulus* and differs from it in having the periphery of the shell well angulated and lacking axial ribs. The spiral cords are smaller and neater; its columella tooth is never colored. Lives in water 6 to 18 feet deep. This species is listed as *Modulus catenulata* Philippi by Dall and Simpson.

Family POTAMIDIDAE
Subfamily POTAMIDINAE
GENUS *Cerithidea* Swainson, 1840

Cerithidea costata da Costa, 1778   Turret Horn Shell
                                                                   Plate 13 s

Florida and the West Indies.

½ inch in length, tan to dark-brown in color. Whorls 9 to 12, very convex. Sculpture consists of prominent, thick ribs, of which there are 25 to 30 on the whorl above the body whorl. Found in large numbers on the mud flats and mangrove swamps. A form, *C. c. turrita* Stearns, differs in having only 15 to 20 axial ribs on the next to the last whorl.

Cerithidea beattyi Bequaert, 1942   Beaded Horn Shell
                                                                   Plate 13 t

Bahamas, Puerto Rico, Virgin Islands, Bermuda, and Trinidad.

Differs from the above species by having 2 or 3 spiral grooves which divide the vertical ribs into tubercles. Tubercles vary from low and elongated to rounded and bead-like. Some of the specimens of this species are pure-white, others are yellow to dark-brown. Found on the mudflats with *C. costata*. A brackish-water species. This may be a form of *costata*.

Cerithidea pliculosa Menke, 1829   Plicate Horn Shell
                                                                   Plate 13 u

Texas, Louisiana, and the West Indies.

About 1 inch in length, brown, with 11 to 13 slightly convex whorls. Sculpture consists of many vertical ribs and spiral threads and prominent former varices. The base of shell has 6 to 9 spiral ridges. A brackish-water snail.

Subfamily BATILLARIINAE
GENUS *Batillaria* Benson, 1842

Batillaria minima Gmelin, 1791   False Cerith
Plate 13 v

South half of Florida and the West Indies.

½ to ¾ inch in length. Variable in size, shape, and sculpture. 10 to
20% of shells deformed in some localities. Color varies from light-gray
to completely black; most shells have dark and light spiral bands.
Sculpture consists of uneven spiral threads and coarse axial swellings
Lip simple, mouth smooth inside. Operculum multispiral. An abundant
shallow brackish-water species. Dall and Simpson reported a variety of
this species from San Juan Harbor as *Pyrazus degeneratus* Dall, 1894.

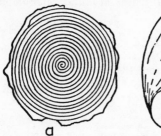 

TEXT FIG. 16. Opercula of a, *Batillaria*, multispiral; b, *Cerithium*,
paucispiral.

Family CERITHIIDAE
GENUS *Cerithium* Bruguière, 1789

Cerithium litteratum Born, 1778   Stocky Cerith
Plate 13 o

Southeast Florida, Bermuda, and the West Indies.

About 1 inch long and ½ inch wide. Sculptured with numerous
spiral threads; there is a shoulder just below the suture on which there
is a spiral row of 9 to 12 prominent sharp nodules. Color whitish, finely
maculated with brown to black. Not uncommon in shallow water where
there is sand and algae. *C. litteratum* form *semiferrugineum* Lamarck
was reported from Vieques and Culebra by Dall and Simpson.

Cerithium variabile C. B. Adams, 1845   Dwarf Cerith
Plate 13 w

South half of Florida to Texas and the West Indies.

⅓ to ½ inch in length, not elongate. Color tan to dark-brown.
Often confused with *Batillaria minima*. The *Cerithium* differs, however,
in the more rounded nodules, and the inside of the mouth is thickened
and toothed; there is also a broad channel in the upper corner where
the outer lip joins the body whorl. Operculum paucispiral with an

eccentric nucleus. Common under rocks in shallow water. Some authorities use *lutosum* Menke, 1828, for this species.

Cerithium eburneum Bruguière, 1792   Ivory Cerith
Plate 13 n

Southeast Florida, the Bahamas, and the Greater Antilles.

¾ to 1 inch in length, moderately elongated. Similar to *algicola* but each whorl has 4 to 6 rows of from 18 to 22 small rounded beads. There are usually a number of former varices. Color variable; all white or cream, or speckled with brown. A shallow-water species: Dall and Simpson (1901) reported this species in Puerto Rico under the dubious name of *uncinatum* Gmelin.

Cerithium algicola C. B. Adams, 1845   Middle-spined Cerith
Plate 13 p

Southern Florida and the West Indies.

1 to 1½ inches in length. Differs from *litteratum* in being more elongate and having its most prominent nodules in the middle of the whorl instead of just below the suture. Former varices seldom present. Color whitish with light- or dark-brown spiral lines or blotches. This species may only be a form of *C. eburneum* Bruguière. Common in shallow water.

Cerithium auricoma Schwengel, 1940   Schwengel's Cerith
Plate 13 q

Florida and Puerto Rico.

About 1¾ inches in length, strong, solid. Color white with light-brown spiral striae. The last 4 whorls are sculptured with 8 rounded axial ribs per whorl; over all is a sculpture of fine spiral threads. On the last whorl there is a strong varix opposite the aperture. Dead specimens of this species were obtained from dredgings at the U. S. Naval Base, Roosevelt Roads, by James Poling, and from San Juan Bay by T. and L. Arnow. Rare.

Genus Bittium Gray, 1847
Subgenus Bittiolum Cossmann, 1906

Bittium varium Pfeiffer, 1840   Variable Bittium
Plate 13 h

Maryland to Florida, Texas, Mexico, and the West Indies.

⅛ inch in length, light to dark-brown in color, commonly translucent. Whorls rounded, with a well-marked suture; delicately cancellate, usually with a thickened former varix. Very abundant in shallow water.

Genus Alabina Dall, 1902

Alabina cerithidioides Dall, 1889   Miniature Horn Shell
Plate 13 b

Florida and the West Indies.

2 to 4 mm. in length, slender. Color cream to light-brown. 8 to 10 whorls, the first 3 smooth. Remaining whorls with narrow, curved axial ribs and faint revolving threads. Aperture somewhat rounded, outer lip thin. Columella feebly curved and ending in a slight lip below, behind which is a small narrow umbilicus. Reported as *Bittium cerithidioide* by Dall and Simpson.

Subfamily *LITIOPINAE*
GENUS *Litiopa* Rang, 1829

Litiopa melanostoma Rang, 1829   Brown Sargassum Snail
                                                                      Plate 13 g

In floating sargassum weed.

⅛ to ¼ inch in length, moderately elongated, with 7 whorls, the last being larger than all the other whorls combined. Color light-brown and translucent. Devoid of sculpture, except for numerous microscopic, revolving threads. There is a strong ridge just inside the aperture on the columella.

Subfamily *CERITHIOPSINAE*
GENUS *Alaba* H. and A. Adams, 1853

Alaba incerta Orbigny, 1842   Uncertain Miniature Cerith
                                                                      Plate 13 r

Bermuda, Bahamas, southeast Florida to the Lesser Antilles and Central America.

¼ inch in length, elongated, with about 13 rounded whorls which gradually increase in size. Nuclear whorls dark-brown and smooth, remainder whitish, often mottled with light-brown and sculptured with numerous fine spiral lines. Usually with a number of rounded varices on the whorls. A later name for this is *A. tervaricosa* C. B. Adams. A common shallow-water species.

GENUS *Cerithiopsis* Forbes and Hanley, 1851

Cerithiopsis greeni C. B. Adams, 1839   Green's Miniature Cerith

Cape Cod to Florida and the West Indies.

⅛ inch in length, elongate, glossy-brown. Whorls 9-12, embryonic ones smooth, translucent; other whorls sculptured with 3 spiral rows of glossy beads connected by spiral and axial threads. A shallow-water species.

Cerithiopsis emersoni C. B. Adams, 1838   Awl Miniature Cerith
                                                                      Plate 13 c

Massachusetts to the West Indies.

½ to ¾ inch in length, slender, and with about 16 whorls. Color tan and brown with the suture sometimes darker. Suture well-marked.

Sculpture consists of 2 revolving rows of many distinct, raised, rounded beads, with a revolving thread between them. In some specimens faint axial riblets connect the beads. Base concave with curved radiating growth lines. Common in shallow dredgings and in drift sand. Previously listed as *Cerithiopsis subulatum* Montagu. The genus is neuter in gender.

Cerithiopsis pupa Dall and Simpson, 1901   Pupa Miniature Cerith
    Puerto Rico.

⅛ inch in length, white, with a brown spiral row of nodules just above the suture. Nuclear whorls usually missing; 6 remaining whorls with 2 rows of white nodules in front of the suture followed by a single brown row. The base has 3 strong spirals. Uncommon.

Cerithiopsis latum C. B. Adams, 1850   Latum Miniature Cerith
                                                Plate 13 e
    Jamaica and Puerto Rico.

About 3 mm. in length, white, with a spiral brown band occupying the suture and upper spiral ridge. Whorls about 8, of which the first 2 are nuclear and smooth; remaining whorls sculptured with 3 spiral, nodulous ridges. Aperture broadly ovate, canal short and wide. Similar to *Cerithiopsis pupa* Dall and Simpson but with the brown row of nodules just below the suture instead of just above the suture. Not very common. *C. cruzanum* Usticke, 1959 and *C. vicola* Dall and Bartsch, 1911, are probably synonyms.

Cerithiopsis crystallinum Dall, 1889   Crystalline Miniature Cerith
    Puerto Rico.

⅝ inch in length, elongated, with 20 or more whorls. Color white. Sculptured with 3 revolving rows of strong tubercles. Reported from Aguadilla by Dall and Simpson.

Cerithiopsis pulchellum Jeffreys, 1858   Beautiful Miniature Cerith
    Puerto Rico.

Reported by Dall and Simpson from Mayagüez, but has not been found since 1901.

GENUS *Seila* A. Adams, 1861

Seila adamsi H. C. Lea, 1845   Adams' Miniature Cerith
                                                Plate 13 m
    Massachusetts to Florida, Texas, and the West Indies.

¼ to ½ inch in length, elongated, and regularly increasing, with about 12 flat whorls. Color light orange-brown, to dark-brown, with 3 smooth, glassy nuclear whorls. Characterized by 3 strong, flattened revolving ridges on each whorl, the spaces between them sculptured with delicate longitudinal threads. Base of shell concave, columella twisted, canal truncated. Common from shore to 40 fathoms.

Family MATHILDIDAE
Genus *Mathilda* Semper, 1865
Subgenus *Fimbriatella* Sacco, 1895

Mathilda barbadensis Dall, 1889   Barbados Mathilda
                                                                    Plate 13 d

Grand Cayman Island, Barbados, Puerto Rico.

About ¼ inch in length, elongate; whorls rounded between sutures. Color light-brown. 3 to 4 nodulous spiral cords per whorl. Two dead specimens of this species were found in beach drift at Ramey Air Force Base near Aguadilla, Puerto Rico.

Family TRIPHORIDAE
Genus *Triphora* Blainville, 1828

Triphora turris-thomae Holten, 1802   Thomas' Trifora
                                                                    Plate 13 j
West Indies.

About ¼ inch in length, sinistral (or left handed), with about 16 slowly increasing whorls. Sculpture consists of 2 spiral rows of nodules on each whorl; the upper row white, the lower row superimposed with a brown line. Last whorl smaller than the preceding one, with 2 small canals which open only at the ends. Common in Puerto Rico.

Triphora melanura C. B. Adams, 1850   Black-tipped Trifora
                                                                    Plate 13 - 1
West Indies.

¼ to ⅜ inch in length, sinistral (or left handed). Whorls about 15, with 3 oblique spiral rows of large beads on each whorl. Color pure-white except for the 4 brown nuclear whorls. Aperture small, canal short, turning slightly to the right. Reasonably common in Puerto Rico.

Triphora nigrocincta C. B. Adams, 1839   Black-lined Trifora
                                                                    Plate 13 k
Massachusetts to Florida, Texas, and the West Indies.

⅛ to ¼ inch in length, left handed. Whorls 10 to 12, slightly convex, pure brown. Sculptured with 3 spiral rows of glossy beads. Found clinging to seaweed at low tide.

Triphora ornata Deshayes, 1832   Ornate Trifora
                                                                    Plate 13 i
Florida and the West Indies.

About ¼ inch in length, left handed. Whorls about 12, almost flat-sided, white with irregular brown splotches. Sculptured with 3 spiral rows of large beads. Uncommon, but found all around the island in beach drift. *Triphora decorata* C. B. Adams also from this area is very similar, but twice as large and with the spire flat instead of concave. Not yet reported from Puerto Rico.

Triphora intermedia C. B. Adams, 1850   Intermediate Trifora
Puerto Rico.

Resembling *T. decorata,* but whitish, except for a pale, solid-brown spiral line on the row of beads just below the suture. Reported from Mayagüez by Dall and Simpson, but not found since 1901.

Triphora samanae Dall, 1889   Samana Trifora
Santo Domingo and Puerto Rico.

About ⅜ inch in length, with 12 to 14 whorls. Color white. Sculpture consists of 3 coarse, close-set spiral rows of tubercles, also arranged in longitudinal rows. Canal short, aperture short, squarish. Dall and Simpson reported one badly worn shell of this species from Mayagüez.

Superfamily *EPITONIACEA*
Family *JANTHINIDAE*
GENUS *Janthina* Röding, 1798
Subgenus *Janthina* Röding, 1798

Janthina janthina Linné, 1758   Common Purple Sea-snail
                                                    Plate 3 h; 15 c
Pelagic in warm waters.

Shell 1 to 1½ inches in diameter, thin and fragile. Pale violet above and deep purple below. Outer lip thin and expanded. For some reason this pelagic mollusk seldom lands on the Puerto Rican beaches. In our 10 years of collecting, we have seen less than a dozen isolated specimens, and these were all less than 1 inch in diameter. The live animal hangs upside-down from a small "frothy" float.

Subgenus *Violetta* Iredale, 1929

Janthina globosa Swainson, 1822   Globe Purple Sea-snail
                                                    Plate 15 b
Pelagic in warm waters.

Shell ½ to ¾ inch in diameter with globose, well-rounded whorls. Color pale violet throughout. Like *J. janthina,* it is uncommon in Puerto Rico.

Family *EPITONIIDAE*
GENUS *Cirsotrema* Mörch, 1852

Cirsotrema dalli Rehder, 1945   Dall's Wentletrap
                                                    Plate 14 h
Southeast U. S. to the West Indies and Brazil.

About 1½ inch in length, chalky grayish-white in color. Whorls about 9, strongly shouldered. Elaborately sculptured with numerous foliated axial costae. These occasionally touch one another, leaving small holes or gaps which lead to the shell surface below. The gaps are largest on the lower portion of the whorl, exposing the reticulated shell surface below. A rare species. The only specimen we have was found on Mona Island by Kayo Phares.

GENUS *Opalia* H. and A. Adams, 1853
Subgenus *Dentiscala* de Boury, 1886

Opalia crenata Linné, 1758   Crenulated Wentletrap
                                                 Plate 14 f

Lower Florida south to Trinidad.

Up to 1 inch in length, grayish-white in color. Fresh specimens are sometimes tinted purple from the animal. Ribs weak, whorls shouldered, suture crenulated. Surface microscopically pitted. Basal ridge usually well-developed. Reasonably common in Puerto Rico.

Opalia hotessieriana Orbigny, 1842   Hotessier's Wentletrap

Southeast Florida and the Caribbean.

Between ¼ and ½ inch in length. Similar to *O. crenata* but smaller, more slender, and its whorls are not shouldered. Operculum corneous, subcircular and paucispiral. Found in shallow dredgings and beach drift.

Subgenus *Nodiscala* de Boury, 1889

Opalia pumilio Mörch, 1874   Pumilio Wentletrap
                                                 Plate 14 g

Southeast U. S. and West Indies.

About ⅜ inch in length, attenuate, with numerous rounded costae (14-16 on body whorl). Outer lip thickened and rounded. There may be 2 or 3 former varices. Microscopically pitted. A form, *O. pumilio morchiana* Dall, 1889, has between 9 and 15 axial costae which are strongly angulated at the periphery of the whorl. Dead shells are reasonably common on beaches.

GENUS *Amaea* H. and A. Adams, 1853
Subgenus *Ferminoscala* Dall, 1908

Amaea retifera Dall, 1889   Reticulated Wentletrap
                                                 Plate 14 c

Southeast U. S. and the West Indies to Barbados.

1 inch in length, elongate, with about 16 whorls. Color yellow to pale-brown. This distinctive species is characterized by its reticulated surface. The only record from Puerto Rico is based on dredgings from off Mayagüez.

Genus *Epitonium* Röding, 1798
Subgenus *Cycloscala* Dall, 1889

Epitonium echinaticostum Orbigny, 1842   Widely-coiled Wentletrap
Plate 14 q
Southern Florida and the West Indies.

About ¼ to ⅜ inch in length, fragile, widely umbilicate, shiny-white. The nuclear whorls are often set at a different angle from those that develop later. The last whorls are widely coiled and very often free. Sculptured with numerous blade-like axial costae. Common in shallow dredgings.

Subgenus *Epitonium* Röding, 1798

Epitonium krebsi Mörch, 1874   Krebs' Wentletrap
Plate 14 r
South half of Florida to the Lesser Antilles.

Up to ¾ inch in length, globose, spire moderately extended and forming an angle of about 45°. Color glossy white. The blade-like costae (10-12 on body whorl) are slightly recurved and have a rather strong angulation at the shoulder of the whorl. The stout form and the open and deep umbilicus help to separate this species from the others. Rare in Puerto Rico.

Epitonium occidentale Nyst, 1871   West Atlantic Wentletrap
Plate 14 p
Southern Florida to the Lesser Antilles.

¾ to 1 inch in length, moderately globose. Color glossy white. There is no indication of spiral sculpture. The numerous thin, axial costae (12-15 on the body whorl) are acutely angled at the whorl's shoulder. Should not be confused with *E. foliaceicostum*, which is more slender and has fewer costae per whorl. Dead specimens are reasonably common on the beaches.

Epitonium albidum Orbigny, 1842   Bladed Wentletrap
Plate 14 n
Southern Florida to Argentina.

½ to ¾ inch in length, rather light in structure, white. Sculptured with numerous, low, blade-like costae (12-14 on body whorl). The costae are not angled at the whorl's shoulder and generally fuse with those of the whorl above. Reasonably common.

Epitonium foliaceicostum Orbigny, 1842   Wrinkled-ribbed Wentletrap
Plate 14 i
Southern Florida to the Lesser Antilles.

½ to ¾ inch in length, white, somewhat slender, strong, and without an umbilicus. The axial costae (7 or 8 per whorl) are thin and strongly angulated at the shoulder. Not uncommon from shallow water to 120 fathoms. *Scala angulata* Say reported by Dall and Simpson is probably this species.

Epitonium unifasciatum Sowerby, 1844   One-banded Wentletrap
Plate 14 l

South Florida, the Bahamas, and south through the West Indies.

About ½ inch in length. Color white with irregular brown markings near the suture. Axial costae are low, narrow, and rounded. Superficially resembles small *E. lamellosum,* but can easily be separated from this species because it lacks the basal ridge. Reasonably common.

Epitonium eulita Dall and Simpson, 1901   Eulita Wentletrap

Puerto Rico.

About 3/16 inch in length, white, polished. Sculptured with thin, sharp axial costae (15 on body whorl), which show an angle near the suture. Dall and Simpson described this small species from Mayagüez. We have not seen the specimen.

Subgenus *Gyroscala* de Boury, 1887

Epitonium lamellosum Lamarck, 1822   Lamellose Wentletrap
Plate 14 m

South half of Florida and the Caribbean. Also Europe.

Up to 1¼ inch in length. Color whitish, with irregular brown markings. Sculptured with numerous white, thin, high, blade-like axial costae. Can easily be recognized by its color and by the spiral ridge at the base of the shell. Animal white, with bright-yellow tentacles. Dead shells are found on many beaches all around the island. The most common *Epitonium* in Puerto Rico. Found alive in shallow dredgings and under rocks at low tide.

Subgenus *Asperiscala* de Boury, 1909

Epitonium apiculatum Dall, 1889   Dall's Wentletrap

North Carolina and Puerto Rico.

About 3/16 inch in length, white. In this species the axial costae are low, cordlike and numerous on the first 3 postnuclear whorls, and the costae on the later whorls are bladelike and fewer (11 on the body whorl). The spiral sculpture is limited to the first 3 postnuclear whorls. Previously reported only from North Carolina. Rare in Puerto Rico. We have only 3 specimens of this interesting little shell.

Epitonium turritellulum Mörch, 1874   Turreted Wentletrap
                                                   Plate 14 d
West Indies.

⅛-¼ inch in length, elongated. China-white except for the light-brown nuclear whorls. The beauty of this little shell can be seen best under the microscope. There are numerous spiral threads between the many axial costae. This rare species previously has been reported from fairly deep water. In Puerto Rico, it has been found in beach drift and in shallow dredgings.

Epitonium frielei Dall, 1889   Friele's Wentletrap
                                                   Plate 14 a
Southeastern U. S. and Puerto Rico.

Reaching ⅝ inch in length, white, conic, umbilicate and very light in structure. Sculpture consists of numerous (52 on the body whorl) very low, thin axial costae; in addition there are numerous spiral threads. To date we have found only 2 specimens of this rare species in Puerto Rico.

Epitonium candeanum Orbigny, 1842   Candé's Wentletrap
                                                   Plate 14 b
Florida south to Barbados.

This species is similar to *E. novangliae,* but it lacks the angles or hooks on the costae at the whorl shoulder. It also has more costae (18 to 25 on the body whorl of *E. candeanum,* as compared to 9 to 16 in *E. novangliae*). Not common. Reported from Mayagüez as *Scala turricula* Sowerby, by Dall and Simpson.

Epitonium novangliae Couthouy, 1838   New England Wentletrap
                                                   Plate 14 e
Massachusetts south to Brazil.

¼ to ½ inch in length, color white to light-brown. Sculptured with many axial costae, which usually develop a hook-like projection on the whorl's shoulder. Between the costae there are numerous spiral threads crossed by microscopic axial lines. This beautiful little *Epitonium* is quite common from shallow dredgings to very deep water.

Epitonium tiburonense Clench and Turner, 1952   Tiburon Wentletrap
                                                   Plate 14 k
Haiti and Puerto Rico.

¼ to ⅜ inch in length, attenuate. Color a light reddish brown throughout, except for white costae. Axial sculpture consists of somewhat thickened costae (12 to 14 on body whorl) which do not produce angles or hooks at the shoulder. The costae merge at the parietal area where they become somewhat flattened to form a thickened pad. Spiral sculpture consists of very fine threads. This species was formerly known only from Haiti. Most of our specimens lack the brown color and are from the west and northwest coast of Puerto Rico.

Epitonium denticulatum Sowerby, 1844   Dentate Wentletrap
Plate 14 o

Florida to the Virgin Islands.

About ⅝ inch in length, attenuate and umbilicate. Dull-white in color. Axial sculpture consists of numerous well-developed bladelike costae (11 to 12 on body whorl), which are strongly angled at the whorl's shoulder. The microscopic reticulate sculpture between the costae makes it easy to separate this species from all others. This species has recently been found in Puerto Rico, but it is not uncommon in the Virgin Islands.

Genus *Depressiscala* de Boury, 1909

Depressiscala nautlae Mörch, 1874   Brown Wentletrap
Plate 14 j

Southeast U. S. to the West Indies.

About ⅝ inch in length, elongate. Color light-tan to brown; shiny. Axial sculpture consists of numerous, rather low, reflected costae which usually have a small angle or hook on the shoulder of the whorl. Uncommon in Puerto Rico.

Genus *Cylindriscala* de Boury, 1909

Cylindriscala acus Watson, 1883

Culebra Island, Puerto Rico.

A small (5 mm.) deep-water species, reported off Culebra Island, Challenger station 24, in 390 fathoms.

Cylindriscala tortilis Watson, 1883

Culebra Island, Puerto Rico.

10 mm. in length, attenuate, strongly sculptured and imperforate. A deep-water form known only from north of Culebra Island in 390 fathoms.

Genus *Solutiscala* de Boury, 1909
Subgenus *Foratiscala* de Boury, 1909

Solutiscala pyrrhias Watson, 1886

Culebra Island, Puerto Rico.

A small (5 mm.), white, highly sculptured (11 axial costae on body whorl, 3 to 4 spiral threads) deep-water species. Known only from off Culebra Island in 390 fathoms.

Superfamily *AGLOSSA*
Family *EULIMIDAE*
GENUS *Balcis* Leach, 1847

Balcis intermedia Cantraine, 1835   Cucumber Melanella
                                             Plate 26 h
                                             Text fig. 13 c
New Jersey to the West Indies, Europe.

¼ to ½ inch long, elongate, with 10 to 13 whorls which taper very gradually to a sharp apex. Glossy white. Aperture narrow; outer lip thin and sharp; operculum horny. Very common; found living as a parasite on the sea cucumber (*Holothuria impatiens*). This family is in need of revision.

Balcis conoidea Kurtz and Stimpson, 1851   Conical Melanella
                                                    Plate 26 p
Florida and the West Indies.

About ¼ inch in length, slender. Last whorl faintly subangulate at the base. Highly polished, all-white, or slightly touched with brown. Reasonably common from shallow dredgings on the southwestern coast of Puerto Rico.

Balcis oleacea Kurtz and Stimpson, 1851   Oily Melanella
Puerto Rico

Reported from Mayagüez by Dall and Simpson.

GENUS *Eulima* Risso, 1826

Eulima patula Dall and Simpson, 1901   Large-mouthed Melanella
                                                Plate 29 - 1
Puerto Rico.

Less than ¼ inch in length, translucent-white. Whorls about 9, with a rapidly diminishing spire, blunt at the extreme tip. Characterized by the large, flaring aperture. Reasonably common from shallow dredgings.

Eulima bifasciata Orbigny, 1842   Double-banded Eulima
                                           Plate 26 i
                                           Text fig. 13 b
West Indies.

About ¼ inch in length, slender, elongate. Highly polished, semi-translucent. White with 2 narrow, brown bands per whorl. Common from shallow dredgings.

Eulima auricincta Abbott, 1958   Single-banded Eulima
                                          Plate 26 j
Southern U. S. to Puerto Rico.

Between ⅛ and ¼ inch in length. Similar to *bifasciata* but smaller and with only one narrow, yellowish brown band per whorl. Listed as *Eulima acuta* Sowerby by Dall and Simpson.

GENUS *Niso* Risso, 1826

Niso portoricensis Dall and Simpson, 1901   Puerto Rican Niso

Plate 28 - 1

Puerto Rico.

Between ¼ to ½ inch in length, conical, with about 13 flat whorls. Brilliantly polished, brown, with a paler zone at the base of each whorl. Base rounded; umbilicus deep and funicular. Operculum thin, light-brown, transparent. This beautiful little shell was discovered for the first time off Mayagüez, Puerto Rico, and described by Dall and Simpson in 1901. Since then, several live specimens have been dredged in relatively shallow water off Mayagüez, Puerto Rico.

Family STILIFERIDAE
GENUS *Stilifer* Broderip, 1832

Stilifer subulatus Broderip and Sowerby, 1832   Thomas' Stilifer

Text fig. 13 d

West Indies.

½ to ¾ inch in length, attenuate, and suddenly contracted towards the apex. White, semi-transparent. Last whorl obtusely angular; aperture obliquely subquadrate. Uncommon. *Melanella bibsae* Usticke, 1959 is probably this species. It appears that *thomasiae* Sowerby, 1878 is closely related, if not this species.

Superfamily HIPPONICACEA
Family HIPPONICIDAE
GENUS *Cheilea* Modeer, 1793

Cheilea equestris Linné, 1758   False Cup-and-saucer

Plate 15 m

Southeast Florida and the West Indies.

½ to 1¼ inch in size, cap-shaped, with an internal half cup. Color dull-white on the outside with a glossy-white interior. Sculpture consists of irregular folds or ridges crossed by numerous, fine radiating threads. About 1½ nuclear whorls, minute, spiral and glossy white. Fairly common in Puerto Rico.

GENUS *Hipponix* Defrance, 1819

Hipponix antiquatus Linné, 1767   White Hoof-shell

Plate 15 h

Southeast Florida and the West Indies.

½ inch in size, heavy, cap-shaped. Color dull-white. Sculpture consists of numerous concentric folds or ridges crossed by microscopic in-cised lines. Very common all around the island on rocks or attached to other shells.

Hipponix subrufus subrufus Lamarck, 1822   Orange Hoof-shell
Plate 15 g

Southeast Florida and the West Indies.

About ½ inch in size, similar to *antiquatus*, but usually stained orange and with numerous radiating cords crossing concentric ridges of about the same size. Common near Aguadilla, Puerto Rico.

Family FOSSARIDAE
GENUS *Fossarus* Philippi, 1841

Fossarus orbignyi Fischer, 1864   Orbigny's Fossarus
Plate 15 d

West Indies.

Shell 2 to 3 mm. in length, turbinate in shape. Color glossy-white, with about 3 brown, smooth, nuclear whorls. Last 4 whorls sculptured with strong revolving cords (5 on the body whorl) and less conspicuous revolving threads between them. Umbilicus chink-like. Outer lip dentated by the spiral cords. Fresh specimens are not uncommon on the beach. *F. tridentata* Usticke, 1959, is a synonym.

GENUS *Iselica* Dall, 1918

Iselica anomala C. B. Adams, 1850   Anomalous Fossarus
Plate 15 e

West Indies.

2 to 5 mm. in length, ovate, white. Sculptured with prominent spiral cords (8 on the body whorl) and numerous axial lines between the cords, giving the shell a cancellate pattern. Aperture large, ovate; columella with a small transverse plait opposite the umbilicus. Un-common from shallow dredgings.

Family VANIKOROIDAE
GENUS *Vanikoro* Quoy and Gaimard, 1832

Vanikoro sulcata Orbigny, 1842   Sulcate Vanikoro
Plate 15 a

West Indies.

Shell ¼ to ⅜ inch in size. Color white, whorls 4. Body whorl sculptured with many prominent, nodulous spiral ridges. Suture deep, whorls rounded. Aperture large, ovate. Umbilicus expanded, flattened below. Common only around Aguadilla. See Abbott, 1958, p. 45.

Superfamily CALYPTRAEACEA
Family CAPULIDAE
GENUS *Capulus* Montfort, 1810
Subgenus *Krebsia* Mörch, 1877

Capulus intortus Lamarck, 1822   Incurved Cap-shell
                                                    Plate 15 f
Florida and the West Indies.

¼ to ½ inch in size, cap-shaped; white with a light-brown periostracum. Apex spirally curved; aperture large, circular, ovate. Sculptured with numerous spiral cords, crossed by irregular growth lines. Resembles *Hipponix subrufus* Lam. but has a much more delicate sculpture, has the apex coiled, and is completely white. Lives on rocks in shallow water and is comparatively rare in Puerto Rico.

Family CALYPTRAEIDAE
GENUS *Calyptraea* Lamarck, 1799

Calyptraea centralis Conrad, 1841   Circular Cup-and-saucer
                                                    Plate 15 o
North Carolina to Texas and the West Indies.

About ¼ inch in diameter, thin, cap-shaped with round base. Dull-white on the outside and shiny-white inside. Sculpture consists of numerous growth lines and finely radiating striae. The flat inner cup is attached to the apex and only about ½ of its outer edge is free. Fairly common on the beach and dredged in shallow water. Commonly found adhering to dead shells. Previously reported as *Calyptraea candeana* Orbigny.

GENUS *Crucibulum* Schumacher, 1817

Crucibulum auricula Gmelin, 1791   West Indian Cup-and-saucer
                                                    Plate 15 n
West Florida to the West Indies.

1 inch in diameter, cap-shaped, moderately heavy. All edges of small inner cup are entirely free. Color dull-white on the outside, interior sometimes with a tinge of orange-pink. Smooth inside; outside coarsely ribbed; edge crenulated. A shallow-water species which sometimes lives attached to scallops or other mollusks. Not common, except on the northwest coast of Puerto Rico.

GENUS *Crepidula* Lamarck, 1799

Crepidula aculeata Gmelin, 1791   Spiny Slipper-shell
                                                    Plate 15 i
Southeast U. S. and the West Indies.

½ to 1 inch in size, boat-shaped; base irregularly oval. Horizontal shelf or deck extends over the posterior ½ on the inside of the shell. Exterior surface rough, usually spiny. Color cream to tan, often mottled with reddish brown; interior smooth, shelf white with an irregular edge. Common in shallow water where it is found attached to rocks, mangrove roots, and other shells.

Crepidula convexa Say, 1822   Convex Slipper-shell
                                                                    Plate 15 k
Eastern U. S. and the West Indies.

¼ to ½ inch in size. Color dark-brown or streaked with reddish brown inside and outside, including the deck. Highly arched or deeply convex. The edge of the deck is almost straight. Often found attached to *Cerithium* and *Modulus*. *C. fornicata cruzana* Usticke, 1959, is possibly this species.

Crepidula glauca Say, 1822   Faded Slipper-shell
                                                                    Plate 15 l
Eastern U. S. and Puerto Rico.

½ inch or less in size, thin. Translucent-tan or mottled with dark-brown. Apex central, projecting, and pointed. Similar to *C. convexa* but flatter and with a white deck. Not very common in Puerto Rico. This may be a form of *convexa*.

Crepidula protea Orbigny, 1845

Cuba and Puerto Rico.

Reported from Mayagüez by Dall and Simpson. We have not seen this species.

Subgenus *Ianacus* Mörch, 1852

Crepidula plana Say, 1822   Eastern White Slipper-shell
                                                                    Plate 15 j
Eastern U. S. and the West Indies.

About 1 inch in size, thin, very flat, convex or concave, and pure white. The shelf is less than ½ the length of the shell. Its shape varies according to the surface it adheres to, usually a large dead shell. Rare on the beach and moderately common in shallow dredgings.

Crepidula riisei Dunker, 1877   Riise's Slipper-shell

West Indies.

Resembling *C. plana*, but separated from it by faint longitudinal brown lines near the apex and its fringed and conspicuous periostracum. Reported from San Juan and Mayagüez by Dall and Simpson. It is so similar to *C. plana* that it is difficult to believe it is a distinct species.

Superfamily STROMBACEA
Family XENOPHORIDAE
GENUS *Xenophora* G. Fischer, 1807
Subgenus *Xenophora* G. Fischer, 1807

Xenophora conchyliophora Born, 1780   Atlantic Carrier shell
                                                                      Plate 12 b
Southeast U. S. to the West Indies.

Up to 2½ inches in diameter, not including foreign attachments; heavy. Base flattish; whorls regularly increasing in size, bearing numerous shell fragments, stones and bits of coral, so that it is well camouflaged. Adult without umbilicus. A common shallow-water species. This is *trochiformis* Born, 1780, not 1778.

Xenophora caribaea Petit, 1856   Caribbean Carrier shell

Florida Keys and the West Indies.

Similar to *conchyliophora* but much lighter in structure, has fewer attachments, is umbilicated, and has a cape which extends below the body whorl. A deep-water species reported from Aguadilla by Dall and Simpson.

Family STROMBIDAE
GENUS *Strombus* Linné, 1758

Strombus gigas Linné, 1758   Queen Conch
                                                    Plate 1 h
Southeast Florida and the West Indies, Bermuda.

6 to 12 inches in length, solid, massive, spinose. Aperture and large flaring outer lip colored with rich shades of pink, peach, or yellow. The shell is covered with a brown-colored periostracum. A beautiful and fairly common shell. Fishermen find them on grassy or sandy bottoms in fairly shallow water. It is employed extensively for food and fish bait in Puerto Rico and throughout the West Indies. *S. samba* Clench, 1946 is a thickened adult form. *S. gigas verrilli* McGinty is a synonym. A young shell is illustrated on plate 24, fig. b. Members of this genus feed on algae, and are not carnivorous.

Strombus pugilis Linné, 1758   West Indian Fighting Conch
                                                        Plate 1 d
Southeast Florida and the West Indies.

3 to 4 inches in length. Bright, deep orange in color, covered with a rather thin periostracum. Early whorls with fine longitudinal ribs which develop into nodules later and into spines on the last 2 whorls. The spines on the next to the last whorl usually are the largest. Operculum smaller than aperture, sickle-shaped, brown and chitinous, and with 7 to 10 small saw-like teeth on its outer margin. One of the most

abundant and most beautiful shells found on the beaches in Puerto Rico. A young shell is illustrated on plate 24, fig. a.

Strombus raninus Gmelin, 1791   Hawk-wing Conch

Plate 1 g

Southeast Florida and the West Indies.

2 to 4 inches in length, solid, bluntly spinose, the largest spines being the last 2 on the body whorl. Aperture and outer lip glazed; salmon-pink inside. Color of outer shell grayish with brown mottling. There are usually heavy folds in the upper and parietal corner of the aperture. Common everywhere in Puerto Rico and the West Indies. Formerly known as *S. bituberculatus* Lamarck. A young specimen is illustrated on plate 24, fig. c.

Strombus costatus Gmelin, 1791   Milk Conch

Plate 1 i

Southeast Florida and the West Indies.

4 to 7 inches in length, solid, very heavy, with blunt spines. Color uniform yellowish white. Parietal wall and outer lip glazed white or yellow; some specimens have an aluminum-like gray glaze. Not as common as *S. pugilis* and *S. gigas*. *S. spectabilis* Verrill, 1950 is a synonym.

Strombus gallus Linné, 1758   Rooster-tail Conch

Plate 1 c

Southeast Florida (rare) and the West Indies.

4 to 6 inches in length. Similar to *S. raninus* but characterized by the long extension or wing of the outer lip, the higher spire, and the lack of folds on the upper inner parietal wall. There are 3 to 5 moderately long spines on the body whorl of *gallus,* as compared to 2 in *raninus.* The least common species of *Strombus* in Puerto Rico.

Superfamily *CYPRAEACEA*
Family *LAMELLARIIDAE*
GENUS *Lamellaria* Montagu, 1815

Lamellaria rangi Bergh, 1853   Rang's Lamellaria

Plate 17 b

Gulf of Mexico and Puerto Rico.

About ¼ inch in length, 2/3 as wide, very fragile, thin, glassy. 2½ to 3 whorls, slightly globose; the last whorl very large. Surface sculptured with fine, irregular growth lines. Aperture large, columella very thin. Uncommonly washed ashore. The soft parts envelop the shell.

Family ERATOIDAE
Subfamily ERATOINAE
GENUS *Erato* Risso, 1826
Subgenus *Hespererato* Schilder, 1932

Erato maugeriae Gray, 1832   Mauger's Erato
                                                       Plate 23 c
   Southeast U. S. and the West Indies.

¼ inch in length, somewhat pear-shaped. Outer lip thickened,
toothed within, and well-shouldered at upper end. Color drab-green;
lip whitish. Spire short with a bulbous apex. Common in drift sand
and from shallow dredgings in Puerto Rico.

Subfamily TRIVIINAE
GENUS *Trivia* Broderip, 1837

Trivia pediculus Linné, 1758   Coffee Bean Trivia
                                                       Plate 16 f
   South half of Florida and the West Indies.

About ½ inch in length, resembling a miniature cowrie (*Cypraea*).
Color tan to brownish pink with 3 pairs of large, irregular dark-brown
spots on the back. Shell with a deep, straight, longitudinal dorsal
furrow and 16 to 19 ribs crossing the outer lip. A very common shallow-
water species.

Trivia suffusa Gray, 1832   Suffuse Trivia
                                                       Plate 16 a
   Southeast Florida and the West Indies.

¼ to ⅓ inch in length, bright-pink with suffused brownish spots
and fine specklings. White outer lip crossed by 18 to 23 riblets. Weak
dark-pink blotch on each side of anterior canal. Dorsal riblets somewhat pustulose. A common shallow-water species.

Trivia quadripunctata Gray, 1827   Four-spotted Trivia
                                                       Plate 16 d
   Southeast Florida, Yucatan, and the West Indies.

About ¼ inch in length, characterized by its bright pink color and
4 very small, dark-brown dots on the dorsal center line. 19 to 24 riblets
cross the outer lip. Do not confuse with *suffusa* which has beaded rather
than very fine riblets; also the fine color speckling of *suffusa* is absent in
this species. Not as common as *T. pediculus* or *T. suffusa*.

Trivia antillarum Schilder, 1922   Antillean Trivia
                                                       Plate 16 e
   Southeast Florida and the West Indies.

⅛ to ¼ inch in length, elongate, globular. Deep purple in color with 18 to 22 teeth crossing the outer lip. The smooth riblets usually cross the faint dorsal groove. Commonly dredged from 30 to 100 fathoms. *T. subrostrata* Gray is this species.

Trivia leucosphaera Schilder, 1931   Little White Trivia
Plate 16 c

Southeast U. S. and the West Indies.

⅛ to ¼ inch in length, globular, pure-white in color, and with 20 to 24 riblets over the outer lip. With or without a dorsal groove over which the riblets usually cross. Can be easily separated from *T. nix* by its small size. Not common.

Trivia nix Schilder, 1922   White Globe Trivia
Plate 16 b

Southeast Florida and the West Indies.

⅜ inch in length, globular. Characterized by its white color, with a strong dorsal groove, and about 22 to 26 riblets which are interrupted by a strong dorsal groove. Relatively uncommon.

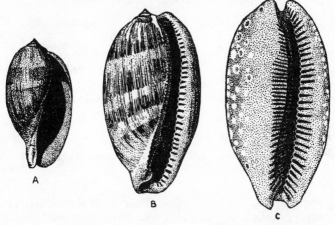

TEXT FIG. 17. Growth and development of the outer lip in *Cypraea zebra*. a, young "bulla" stage; b, immature shell; c, adult shell.

Family CYPRAEIDAE
GENUS *Cypraea* Linné, 1758
Subgenus *Trona* Jousseaume, 1884

Cypraea zebra Linné, 1758   Measled Cowrie
Plate 2 e; 16 n

Southeast Florida and the West Indies.

1¼ to 3½ inches in length, oblong. Young specimens are strongly banded with gray and brown. These bands are later covered by a brightly polished, chocolate-brown layer with round whitish spots. The spots at the base are often ringed. Common in moderately shallow water. The light orange form, *Cypraea zebra vallei* Jaume and Borro, is equally as common and seems to be smaller, the smallest adult being 1¼ inch and the largest 2½ inches in length. The color and size difference of this form may be due to the animal's environment. Previously reported as *C. exanthema* Linné, 1767. *C. cervus* L. may be the female form.

Subgenus *Luria* Jousseaume, 1884

Cypraea cinerea Gmelin, 1791   Atlantic Gray Cowrie
                                                                Plate 16 h
Southeast Florida and the West Indies.

¾ to 1½ inches in length, rotund. Color orange to ashy-brown, usually with 2 faint lighter bands. Base white to ivory, interspaces between the teeth sometimes purple. A very common species found under rocks and on reefs.

Subgenus *Erosaria* Troschel, 1863

Cypraea spurca acicularis Gmelin, 1791   Atlantic Yellow Cowrie
                                                                Plate 16 i
South half of Florida, Yucatan and the West Indies.

½ to 1¼ inches in length. Color whitish, clouded and flecked with orange-brown. Teeth and interspaces between the teeth at the base always ivory-white. Moderately common under rocks at low tide.

Family OVULIDAE
GENUS *Neosimnia* Fischer, 1884

Neosimnia acicularis Lamarck, 1810   Common West Indian Simnia
                                                                Plate 16 - l
Southeastern U. S. to the West Indies.

½ inch in length, narrow, glossy, and with a toothless aperture. Color purple or yellowish. Columella area flattened or sometimes slightly dished and, in adults, always bordered by a long, whitish ridge. Posterior end of columella sometimes slightly swollen. A common species which lives on purple or yellow seafans.

Neosimnia uniplicata Sowerby, 1848   Single-toothed Simnia
                                                                Plate 16 m
Virginia to Florida and the West Indies.

½ to ¾ inch in length, similar to *acicularis,* but with only one innermost longitudinal ridge on the columella, and with a twisted, spiral plication at the posterior end of the columella. Moderately common on seafans.

GENUS *Cyphoma* Röding, 1798

Cyphoma gibbosum Linné, 1758   Flamingo tongue
                                                               Plate 16 k
Southeast U. S. and the West Indies.

¾ to 1 inch in length, smooth, solid. Fresh specimens are bright, glossy orange in color. Aperture narrow, running the length of the shell. Dorsal transverse ridge conspicuous near the center. When the animal has its mantle extended, it covers most of the shell and is orange in color with numerous squarish, black rings. This beautiful animal lives on gorgonians. Common.

Cyphoma signatum Pilsbry and McGinty, 1939   Fingerprint Cyphoma
                                                               Plate 16 g
Lower Florida Keys to the West Indies.

Shell similar to *C. gibbosum,* but more elongate, color light-buff with a cream-buff tint deep inside the aperture. Mantle pale-yellow with numerous, crowded, long, black transverse lines. Rare.

Cyphoma intermedium Sowerby, 1828   Weak-ridge Cyphoma
                                                               Plate 16 j
Greater Antilles to Brazil. Bermuda, deep water.

About 1½ inches in length, elongately ovate, rather solid, reddish yellow when fresh. Dorsal ridge weak or absent, columella twisted; callus at the upper part. The weak transverse ridge and columellar twist help to separate this species from the common *gibbosum.* Rare.

Superfamily *HETEROPODA*
Family *ATLANTIDAE*
GENUS *Atlanta* Lesueur, 1817

Atlanta peroni Lesueur, 1817   Peron's Atlanta
                                                               Plate 28 k
Atlantic and Pacific warm water; pelagic.

About ½ inch in diameter, planorboid, compressed, fragile. Color whitish. Sometimes washed ashore after storms; may also be obtained by dredging. D. S. Erdman found one specimen in excellent condition in the stomach of a yellowfin tuna. Uncommon.

Superfamily NATICACEA
Family NATICIDAE
Subfamily POLINICINAE
GENUS *Polinices* Montfort, 1810

Polinices lacteus Guilding, 1834   Milk Moon-shell

Southeastern U. S. and the West Indies.   Plate 17 a

¾ to 1½ inch in length, solid, smooth, glossy, pure white. Last whorl large, rather flattened. Umbilicus deep, small, partially covered by callus. Periostracum yellowish, thin, smooth. Operculum wine-red or yellow, thin, corneous, paucispiral. Lives in sandy intertidal areas. Dead shells commonly wash up on the beaches.

Polinices uberinus Orbigny, 1842

West Indies.

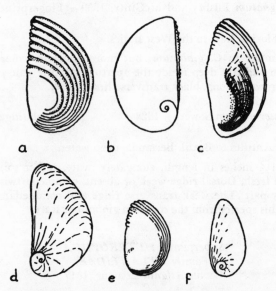

TEXT FIG. 18. Various *Naticidae* opercula. a, *Natica canrena*, outer calcareous surface with many strong spiral grooves; b, muscle attachment of same; c, *N. cayennensis*, outer calcareous surface with a large brown, arching ridge in the center; d, *Polinices hepaticus*, corneous, thin, light-brown; e, *N. menke-ana*, outer calcareous surface with few spiral grooves; f, *Polinices lacteus*, corneous, thin, transparent, wine red.

Reported from Mayagüez and Culebra by Dall and Simpson. It is extremely close to *P. lactea* and may only be a form.

Polinices hepaticus Röding, 1798   Brown Moon-shell
                                                      Plate 3 f; 17 i

Southeast Florida and the West Indies.

1 to 2 inches in length, oval, elongate, heavy. Glossy-smooth, orange-brown or purple-brown above; columella, umbilicus, and interior of shell white. Umbilicus large and deep. Operculum light-brown, thin, corneous. A common shallow-water species. This is *Natica brunnea* Link, 1807, and *mamillaris* Lamarck, 1822.

Polinices nubilus Dall, 1889   Nubilus Moon-shell

Gulf of Mexico, Puerto Rico, and Barbados.

⅜ inch in length, dirty-white, faintly clouded with brown. Sculptured with strong growth lines and exceedingly faint spiral lines. Umbilicus moderately open, surrounded by a revolving ridge at its base which projects within, partly closing it. Reported from Mayagüez by Dall and Simpson. Rare.

Subfamily SININAE
GENUS *Sinum* Röding, 1798

Sinum perspectivum Say, 1831   Common Baby's Ear
                                                      Plate 17 k
Southeastern U. S., the Gulf States, and the West Indies.

1 to 2 inches in maximum diameter. Flattened, pure white, with a thin yellowish brown periostracum. Sculptured with many fine, wavy spiral lines. Aperture large, columella curved. Usually found on sandy bottoms in shallow water.

Sinum maculatum Say, 1831   Maculated Baby's Ear
                                                      Plate 17 h
Southeastern U. S. to the West Indies.

1 to 2 inches in maximum diameter. Similar to *perspectivum,* but more elevated, with weaker sculpture and all or partly brown in color. Not common. This is probably *S. martinianum* Philippi, 1844. *Sigaretus* Lamarck, 1799, is a synonym of *Sinum.*

Subfamily NATICINAE
GENUS *Natica* Scopoli, 1777

Natica livida Pfeiffer, 1840   Livid Natica
                                                      Plate 17 j
North Carolina to the West Indies.

½ inch in length; color grayish brown with vague, darker, spiral bands. Brown callus almost fills the umbilicus. Aperture and columella stained with light-brown; base white. Less common than the other Naticas.

Natica menkeana Philippi, 1852   Menke's Natica
                                                     Plate 17 c
West Indies.

About ½ inch in length, solid, smoothish. Color yellowish brown with a network of reddish brown markings below the suture and a broken, reddish brown spiral band just below the middle of the body whorl. Callus glazed, barely visible, umbilicus narrow. Operculum shelly, white, its exterior with 3 or 4 spiral grooves on the outer edge. Reasonably common in Puerto Rico. Rare elsewhere in the West Indies.

Natica canrena Linné, 1758   Colorful Atlantic Natica
                                                 Plate 3 d; 17 g
Southeast U. S. and the West Indies.

1 to 2 inches in length with rounded whorls. Color pattern variable; there are many brown, wavy, or zigzag lines usually superimposed on alternating brown and white spiral bands. Callus white, large, and entering narrow umbilicus. Operculum hard, exterior with about 10 spiral grooves. Reasonably common all around the island of Puerto Rico.

Natica marochiensis Gmelin, 1791   Morocco Natica
                                                     Plate 3 g
Florida and the West Indies.

½ to 1 inch in length, whorls rounded. Color uniformly dark- or light-brown with about 4 narrow spiral bands of zigzag brown markings. Do not confuse with *canrena*, which has much larger brown zigzag markings on a white and brown background instead of a solid brown background. Nuclear whorls conspicuously dark. Base of shell and callus white; interior brown. Moderately common.

Natica sagraiana Orbigny, 1842   Sagra's Natica
West Indies.

Reported from San Juan and Quebradillas by Gundlach.

Subgenus *Glyphepithema* Rehder, 1943

Natica cayennensis Récluz, 1850   Cayenne Natica
                                                     Plate 3 e; 17 f
West Indies.

About 1 inch in size, similar to *N. canrena* L. but smaller, with more prominent wrinkles near the suture, color less vivid, and pattern more blurred. The operculum is quite distinct, being calcareous, paucispiral, thick; surface irregularly pustulose and with a large, swollen, arching ridge in the center. Most common on the west coast of Puerto Rico. *Natica haysae* Usticke, 1959, is undoubtedly this species.

GENUS *Stigmaulax* Mörch, 1852

Stigmaulax sulcata Born, 1778   Sulcate Natica
Plate 17 e
West Indies.

½ to ¾ inch in length, with rounded whorls. Color cream with irregular, yellowish brown markings; base white. Sculptured throughout with many strong axial ribs crossed by fine striae. Umbilicus large and deep, the revolving ridge within it wide and rounded. Uncommon.

GENUS *Tectonatica* Sacco, 1890

Tectonatica pusilla Say, 1822   Miniature Natica
Plate 17 d
Eastern U. S., the Gulf States, and the West Indies.

¼ to ⅓ inch in length, glossy-smooth, rotund. Color white, but often with weak, light-brown color markings. Umbilical callus strong, often with a small open chink next to it. Operculum calcareous, smooth. Obtained from shallow dredgings.

Superfamily TONNACEA
Family CASSIDIDAE
GENUS *Morum* Röding, 1798

Morum oniscus Linné, 1767   Atlantic Wood-louse
Plate 23 r
Southeast Florida and the West Indies.

¾ to 1 inch in length; sculptured with 3 spiral rows of blunt tubercles. Colored with a heavy speckling of brown on white background. Parietal wall glazed, usually minutely pustulose. Outer lip thickened, inner side toothed. Spire low, with a pink or white sharply pointed nuclear tip. Periostracum thin and velvety. Animal translucent with large opaque-white and tiny black speckling. A fairly common shallow-water species.

GENUS *Sconsia* Gray, 1847

Sconsia striata Lamarck, 1822   Royal Bonnet
Plate 28 g
Florida Keys and the West Indies.

1½ to 2½ inches in length, solid, polished. Color whitish, with rows of square brown spots. Spirally striated. A rare deep-water species reported from Mayagüez by Dall and Simpson.

GENUS *Phalium* Link, 1807

Phalium granulatum Born, 1778   Scotch Bonnet
                                                                   Plate 3 b

North Carolina to the West Indies.

1½ to 4 inches in length; surface moderately to strongly reticulated by many evenly-spaced spiral grooves and weaker axial grooves. Ground color cream to white overlaid by a series of brown squares. Lower parietal area pustulose. Outer lip toothed, often greatly thickened. Animal cream-colored. Fresh specimens are commonly washed ashore. *P. abbreviata* Lamarck is a synonym.

Phalium cicatricosum Gmelin, 1791   Smooth Scotch Bonnet
                                                              Plate 3 a

Southeast Florida, Bermuda, and the Caribbean.

1½ to 2 inches in length, similar to *P. granulatum* but with a nearly smooth surface, smaller in size and somewhat more attenuated. Less abundant than *P. granulatum*.

GENUS *Cassis* Scopoli, 1777

Cassis tuberosa Linné, 1758   King Helmet
                                                                   Plate 1 b

Southeast Florida and the West Indies.

Adult shell 4 to 9 inches in length, heavy and solid with a fine reticulated surface. Color brownish cream, mottled with dark-brown, crescent-like marks. Parietal shield triangular in shape, with a large patch of brown on the mid area; inner margin plicated. Brown between the teeth on the outer lip. Common in 10 to 20 feet of water, usually on grassy bottoms. Live specimens have been found almost entirely buried in sand.

Cassis flammea Linné, 1758   Flame Helmet
                                                                   Plate 1 e

Bahamas and the Antilles.

3 to 5 inches in length. Similar to *C. tuberosa* but lacking the reticulated sculpture (sculpture consists of axial growth lines only). Has no brown markings between the teeth on the outer lip, and the corners of parietal shield are rounded. Not as common in Puerto Rico as it is in the Virgin Islands.

Cassis madagascariensis Lamarck, 1822   Emperor Helmet
                                                                   Plate 1 f

Southeast Florida, the Bahamas, and the Greater Antilles.

4 to 9 inches in length, solid and strong. Characterized by having the parietal shield and outer lip salmon color and the exterior pale-cream. Parietal shield with rounded corners, stained brown at the aperture and between the teeth on the outer lip. Spear fishermen bring them up from 10 to 20 feet of water.

Cassis madagascariensis form *spinella* Clench, 1944

Florida Keys and Puerto Rico.

Differs from *C. madagascariensis* by its larger size (up to 16 inches in length), and the possession of smaller, more regular and far more numerous tubercles. Previously only known from the Lower Florida Keys. Found on the west and south coasts of Puerto Rico.

GENUS *Cypraecassis* Stutchbury, 1837

Cypraecassis testiculus Linné, 1758   Reticulated Cowrie-helmet
                                                        Plate 3 c
Southeast Florida, Bermuda, and the West Indies.

1 to 3 inches in length, solid and with a reticulated sculpture. Color light orange-brown, blotched with purplish brown and gray. Parietal wall and outer lip with heavy cream-orange glaze, streaked with bright-orange. Adults lack periostracum and operculum. Very common. The form *crumen*a Bruguière which differs from the typical *testiculus* in having a single or double row of short plications or ridges on the upper part of the body whorl, has also been found in Puerto Rico, but it is uncommon.

Family *CYMATIIDAE*
GENUS *Charonia* Gistel, 1848

Charonia variegata Lamarck, 1816   Trumpet Triton
                                                        Plate 1 a
Southeast Florida and the West Indies.

12 to 18 inches in length. Variegated with buff, brown, and purple-pink. Very young specimens (less than an inch in size) have a reticulated surface and are bright coral-pink in color with brown nuclear whorls. As the shell grows it loses its axial sculpture and retains only the revolving cords which encircle the shell. The whorls are elongated and in adult shells the shoulder of the body whorl is decidedly angular. Aperture orange-pink the raised folds on both sides of the aperture are white with brown between them. This is *C. tritonis nobilis* Conrad. Fairly common in Puerto Rico. Spearfishermen find them in caves from 6 to 30 feet under water.

GENUS *Cymatium* Röding, 1798
Subgenus *Linatella* Gray, 1857

Cymatium poulseni Mörch, 1877   Poulsen's Triton
Plate 18 e

Florida south through the West Indies to Venezuela.

2 to 3 inches in length, light-brown in color. Sculpture consists of 18 to 20 flattened spiral cords. The axial sculpture consists of fine growth lines. Outer lip crenulated and slightly expanded. Columella glazed. Rare. Mrs. Ruhl found the only specimen we have from Puerto Rico on the beach of Punta Algarrobo, just north of Mayagüez.

Subgenus *Cabestana* Röding, 1798

Cymatium labiosum Wood, 1828   Lip Triton
Plate 18 a

Florida Keys and the West Indies.

¾ inch in length, heavy and short, yellow, orange, or brown in color. Parietal shield small, with one or no folds. Siphonal canal short, slightly umbilicated. Uncommon.

Subgenus *Ranularia* Schumacher, 1817

Cymatium caribbaeum Clench and Turner, 1957   Dog-head Triton
Plate 2 b; 18 k

Southeast Florida and the West Indies.

1½ to 2½ inches in length, color gray to brown. Whorls globular, with slightly noduled spiral cords, and squarish at the shoulder. Parietal area orange, with a dark-brown area over which run several lighter colored folds. Outer lip usually has 7 large teeth. Animal light reddish brown in color, with dark reddish brown spots. Fairly common in Puerto Rico. Formerly known as *C. cynocephalum* Lam.

Cymatium nicobaricum Röding, 1798   Gold-mouthed Triton
Plate 18 g

Southeast Florida, Bermuda, and the West Indies.

1 to 2½ inches in length, white or gray, mottled with brown. In juvenile specimens the aperture is lined with brown and white spiral bands. In adult specimens these bands disappear, and the aperture is usually bright-orange. The outer lip has a series of single white teeth, and the parietal area has many white folds on the orange background. Fairly common. Formerly known as *C. chlorostomum* Lamarck.

Subgenus *Septa* Perry, 1810

Cymatium pileare Linné, 1758   Atlantic Hairy Triton
Plate 2 a

Southeastern U. S. to the West Indies.

1½ to 3 inches in length, colored brown with occasional lighter bands. Outer lip thickened, possessing small paired teeth; parietal area brown over which run many white folds. Siphonal canal short. Whorls elongated and rounded at the shoulder. Periostracum light-brown and thick. *C. aquatile* Reeve and *C. martinianum* Orbigny are later names for this species. Very common all around the islands.

Cymatium krebsi Mörch, 1877   Krebs' Triton

Florida to the West Indies.

About 3 inches in length. Color pure white or white with yellowish brown spiral bands. Sculpture consists of 5 to 7 strong, nodulose axial ridges; these are crossed by 6 or 7 heavy spiral cords. Outer lip greatly thickened and toothed within. Parietal lip rather narrow and heavily glazed. Columella has 2 rather large lamellae. Periostracum thin, brown. Rare. We have seen only 3 specimens of this species from Puerto Rico, all from the western end.

Cymatium vespaceum Lamarck, 1822   Dwarf Hairy Triton
                                                                   Plate 18 b

Southern Florida to the West Indies.

1 to 1½ inches in length; color uniformly white to light-orange, except for the varix, which is brown and white. Whorls elongated and squarish at the shoulder. Outer lip possessing several small white teeth. Parietal area with a few folds of the same color, the largest fold being the upper-most. Siphonal canal long, slender. Not uncommon in Puerto Rico. *C. gracile* Reeve is probably this species.

Subgenus *Gutturnium* Mörch, 1852

Cymatium muricinum Röding, 1798   Knobby Triton
                                                                   Plate 18 h

Southeast Florida, Bermuda, and the West Indies.

1 to 2 inches in length; color gray to brown, commonly with a lighter spiral band on the last whorl. Large thick parietal shield. The teeth form a notch at the top of the aperture. Siphonal canal short and recurved. Interior of aperture white to dark-orange. *C. tuberosum* Lamarck is a synonym. Fairly common in intertidal reef areas.

Subgenus *Monoplex* Perry, 1811

Cymatium parthenopeum von Salis, 1793   von Salis' Triton
                                                                   Plate 18 f

Bermuda, Florida, Mexico, and the West Indies south to Brazil.

Reaching 5¾ inches in length, heavy. Color brownish yellow. Sculptured by 5 or 6 broad, low, and often nodulose spiral cords, with many finer threads. Axial sculpture consists of numerous fine growth lines. Parietal wall with many irregular, white plicae. Teeth of outer lip are grouped in pairs. Not common; to date we have found only young specimens in Puerto Rico.

Subgenus *Cymatium* Röding, 1798

Cymatium femorale Linné, 1758   Angular Triton
                                                              Plate 2 c
Southeast Florida and the West Indies.

3 to 7 inches in length, color orange to brown with white nodules on the varices of the last 2 or 3 whorls. Outer lip thickened, flaring, triangular in shape, and possessing 6 to 8 nodules; these nodules are separated by brown bands. The whorls are slightly flattened at the top, squarish and nodulous at the shoulder. Operculum small and oval-shaped. Siphonal canal elongated and turning backwards. Periostracum yellow-brown. Animal colored bright reddish brown, spotted with dark-brown. A common shallow-water species.

GENUS *Distorsio* Röding, 1798

Distorsio clathrata Lamarck, 1816   Atlantic Distorsio
                                                              Plate 18 d
Southeast U. S., the Gulf States, and the Caribbean.

¾ to 3 inches in length; whorls distorted, reticulated and knobbed; fairly rounded at the shoulder. Color white to tan, periostracum light-brown. Siphonal canal curved. Teeth of uneven size and shape on both sides of the aperture give the shell a grotesque appearance. Dredged in shallow water. Animal pale-yellow, striated with light-orange and white. Dead shells are commonly cast up on the beach.

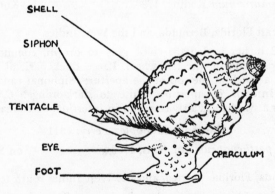

TEXT FIG. 19. *Distorsio clathrata* Lamarck. The living animal carrying its grotesque shell.

Distorsio mcgintyi Emerson and Puffer, 1953   McGinty's Distorsio
Plate 18 c
Florida, south through the West Indies.

A deep-water form similar to *D. clathrata* Lam. It is differentiated from *clathrata* by its smaller size (1 to 1¾ inches in length), its shorter siphonal canal, and more irregular coiling of the whorls. In addition, *D. mcgintyi* has only one parietal plica near the siphonal canal, while there are 2 in *clathrata*. Uncommon. Kay Yates found the only Puerto Rican specimen we have seen, at Aguadilla.

Family *BURSIDAE*
GENUS *Bursa* Röding, 1798

Bursa thomae Orbigny, 1842   St. Thomas Frog-shell
Plate 18 j
Southeast Florida and the West Indies.

½ to 1 inch in length. White with a tinge of pink or lavender, some brown on the varices and on top of the nodules. Two prominent varices per whorl, placed axially one below the other. Aperture a delicate shade of lavender. Not common. Listed as *Gyrineum cruentatum* Reeve by Dall and Simpson.

Subgenus *Colubrellina* Fischer, 1884
Bursa cubaniana Orbigny, 1842   Granular Frog-shell
Plate 18 i
Southeast Florida and the West Indies.

¾ to 2 inches in length, flattened laterally. Color orange-brown with 3 narrow white bands which sometimes only show up as white bands on the varices. Varices axially placed one below the other. Surface covered with several spiral rows of small beads. Parietal shield with many white folds. Dead shells often thrown up on the beach. *B. granularis* Röding is closely related and known only from the Indo-Pacific region.

Bursa corrugata Perry, 1811   Gaudy Frog-shell
Plate 18 m
Southeast Florida and the Caribbean.

2 to 3 inches in length, heavy. Orange-brown in color. The 2 large knobbed varices on each whorl do not exactly line up under each other. There are generally 1 or 2 rows of blunt nodules on the body whorl. Parietal shield tan, with many minute folds and pustules. Not common.

Subgenus *Bufonaria* Schumacher, 1817
Bursa spadicea Montfort, 1810   Chestnut Frog-shell
Plate 18 - 1
Southeast Florida and the Caribbean.

1 to 2 inches in length, flattened laterally. Yellowish with diffused markings of orange-brown. The 2 strong rounded varices on each whorl line up axially one under the other. Surface covered with spiral rows of numerous, small beads. R. Burden found a fresh specimen of this rare species at Punta Algarrobo, just north of Mayagüez, Puerto Rico.

Family TONNIDAE
GENUS *Tonna* Brünnich, 1772

Tonna maculosa Dillwyn, 1817   Atlantic Partridge Tun
                                                              Plate 2 f

Southeast Florida and the West Indies.

2 to 5 inches in length, thin but strong. Mottled with brown and white. Spire moderately extended. Suture deeply impressed but not channeled as in *T. galea*. Sculpture consists of many fine and irregular axial growth lines in addition to the broad, flattened spiral ridges. Animal with large foot, truncate in front and ending in a point posteriorly. Adults do not have an operculum in this genus. Reasonably common all around Puerto Rico.

Tonna galea Linné, 1758   Giant Tun

Circumtropical.

5 to 7 inches in length, thin but strong. Color white to dark-brown, generally uniform, but occasionally indistinctly mottled. Spire slightly extended. Suture deep, forming a channel. Sculpture consists of many broad, flattened spiral ridges. Animal with a large foot and lengthy proboscis. In one specimen approximately 40 mm. in length, the elongated proboscis measured 50 mm. in length and 5 mm. in width. The animal is yellowish in color, heavily mottled with black. The eyes are small and at the base of the tentacles. Uncommon in Puerto Rico.

Order NEOGASTROPODA
Superfamily MURICACEA
Family MURICIDAE
Subfamily MURICINAE
GENUS *Murex* Linné, 1758
Subgenus *Phyllonotus* Swainson, 1833

Murex pomum Gmelin, 1791   Apple Murex
                                                              Plate 2 g

Southeast U. S. to the West Indies.

2 to 4½ inches in length, thick and strong with a rough surface. Color cream, tan, or brown. Interior of aperture polished and colored ivory, tan, yellow, or orange, usually with brown spots on the upper end

of parietal wall and on the outer lip. It can easily be separated from
M. brevifrons by its colored aperture and the lack of large spines on
the varices. A common shallow-water species.

Subgenus *Chicoreus* Montfort, 1810

Murex brevifrons Lamarck, 1822   West Indian Murex
                                                            Plate 2 h
Lower Florida Keys and the West Indies.

3½ to 6 inches in length, very spinose. Color variable. It may be
unicolor cream to dark-brown or with many brown spiral bands. Interior
of aperture glossy-white. There are 3 axial varices which possess many
frond-like spines (the spines are sometimes lost in beach-worn specimens). A common shallow-water species, commonly found on the mangrove roots where it feeds on oysters.

Subgenus *Murex* Linné, 1758

Murex woodringi Clench and Farfante   Woodring's Murex
                                                            Plate 19 m
Jamaica, Puerto Rico, and northern South America.

2 to 2¾ inches in length. Color cream to gray. Spire acute and extended. Characterized by its long, narrow siphonal canal. The 3 axial
varices are moderately spinose. Two live specimens of this beautiful
species were dredged in about 20 feet just south of Mayagüez, Puerto
Rico.

Murex recurvirostris rubidus F. C. Baker 1897   Rose Murex
                                                            Plate 19 n
Florida, Bahamas and Puerto Rico.

1 to 2 inches in length. Color cream, pink, orange or red. Siphonal
canal rather long and slender. Can be separated from *M. woodringi* by
its short spire and its short body whorl. This species was reported from
Mayagüez by Dall and Simpson as *Murex messorius* Sowerby. Luis
Almodóvar dredged 2 beautiful specimens of this species off La Parguera,
on the southwest coast of Puerto Rico. Rare in Puerto Rico; common in
Florida.

Murex antillarum Hinds, 1844   Antillean Murex

Southern Florida through the Lesser Antilles.

2 to 4 inches in length, solid and very spinose. Color cream to
purple-brown with 3 rather indistinct bands of a darker color on each
whorl. Siphonal canal greatly extended in adults. A fairly deep-water
species reported from Mayagüez by Dall and Simpson.

Subgenus *Favartia* Jousseaume, 1880

Murex cellulosus Conrad, 1846   Pitted Murex
                                                          Plate 19 f

Bermuda, southeast U. S., and the Greater Antilles.

1 inch in length. Color dull grayish white. Axial sculpture consists of 5 to 7 low, fluted, axial varices. Spiral sculpture consists of many strong ridges which sometimes form low spines at each varix. Siphonal canal curved and broad at the base.

A globose form, *Murex cellulosus nuceus* Mörch, 1850 (plate 19 g) has heavily scaled varices, a shorter and wider siphonal canal, and more rounded aperture. A shallow-water species and the most common of the three forms in Puerto Rico.

A narrow form, *Murex cellulosus leviculus* Dall, 1889 (plate 19 h) is colored yellowish brown, has delicate sculpturing and irregular brown markings. Occurs in deep water.

GENUS *Muricopsis* Bucquoy, Dautzenberg and Dollfus, 1882

Muricopsis oxytatus M. Smith, 1938   Hexagonal Murex
                                                          Plate 19 e

Florida Keys and the West Indies.

1 to 1½ inches in length. Color whitish, sometimes tinted with purple or orange-brown. Shell elongated, with a high spire and 6 spiny rib-like varices on the body whorl. Aperture white. Moderately common in shallow dredgings. This is *Murex hexagonus* Lamarck, 1816, not Gmelin 1791. See Abbott, 1958, p. 63.

Subfamily *PURPURINAE*
GENUS *Drupa* Röding, 1798
Subgenus *Morula* Schumacher, 1817

Drupa nodulosa C. B. Adams, 1845   Blackberry Drupe
                                                          Plate 19 a

South half of Florida and the West Indies.

½ to 1 inch in length, elongate. Color dark reddish brown to black, with a purple-black aperture. Sculpture consists of about 10 longitudinal beaded ribs. Outer lip thickened with 4 or 5 white teeth. Common shallow-water species found living under rocks all around Puerto Rico.

GENUS *Risomurex* Olsson and McGinty, 1958

Risomurex roseus Reeve, 1856   Pink Drupe
                                                          Plate 19 b

West Indies.

About ½ inch in length, rose-colored with brown spiral bands. Whorls axial and nodosely ribbed. Aperture small; outer lip thickened, toothed within. Uncommon in shallow-water.

Genus *Purpura* Bruguière, 1789

Purpura patula Linné, 1758   Wide-mouthed Purpura
                                                           Plate 19 o

Southeast Florida and the West Indies.

2 to 3½ inches in length, ovate, with a short spire. Color dull brownish gray on the outside. Columella salmon-pink. Aperture very large, elliptical; inside of outer lip crenulated, irregularly blotched with brown. Sculpture consists of 6 or 7 revolving rows of rather sharp nodules. The younger shells are the most nodulose; adult shells are sometimes nearly smooth. The animal produces a harmless purple dye. A very common species living on rocks at the intertidal zone, all around Puerto Rico.

Genus *Thais* Röding, 1798
Subgenus *Stramonita* Schumacher, 1817

Thais rustica Lamarck, 1822   Rustic Rock shell
                                                           Plate 19 k

Southeast Florida, Bermuda, and the West Indies.

1½ inches in length, solid. Color dull-gray, often spirally banded with brown. Interior of aperture white, sometimes with brown spots along the outer lip. Parietal wall glossy-white; columella slightly twisted and stained purple at the lower inner corner. Outer lip strongly crenulated, usually with a second series of ridges within the aperture. Sculpture consists of 1 or more rows of rather well-developed nodules on the shoulder and mid-area of the whorl. In addition there are many fine growth lines and spiral threads. Fairly common on intertidal rocks all around the island of Puerto Rico.

Thais haemastoma floridana Conrad, 1837   Florida Rock shell
                                                           Plate 19 j

Southeastern U. S. and the Caribbean.

2 to 3 inches in length, solid. Color light-gray to yellow with brown mottling. This species is quite variable in color pattern and in shape. Sculpture consists of many fine spiral lines, sometimes with 2 or more rows of small nodules; there are also some axial growth lines. The shell appears smooth to finely nodulose. Above the columella there is a strong ridge that runs back within the aperture. Common under rocks in shallow-water. This is probably what Dall and Simpson reported as *Thais haemastoma* var. *undata* Lamarck, 1822.

Subgenus *Mancinella* Link, 1807

Thais deltoidea Lamarck, 1822   Deltoid Rock-shell
                                                            Plate 19 - 1
Florida and Bermuda to the West Indies.

1 to 2 inches in length, heavy. Color grayish, usually mottled with
brown or black. Specimens are often covered with coralline algae. Interior of aperture glossy white. Parietal wall tinted with light-purple or
pink. Columella with a small but distinct ridge at the base which forms
the margin of the siphonal canal. Sculpture consists of 1 or 2 spiral rows
of large, blunt nodules. In addition, there are numerous fine, spiral,
incised lines, no apparent axial sculpture. Operculum semicircular,
corneous, rough, with strong wavy growth lines. Found living on rocks
which are exposed to the ocean surf. Common in Puerto Rico.

GENUS *Aspella* Mörch, 1877
Subgenus *Aspella* Mörch, 1877

Aspella anceps Lamarck, 1822   Two-sided Aspella
                                                            Plate 19 c
Australia, Japan, Panama, and the West Indies.

About ½ inch in length, elongated, with elevated spire. Color white
or yellow. Shell flattened, with a double row of varices on each edge.
There is usually a smaller secondary varix in the center of the space
between the double varices. Spiral sculpture consists of a few revolving
threads. Suture deep and pitted. Aperture small, elliptical. Canal short,
narrow, recurved. Fairly common in drift sand and shallow dredgings.

Aspella paupercula C. B. Adams, 1850   Little Aspella
                                                            Plate 19 d
West Indies.

About ¾ inch long, elongated, with elevated spire. Color yellowish.
There are 3 principal axial varices and a smaller secondary one between
each of these. Spiral sculpture consists of a few revolving ridges and
many fine revolving threads. Spaces between the revolving ridges pitted
at the principal varices. Suture deep and pitted. Aperture small, elliptical; outer lip feebly toothed within. Canal short, recurved. Uncommon
shallow-water species. *A. scalaroides* Blainville may be this species.

GENUS *Ocenebra* Gray, 1847

Ocenebra intermedia C. B. Adams, 1850   Frilly Dwarf Triton
                                                            Plate 19 i
West Indies.

About 1 inch in size, elongated, ovate, fusiform. Color whitish, often
faintly banded with brown. Sculptured with 6 or 7 frilled axial varices

and a series of strong revolving ridges. Suture deep, whorls more or less shouldered. Aperture ovate, outer lip delicately frilled. Canal rather short, nearly closed. Reasonably common from shallow dredgings and on the beaches.

Subgenus *Ocinebrina* Jousseame, 1880

Ocenebra minirosea Abbott, 1954   Rose Dwarf Triton
                                                                             Plate 29 q
    Florida and West Indies.

    Small (about 5 mm. in length), salmon-red in color. Spire somewhat elevated; canal rather short. Reported from Boquerón, Puerto Rico, by Dall and Simpson as *Murex micromeris* Dall, 1890.

Family *MAGILIDAE*
Genus *Coralliophila* H. and A. Adams, 1853

Coralliophila abbreviata Lamarck, 1816   Short Coral-shell
                                                                             Plate 20 c
    Southeast Florida and the West Indies.

    About 1 inch in length, heavy, with rounded whorls. Color grayish white; aperture white, commonly tinted with yellow or orange. Widely umbilicate. Sculptured with numerous, crowded spiral cords and rounded axial ridges. Operculum chitinous, opaque, yellowish brown. It lives on or near coral in shallow water.

Coralliophila caribaea Abbott, 1958   Caribbean Coral-shell
                                                                             Plate 20 b
    Southeast Florida and the West Indies.

    ½ to 1 inch in length. Characterized by its triangular shape and purple-tinted aperture. Whorls angulate at the shoulder. Spire high. Sculpture consists of numerous crowded cords and about a dozen rounded plications, which form rounded nodules at the periphery. Umbilicus slit-like. Operculum corneous, elongate, opaque, wine-red, with a marginal nucleus. Very common at base of sea fans.

Coralliophila aberrans C. B. Adams, 1850   Globular Coral-shell
                                                                             Plate 20 e
    West Indies.

    About ½ inch in length, ovate. Color white. Sculpture consists of many rounded axial ribs and numerous close-set spiral ridges which are continuous over the longitudinal ribs. Apex acute. Whorls quite convex with a rather deep suture. Rare; only dead shells of this species were found on the southeastern and northwestern coasts of Puerto Rico.

Coralliophila scalariformis Lamarck, 1822   Pagoda Coral-shell
Plate 20 d
Florida and the Gulf of Mexico to the Virgin Islands.

About 1 inch in length, solid. White throughout. Sculpture variable,
usually consisting of numerous, close, scaly spiral cords and strong axial
waves. Characterized by the short triangular spines at the periphery of
the whorls. Operculum yellow. McGinty reports that the male is usually
much smaller than the female. Found under stones.

Superfamily *BUCCINACEA*
Family *COLUMBELLIDAE*
GENUS *Columbella* Lamarck, 1799

Columbella mercatoria Linné, 1758   Common Dove-shell
Plate 20 a
Southeast Florida and the West Indies.

½ to ¾ inch in length, solid, squat. Color pattern extremely variable; commonly white and brown or white and orange, yellowish brown,
or pink with interrupted spiral bars or zigzag markings. The whorls are
rounded; the surface is covered with many strong revolving ridges. Outer
lip thick, incurved in the middle, and strongly toothed within throughout its length. Columella callus with 6 or 8 teeth at the base. A very
common shallow-water species.

GENUS *Pyrene* Röding, 1798

Pyrene ovulata Lamarck, 1822   Ovate Dove-shell
Plate 20 t
West Indies.

½ to ¾ inch in length, ovate-conic. Color reddish brown with
irregular white markings. Sculpture consists of many faint spiral grooves
which are scarcely visible on the middle of the body whorl. The shell
appears to be smooth. Aperture white, long, and narrow; outer lip
weakly toothed within. Columella slightly curved in the middle to cor-
respond with the incurving of outer lip; slightly plicated below. Dead
shells are frequently cast up on the beaches. *P. ovuloides* C. B. Adams
is a synonym.

GENUS *Anachis* H. and A. Adams, 1853

Anachis catenata Sowerby, 1844   Chain Dove-shell
Plate 20 r
Bermuda and the West Indies.

About ¼ inch in length. Color white to yellow with brown spots
more or less on alternate ribs. Sculptured with rather strong axial ribs
and faint spiral striae. Outer lip thickened, slightly notched above,

toothed within. Columella with feeble pustules. A moderately common shallow-water species all around Puerto Rico.

Anachis sparsa Reeve, 1859   Sprinkled Dove-shell
                                                                        Plate 20 s
West Indies.

¼ to ⅜ inch in length, fusiform. Color yellowish white with many small reddish brown markings. Sculptured with many (14-15 on body whorl) prominent axial ribs and numerous faint, spiral striae which do not cross the axial ribs. There are 6 or 7 revolving cords at the base of the body whorl. Fresh shells are covered with a brown periostracum. Aperture small, outer lip toothed within, notched at upper part. Columella callus faintly nodulous. Very common from shallow dredgings all around Puerto Rico.

Anachis mangelioides Reeve, 1859   Mangelia-like Dove-shell
                                                                        Plate 20 o
West Indies.

About 5/16 inch in length, elongated. Color cream, very commonly sprinkled with some brown markings. Sculptured with very prominent axial ribs (9-12 on body whorl). Whorls numerous, flatly convex; suture impressed; siphonal canal moderately developed. Aperture small and narrow. Outer lip enlarged exteriorly, toothed within. A reasonably common shallow-water species found on all coasts of Puerto Rico. *A. mcgintyi* Usticke, 1959 is probably this species.

Anachis iontha Ravenel, 1883   Iontha Dove-shell

Puerto Rico and southeast United States.

Reported from Mayagüez by Dall and Simpson.

Anachis pulchella Sowerby, 1844   Beautiful Dove-shell
                                                                        Plate 20 g
Florida Keys and the West Indies.

¼ to ⅜ inch in length. Color yellowish white, variegated with brown. Sculptured with many axial ribs, the ribs on the upper whorls being the strongest; numerous spiral striae cross the axial ribs. Outer lip slightly thickened, faintly toothed within. Columella callus raised into a little lip at its edge, faintly nodulous to smooth. A common shallow-water species frequently cast up on the beaches of Puerto Rico.

Anachis obesa C. B. Adams, 1845   Fat Dove-shell
                                                                        Plate 20 q
Virginia to Florida, the Gulf and the West Indies.

3/16 to ¼ inch in length, rather stout. Color whitish or yellowish, usually with 2 to 4 light- or dark-brown spiral bands. Sculptured with numerous small, strong, axial ribs, which fade out on the back of the body whorl, and numerous incised spiral lines which do not cross the ribs. Outer lip thickened, toothed within. Columella callus smooth. A common shallow-water species found all around Puerto Rico.

Anachis calliglypta Dall and Simpson, 1901   Puerto Rican Dove-shell

Puerto Rico.

Reported from Aguadilla by Dall and Simpson.

Anachis crassilabris Reeve, 1859   Thick-lip Dove-shell
Plate 20 h
West Indies.

3/16 to ¼ inch in length. Similar to *Anachis obesa,* but the brown is in the form of arrowheads rather than solid bands. The outer lip is greatly thickened exteriorly, and there are 2 noticeable brown spots on it. One of these is at the base opposite the canal, and the other is about midway on the lip. Common in shallow-water dredgings.

GENUS *Nitidella* Swainson, 1840

Nitidella ocellata Gmelin, 1791   White-spotted Dove-shell
Plate 20 j
Lower Florida Keys, the West Indies and Bermuda.

¼ to ½ inch in length, solid. Color dark-brown, covered with white spots. Smooth except for a few faint revolving striae at the base. Aperture short, narrow. Outer lip thickened, notched, toothed within. Columella smooth. Common under rocks at low tide. Formerly known as *N. cribraria* Lamarck, 1822.

Nitidella dichroa Sowerby, 1858   Two-colored Dove-shell
Plate 20 k
West Indies.

Similar to *N. ocellata,* but smaller in size and with a different color pattern. The white is irregularly streaked and diffused in this species, whereas in *ocellata* the white is in the form of polka dots. Common under stones at low tide.

Nitidella nitida Lamarck, 1822   Glossy Dove-shell
Plate 20 p
Southeast Florida and the West Indies.

½ inch in length, oblong-oval. Color yellowish to purplish brown, blotched and spotted with white. Surface smooth and shiny. Aperture long and narrow; outer lip thickened in the middle, toothed within, the spaces between the teeth darker. Columella has 2 small ridges just below its center. Very common on rocks at low tide. *N. nitidula* Sowerby, 1822 is a synonym.

Nitidella laevigata Linné, 1758 — Smooth Dove-shell
Plate 20 u
Florida Keys and the West Indies.

½ to ¾ inch in length. Color pattern quite variable, usually white with longitudinal zigzag brown markings. There is a row of very dark spots above the suture and on the middle of the body whorl. Surface smooth and shiny. Resembles *N. nitida,* but its aperture is oval rather than narrow, and the outer lip is not thickened in the middle. Columella excavated above, with 2 folds at its base. Fairly common in shallow water.

GENUS *Mitrella* Risso, 1826
Subgenus *Mitrella* Risso, 1826

Mitrella lunata Say, 1826 — Lunar Dove-shell
Plate 20 i
Massachusetts to Florida, Texas, and the West Indies.

About 3/16 inch in length, moderately wide. Color glossy-white to yellow, with many fine, zigzag, brown markings. Nuclear whorls sometimes brown. No apparent sculpture except for a few fine spiral lines at the base of the shell. Aperture small, outer lip slightly notched at the top, and toothed within. Very common on weeds at low tide. Found all around the island of Puerto Rico.

Mitrella duclosiana Orbigny, 1847 — Duclos' Dove-shell

Puerto Rico.

Reported by Dall and Simpson from Mayagüez.

Subgenus *Columbellopsis* Bucquoy,
Dautzenberg and Dollfus, 1882

Mitrella fenestrata C. B. Adams, 1850 — Fenestrate Dove-shell
Plate 20 - 1
Southern Florida and the West Indies.

Slightly over ¼ inch in length, elongate, with a narrow, pointed, flat-sided spire. Color white to cream, usually with a row of light brown, flame-like markings on each whorl. Glossy, smooth. Outer lip is slightly thickened and with small teeth within. Common in shallow water. This is *M. fusiformis* Orbigny, 1842, not Anton, 1839.

Mitrella nitens C. B. Adams, 1850 — Shiny Dove-shell
Plate 20 f
West Indies.

About ½ inch in length, ovate, fusiform. Spire rather elongated, apex acute. Color white with spiral series of brown flamulations. Shell shiny and smooth, except for about 14 striae at its base. Aperture a little less than half the length of the shell. Outer lip thickened exteriorly and delicately toothed within. Columella smooth to feebly and obliquely striated near the canal. Canal short and wide. Common on the west coast of Puerto Rico in dredgings from 20 to 100 fathoms. Redescribed by Dall and Simpson as *Columbella perpicta*.

GENUS *Psarostola* Rehder, 1943

Psarostola monilifera Sowerby, 1844   Many-spotted Dove-shell
                                                             Plate 20 m
          Florida and the West Indies.

About 3/16 inch in length, slender. Color white to yellow with 3 to 4 spiral rows of reddish brown spots on each whorl and about 6 rows at the base of the last whorl. Sculptured with narrow axial ribs crossed by strong spiral cords which form nodules on crossing the ribs. Aperture small; interior of outer lip toothed; inner lip smooth. Common. *P. sparsipunctata* Rehder, 1943 is a color form with spots only on the upper 2 cords. A brown color form with white spots is also found in Puerto Rico.

Psarostola minor C. B. Adams, 1845   Banded Dove-shell
                                                             Plate 20 n
          West Indies.

About ¼ inch in length, with slightly rounded whorls. Color whitish, with a spiral brown band below the suture and another on the base of the shell. Sculptured with 9 to 13 rounded longitudinal ribs; these are cut by shallow, revolving grooves into low, irregular nodules. Otherwise resembling *P. monilifera*. Common from shallow dredgings. Listed as *Nassarina glypta* Bush by Dall and Simpson.

GENUS *Nassarina* Dall, 1889

Nassarina metabrunnea Dall and Simpson, 1901 Brown-striped Nassarina
                                                             Plate 29 p
          Puerto Rico.

Reported from Mayagüez by Dall and Simpson.
                    Family *BUCCINIDAE*
          GENUS *Bailya* M. Smith, 1944

Bailya parva C. B. Adams, 1850   West Indian Baily-shell
                                                             Plate 21 a
          Bahamas and the West Indies.

About ¾ inch in length, elongate. Flesh-colored with irregular pale-brown and white revolving stripes. Whorls rounded, deeply sutured.

Sculptured with 10 or 12 narrow, rounded axial ribs which are crossed by less conspicuous spiral lines. At their intersection there are small beads. Outer lip thickened; columella smooth and glossy. Uncommon. Similar to *B. intricata* Dall but is larger, has brown coloring, axial ribs are more prominent, and the whorls are not shouldered.

Bailya intricata Dall, 1883   Intricate Baily-shell
                                                                        Plate 21 b
        Southern half of Florida and the West Indies.

About ½ inch in length, elongate. Color dingy white. Whorls slightly shouldered. Sculpture strongly cancellate, with 12 to 14 low, narrow axial ribs on the body whorl, crossed by alternating strong and weak spiral cords. Aperture about ½ length of shell; outer lip thickened by a frilled varix. Columella smooth. Uncommon under rocks at low tide.

GENUS *Antillophos* Woodring, 1928

Antillophos candei Orbigny, 1853   Beaded Phos
                                                                        Plate 21 h
        Southeast U. S. to the West Indies.

1 to 1¼ inches in length, heavy. Color yellowish white, sometimes with faint-brown bands. Last whorl sculptured with about 16 strong longitudinal ribs, beaded where they are crossed by the revolving threads. Aperture spirally ridged. Columella with 2 folds at the base. Uncommon from shallow dredgings.

Antillophos oxyglyptus Dall and Simpson, 1901   Puerto Rican Phos
                                                                        Plate 21 g
        Puerto Rico.

About ⅝ inch in length. Dirty white in color. Delicately sculptured with about 16 longitudinal ribs and numerous spiral threads. Dall and Simpson described this species from Mayagüez. The only specimen we found came from the same locality. Rare.

GENUS *Engoniophos* Woodring, 1928

Engoniophos guadelupensis Petit, 1852   Guadeloupe Phos
                                                                        Plate 21 f
        West Indies.

About 1 inch in length. Color varying from whitish to light- or dark-brown. Sculptured with about 10 strong longitudinal ribs, crossed by numerous revolving threads (not beaded like *A. candei*). Columella with only one fold at the base. Very common from shallow dredgings.

Engoniophos unicinctus Say, 1826   Lined Phos
Plate 21 j
West Indies.

Similar to *E. guadelupensis* but with slightly shouldered whorls and with a narrow, dark-colored band below the shoulder on the body whorl. On the other whorls the dark color is at the suture. This may be the same species as *E. guadelupensis.*

GENUS *Engina* Gray, 1839

Engina turbinella Kiener, 1836   White-spotted Engina
Plate 21 d
Lower Florida Keys and the West Indies.

About ½ inch in length. Color reddish brown to black with a row of white nodules on the periphery of each whorl. Surface covered with numerous microscopic spiral lines and finer axial threads. Base with 2 to 4 nodulous, spiral cords. Aperture narrow; outer lip thickened and toothed within. Parietal area glazed and nodulous; columella twisted just above the narrow siphonal canal. Common under rocks in shallow water. The subspecies *cruzana* Usticke, 1959 is merely a form which occurs throughout the entire range of the species.

GENUS *Colubraria* Schumacher, 1817

Colubraria lanceolata Menke, 1828   Arrow Dwarf Triton
Plate 21 m
Southeast U. S. and the West Indies.

¾ to 1 inch in length, elongate, slender. Flesh-colored with occasional brown markings. Surface finely reticulate with numerous axial and spiral lines. Former varices distinct. Aperture long, narrow. Parietal shield smooth, white, and elevated. Nucleus brown, smooth, and bulbous. Uncommon.

Colubraria obscura Reeve, 1844   Leaning Dwarf Triton
Plate 21 q
Tortugas and the West Indies.

1 to 2 inches in length, heavy. Color light-brown with zones of darker brown. Surface cancellate and heavily beaded. Former varices large and prominent, marked with dark-brown and white. Parietal shield pustulose at the base, inner margin with numerous folds. Outer lip thickened and toothed within. Nuclear whorls commonly missing, but when present are cream-colored, smooth, and bulbous. This species is much larger and fatter than *C. lanceolata* Menke. Uncommon. Found also in the Indo-Pacific region. *C. testacea* Mörch, 1877 is a synonym.

Subgenus *Monostiolum* Dall, 1904

Colubraria swifti Tryon, 1881   Swift's Dwarf Triton
                                                              Plate 21 i
West Indies.

About ¾ inch in length, slender, elongate. Color yellow, maculated with brown. Sculptured with many axial ribs, crossed by numerous spiral lines. No former varices. Aperture about ⅓ the length of the shell. Outer lip thickened, weakly toothed within, the uppermost tooth being the largest. Parietal wall glazed. Dead shells are commonly washed up on the beaches of Puerto Rico.

GENUS *Pisania* Bivona-Bernardi, 1832

Pisania pusio Linné, 1758   Miniature Triton Trumpet
                                                              Plate 21 e
Southeast Florida and the West Indies.

1 to 1¾ inches in length, solid, somewhat elongated. Color purplish brown with narrow, revolving, dark-brown bands, sometimes in the shape of arrowheads. Surface smooth and glossy. Aperture large, outer lip toothed within. Parietal wall frequently plicate at the base and with a strong ridge at its upper end. Uncommon in Puerto Rico, but common in Grand Cayman Island.

GENUS *Cantharus* Röding, 1798
Subgenus *Pollia* Sowerby, 1834

Cantharus tinctus Conrad, 1846   Tinted Cantharus
                                                              Plate 21 k
Southeast U. S. and the West Indies.

¾ to 1¼ inch in length, heavy, with a conical spire. Color light- to dark-brown, clouded with white or gray. Sculptured with 10-14 low axial ribs crossed by numerous spiral cords. Otherwise similar to *C. auritulus* but not nearly as common. Reported from Cabo Rojo Lighthouse by Dall and Simpson.

Cantharus tinctus var. *bermudensis* Dall, 1901

Similar to the above but more slender and delicate. Reported by Dall and Simpson from Boqueron, Puerto Rico.

Cantharus auritulus Link, 1807   Common Cantharus
                                                              Plate 21 - l
Southeast Florida, south through the Antilles to Brazil.

¾ to 1¼ inches in length, heavy, broad. Color light- to dark-brown with diffused white or gray. Sculptured with 9 to 11 low axial ribs, crossed by many spiral cords. Aperture wide, with a small canal at the top. Outer lip thickened, strongly toothed within. A common shallow-water species.

Cantharus lautus (Reeve, 1846)   Gaudy Cantharus
                                                                     Plate 21 c
West Indies.

About ¾ inch in length. Brown with one or more white bands. Sculptured with 8 to 10 strong axial ribs crossed by beaded spiral cords. Aperture narrower than in *C. auritulus.* This species was reported as the Mediterranean *Tritonidea orbignyi* Payraudeau, 1826 by Dall and Simpson. *C. karinae* Usticke, 1959 is also this species. Uncommon.

Cantharus multangulus Philippi, 1848   False Drill Cantharus

Southeast U. S. and the West Indies.

Dall and Simpson reported this species from Mayagüez, under the name *Muricidea multangula* Philippi. According to Robert Robertson (1957) this record is erroneous, for it is based on a juvenile muricid. This species apparently does not occur in Puerto Rico.

Family NASSARIIDAE
GENUS *Nassarius* Duméril, 1806

Nassarius albus Say, 1826   Variable Nassa
                                                                     Plate 21 o
Southeastern U. S. to the West Indies.

½ inch in length. Color white or yellow, generally spotted or banded with brown. Sculptured with 8 to 14 longitudinal ribs, crossed by numerous revolving threads. Suture deep. Parietal shield usually not well-developed, white. Commonly found on mud bottoms and dredged down to 100 ft. This is *Nassarius ambiguus* Pulteney, not Solander, 1766.

Nassarius nanus Usticke, 1959   Dwarf Nassa
                                                                     Plate 21 n
West Indies.

Resembles *N. albus* but is smaller, more elongate, with acute spire.

Nassarius vibex Say, 1822   Common Eastern Nassa
                                                                     Plate 21 p
Cape Cod to Florida, the Gulf States, and the West Indies.

⅜ inch in length, heavy. Color light- to dark-brown. Last whorl sculptured with about 12 longitudinal ribs, crossed by finer revolving threads. Parietal shield well-developed, glazed, white or yellow. A common sand or mudflat species. *N. sturmi* Philippi, 1848 is probably this species.

Family *FASCIOLARIIDAE*
Subfamily *FASCIOLARIINAE*
GENUS *Fasciolaria* Lamarck, 1799

Fasciolaria tulipa Linné, 1758   True Tulip
                                                                   Plate 2 d
Southeastern U. S. and the West Indies.

3 to 9 inches in length, fusiform, with rounded whorls. Color variable, orange, red, or mahogany brown, clouded with white, yellow or tan and overlaid with numerous brown spiral lines. Fairly smooth except for the wrinkles and 2 or 3 spiral grooves just below the suture. Commonly found on grass bottoms in shallow water all around the island of Puerto Rico.

GENUS *Pleuroploca* P. Fischer, 1884

Pleuroploca gigantea Kiener, 1840   Florida Horse Conch
North Carolina to Florida.

One very young shell of this species was reported as *Fasciolaria gigantea,* from Mayagüez by Dall and Simpson. The shell must have been too young for correct identification, as this species does not occur in Puerto Rico.

GENUS *Latirus* Montfort, 1810

Latirus infundibulum Gmelin, 1791   Brown-lined Latirus
                                                                   Plate 2 i
Florida Keys and the West Indies.

2 to 3 inches in length, elongate, fusiform, heavy. Color light brown, with darker revolving cords. Whorls sculptured with 7 or 8 strong, rounded longitudinal ridges. Aperture long, ovate, usually with many spiral threads within; 3 weak columella plaits. Canal long, narrow. Imperfect umbilicus at base of shell. Animal bright red, finely speckled with white. A moderately common shallow-water species.

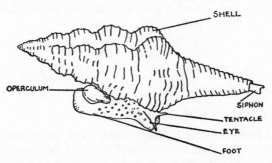

TEXT FIG. 20. *Latirus infundibulum* Gmelin, showing the visible parts of the living animal.

Latirus brevicaudatus Reeve, 1847   Short-tailed Latirus
Plate 22 - 1
Lower Florida Keys and the West Indies.

1 to 2½ inches in length. Color reddish brown. Sculpture with 8 or 9 long, rounded axial ribs, crossed by numerous spiral threads. Canal short. Similar to *L. infundibulum* but smaller, broader, and shorter. A moderately common shallow-water species.

Latirus virginensis Abbott, 1958   Virgin Island Latirus
Plate 22 n
Greater Antilles.

1 to 1½ inches in length, solid, elongate, fusiform. Color yellowish brown. Sculptured with 7 to 9 strong, rounded axial ribs. There is a prominent row of 7 to 9 large white nodules on each whorl, corresponding with each rib. Surface covered with many spiral cords. Siphonal canal narrow, long, open along its length. Lower half of columella with 4 to 5 weak plicae. Outer lip crenulated. Aperture with many spiral threads within. There is usually a tooth at the upper left-hand side of the aperture. Originally described from the Virgin Islands, this species also lives in Puerto Rico.

GENUS *Fusilatirus* McGinty, 1955

Fusilatirus cayohuesonicus Sowerby, 1878   Key West Latirus

Key West to the West Indies.

About ¾ inch in length, elongate, fusiform. Color dark-brown throughout. Resembles a miniature *Latirus infundibulum*. Sculptured with 6 or 8 large, rounded axial ribs, which are crossed by strong spiral cords. Between the spiral cords, the surface is covered with a network of microscopic axial and spiral threads. Aperture small, notched at the upper end, bearing many spiral threads within. Parietal wall glazed, bearing 3 large folds, the lowermost sometimes being obsolete. Canal narrow. Rare in Puerto Rico.

GENUS *Leucozonia* Gray, 1847
Subgenus *Leucozonia* Gray, 1847

Leucozonia nassa Gmelin, 1791   Chestnut Latirus
Plate 22 m
Florida to Texas and the West Indies.

1½ to 2 inches in length, heavy. Color light- to dark-brown, usually with a narrow white band at the base of the shell. Sculptured with about 9 longitudinal nodules which are most pronounced at the shoulder of the whorl. The surface is covered with faint revolving threads. Aperture elliptical, generally with spiral threads within. Columella with 3 or 4 weak folds at the base. Canal short. Moderately common under rocks. The animal is bright red in color. *L. cingulifera* Lamarck is this species.

Leucozonia ocellata Gmelin, 1791   White-spotted Latirus
Plate 22 k
    Florida and the West Indies.

1 inch in length, solid. Color light- or dark-brown, with a row of about 9 large, white rounded nodules at the periphery of .each whorl. 3 or 4 spiral rows of broken white bands at the base of the shell. Aperture with many spiral threads within. Columella with 3 small folds, canal short. A moderately common shallow-water species found all around Puerto Rico.

Family XANCIDAE
Subfamily VASINAE
Genus *Vasum* Röding, 1798

Vasum muricatum Born, 1778   Caribbean Vase
Plate 22 p
    South half of Florida and the West Indies.

2½ to 4 inches in length, bearing short blunt spines at the shoulder of the whorls. Color dull-white, usually covered with a thick dark-brown periostracum. Spire flat-sided. Columella bears 5 folds. Aperture large, elongate, shiny-white, usually tinged with purple. Operculum dark-brown, thick, horny, and filling most of the aperture. Very common in shallow water.

Vasum capitellus Linné, 1758   Spiny Vase
Plate 22 q
    Puerto Rico and the Lesser Antilles to Colombia.

2 to 3 inches in length, bearing prominent spines at the shoulder of the whorls. Color cream, usually covered with a thick, light-brown periostracum. Spire elongated and pointed. Columella bears 3 folds. Aperture small, oval, shiny-white, usually tinged with bright-orange. Operculum brown with many growth lines. Rare except at Cabo Rojo Lighthouse.

Superfamily VOLUTACEA
Family OLIVIDAE
Genus *Oliva* Bruguière, 1789

Oliva reticularis Lamarck, 1811   Netted Olive
Plate 3 j: 23 s
    Southeast Florida and the West Indies.

1½ to 1¾ inches in length, rather elongated, slightly swollen at the middle; spire somewhat elevated. Ground color whitish, overlaid with purplish brown reticulations. Aperture white. A fairly common shallow-water species.

A form, *O. reticularis olorinella* Duclos, has an elongated spire, glossy surface, and is almost completely cream or white. Uncommon.

Oliva caribaeensis Dall and Simpson, 1901   Caribbean Olive
                                                          Plate 3 k; 23 t
Caribbean.

About 1 to 2 inches in length. Similar to *reticularis* but with a lower spire and having the suture deeply channeled. Surface glossy; the interior is purple in fresh specimens. Reasonably common. *O. trujilloi* Clench, 1938 appears to be this species. This is also what Usticke erroneously called *sayana* Ravenel.

GENUS *Olivella* Swainson, 1831
Subgenus *Olivella* Swainson, 1831

Olivella nivea Gmelin, 1791   West Indian Dwarf Olive
                                                          Plate 23 n
Southeast Florida, the West Indies, and Bermuda.

½ to 1 inch in length, apex sharply pointed. Color mostly white or with shadings of purple-brown. Suture channel is deep and fairly wide. Reported from San Juan by Gundlach. Harold Winters also found this species on Mona Island, but it is rare in Puerto Rico.

Olivella petiolita Duclos, 1835   Caribbean Dwarf Olive
                                                          Plate 23 p
West Indies to Venezuela and Panama.

½ to ¾ inch in length, solid, with high, conic spire. Color white or yellow, overlaid by brown or orange coalescing arrow-shaped lines. Suture grooved, parietal callus strong. This is the commonest *Olivella* in Puerto Rico. Dall and Simpson reported this species as *Olivella esther* Duclos.

Olivella floralia Duclos, 1835   Florida Dwarf Olive
Florida and the West Indies.

Reported from Mayagüez as *Olivella oryza* Lamarck by Dall and Simpson. Rare.

Subgenus *Dactylidia* H. and A. Adams, 1853
Olivella dealbata Reeve, 1850   White Dwarf Olive
                                                          Plate 23 m
Florida and the West Indies.

About ¼ inch in length, with a stubby apical tip. Color white or cream; the midzone of the body whorl is often brownish as a result of irregular zigzag lines. Reasonably common from shallow dredgings on the west coast of Puerto Rico.

Subgenus *Niteoliva* Olsson, 1956

Olivella minuta Link, 1807   Minute Dwarf Olive
                                                                    Plate 23 u
West Indies and Caribbean.

¼ to ½ inch in length, fat, with a sharp apex; glossy. Color pattern is quite variable, usually light-gray or brownish with darker, indistinct zigzag lines. There is usually a darker colored band just below the suture on the body whorl and towards the base of the body whorl. Parietal callus strong, extending upward towards the suture. The sutures are open and grooved. This is probably what was referred to as *O. mutica* Say by Dall and Simpson. Reasonably common from shallow dredgings and in beach drift.

Olivella verreauxi Ducros, 1857   Verreau's Dwarf Olive
                                                                    Plate 23 v
West Indies.

Closely related to *O. minuta*, but generally much slenderer. Reported from Quebradillas and Aguadilla by Gundlach.

Subgenus *Mcgintiella* Olsson, 1956

Olivella rotunda Dall, 1889   Stout Dwarf Olive

Puerto Rico and Barbados.

A little less than 1 inch in length, stout, inflated, with a small pointed spire. Color pale-yellow, with faint, irregular, broken zigzag markings. Suture deeply grooved, forming a lengthened, appressed anal canal at the end of the aperture. Parietal callus strong, extending to the end of the aperture. Columellar plications strong and numerous. Reported from Mayagüez and Aguadilla by Dall and Simpson.

Subgenus *Minioliva* Olsson, 1956

Olivella perplexa Olsson, 1956   Tiny Dwarf Olive
                                                                    Plate 23 - l
Florida and the West Indies.

Less than 5 mm. in length, with an elevated stubby spire. Porcellaneous-white, glossy. Sutures deeply channeled. Parietal callus thick. Very common in beach drift and from shallow dredgings.

Olivella acteocina Olsson, 1956   Olsson's Dwarf Olive
                                                                    Plate 23 k
West Indies.

About 4 mm. in length. Close to *O. perplexa* but more cylindrical in form, generally with a higher spire and larger nucleus. Common from shallow-water dredgings.

GENUS *Jaspidella* Olsson, 1956

Jaspidella jaspidea Gmelin, 1791   Jasper Dwarf Olive
                                                         Plate 23 q
     Southeast Florida to Barbados.

½ to ¾ inch in length, rather thin and elongate. Whorls 5, apex blunt, nuclear whorls large and bulbous. Compared to *O. nivea*, the sutural channel is moderately deep, narrow, but without an etched indentation on the side of preceding whorl. Color variable, usually grayish with faint brown or purple markings. Columella not calloused; with 4 strong plaits at the base. Operculum chitinous. A shallow-water species. Formerly placed in the genus *Olivella*.

Family *MITRIDAE*
GENUS *Mitra* Lamarck, 1799

Mitra nodulosa Gmelin, 1791   Beaded Miter
                                                         Plate 22 j
     Southeast U. S. and the West Indies.

¾ to 1 inch in length, color orange to brown. Surface sculptured by neatly beaded longitudinal ribs of which there are 15-17 on the body whorl. Columella with 4 white folds; the uppermost is strongest and the lowest very faint. Lives under rocks. Reasonably common all around Puerto Rico.

Mitra barbadensis Gmelin, 1791   Barbados Miter
                                                         Plate 22 o
     Southeast Florida and the West Indies.

1 to 1½ inches in length, elongate. Color yellow-brown, with few small grayish white flecks. Surface sculptured with raised revolving threads. Aperture long and widened below. Columella with 4 or 5 white, slanting folds. Reasonably common under rocks at low tide.

Mitra fluviimaris Pilsbry and McGinty, 1949   Gulf Stream Miter
                                                         Plate 22 d
     Florida and Puerto Rico.

About 1 inch in length, fusiform. Color white with some brown stain. Body whorl sculptured with 14-18 spiral cords. Aperture is more than ½ the length of shell; narrow. There are 4 columellar folds. A deep-water species previously known only from the border of the Gulf Stream in Florida. A single 7 mm. specimen was found in beach drift at Ramey Base on the northwest coast of Puerto Rico.

GENUS *Pusia* Swainson, 1840

Pusia hanleyi Dohrn, 1861   Hanley's Miter
                                                      Plate 22 b
Florida to the West Indies.

¼ inch or less in length. Tan to brown in color with a white or
cream spiral band. Sculpture consists of 13 to 16 axial ribs per whorl
and numerous crinkles or riblets just below the suture. Columella with
4 brown folds. Reasonably common shallow-water species.

Pusia gemmata Sowerby, 1874   Little Gem Miter
                                                      Plate 22 a
Florida and the West Indies.

¼ inch or slightly more in length. Black-brown in color, with a
broad white peripheral band. 11-13 ribs per whorl. Columella with 4
black spiral folds. Similar to *P. hanleyi* but larger, less elongate, darker
in color, and lacking the riblets just below the suture. Reasonably
common.

Pusia puella Reeve, 1845   Girl Miter
                                                      Plate 22 f
Southeastern U. S. to the Lesser Antilles.

Between ¼ and ½ inch in length, rotund in shape. Color dark-
brown or black with white flamules just below the suture of the whorl.
Faintly sculptured with numerous spiral and axial threads. Columella
with 4 folds, the lower 2 weak and close-set. This is an uncommon
species found on the northeast coast of Puerto Rico.

Pusia staminea A. Adams, 1851

Puerto Rico.

Reported from Mayagüez by Dall and Simpson.

Pusia pulchella Reeve, 1845   Beautiful Miter
                                                      Plate 22 e
West Indies.

A little over ½ inch in length. Color dark-brown or reddish brown
with white maculations. Sculptured with prominent, rounded axial ribs
(17-20 on body whorl) and several spiral lines which do not appear to
cross the ribs. Columella with 4 plaits, the upper 2 large and prominent.
Found at Rincón; rare. *Mitra albicostata* C. B. Adams, 1850 is this
species.

Pusia albocincta C. B. Adams, 1845   White-lined Miter
                                                      Plate 22 c
Florida and the West Indies.

About 1 inch in length, fusiform. Tan to dark-brown in color with a white spiral band on each whorl. Whorls sculptured with 12-14 strong axial ribs; surface microscopically reticulate. 4 large columella folds. Uncommon. *Pusia microzonias* Lamarck, 1811, an Indo-Pacific species was reported from San Juan by Gundlach. He probably had *albocincta*.

Pusia histrio Reeve, 1844   Painted Miter
                                                          Plate 22 i
West Indies.

About ½ inch in length, fusiform. Color dark-brown with a narrow, white, spiral band topped by a bright-orange band on each whorl. Sculptured with about a dozen sharp axial ribs. Columella with 4 folds. One beautiful specimen of this species was dredged off La Parguera on the south coast of Puerto Rico in about 75 feet of water.

Family VOLUTIDAE
Subfamily VOLUTINAE
GENUS *Voluta* Linné, 1758

Voluta musica Linné, 1758   Music Volute
                                                          Plate 22 r
Caribbean.

2 to 2½ inches in length, heavy. Easily recognized by its pinkish cream background and the 2 to 3 spiral bands of fine lines which are dotted with darker brown (the music notes). This moderately common West Indian species is rare in Puerto Rico. A. Oliver found 2 dead specimens of this beautiful species near Guanica, Puerto Rico.

Family CANCELLARIIDAE
GENUS *Cancellaria* Lamarck, 1799

Cancellaria reticulata Linné, 1767   Common Nutmeg
                                                          Plate 22 h
Southeast U. S. and the West Indies.

1 to 1¾ inches in length, strong. Color cream, irregularly banded with reddish brown markings. Surface reticulate. Columella usually with 3 folds; the center one largest; when only 2 folds are present, the upper one is the largest. Outer lip strongly ridged within. Fresh specimens of this rather widespread species are seldom found on the beaches in Puerto Rico.

GENUS *Trigonostoma* Blainville, 1827

Trigonostoma rugosa Lamarck, 1822   Rugose Nutmeg
                                                          Plate 22 g
Caribbean.

About 1¼ inches in length, resembling a huge *Nassarius* in shape. Color dirty white. Surface sculptured with many strong axial ribs, about 14 on the body whorl, crossed by numerous smaller spiral cords. Aperture wide and expanded. Rare. To date, we have only one specimen of this species from the north coast of Puerto Rico found by Margaret Graham.

Trigonostoma agassizi Dall, 1889   Agassiz's Nutmeg

Puerto Rico to Venezuela.

Reported from Mayagüez by Dall and Simpson.

Family *MARGINELLIDAE*
GENUS *Marginella* Lamarck, 1799
Subgenus *Eratoidea* Weinkauff, 1879

Marginella haematita Kiener, 1841   Carmine Marginella
Plate 23 b
Southern Florida and the West Indies.

¼ to ½ inch in length, glossy, and deep-rose color. Inside of outer lip with 15 small teeth; columella teeth 4. Spire pointed. Common all around the island.

Marginella denticulata Conrad, 1830   Tan Marginella
Plate 23 a
Southeast U. S. to the West Indies.

⅛ to ⅜ inch in length, similar to *haematita,* but whitish, with a longer spire, only 7 to 9 teeth on the outer lip, and a shallow U-shaped notch at the top of the aperture. Found on all coasts of Puerto Rico but uncommon.

Marginella lactea Kiener, 1841   White Marginella
Plate 23 j
Florida to the West Indies.

About ¼ inch in length with a moderately-developed glazed spire. Color milk-white throughout. Outer lip slightly thickened, incurved in the middle. Columella nearly straight, with 4 strong folds. Obtained from shallow-water dredgings.

Marginella gracilis C. B. Adams, 1851   Graceful Marginella
Plate 23 g
West Indies.

¼ inch in length, slender, with a tall spire. Color milky-white, glossy. Outer lip smooth and thin; 4 oblique teeth on the columella. Rare in Puerto Rico; found only in beach drift at Aguada.

GENUS *Bullata* Jousseaume, 1875

Bullata ovuliformis Orbigny, 1842   Teardrop Marginella
                                                                    Plate 23 e
Southeast U. S. and the West Indies.

⅛ inch in length, globular, glossy-white. Aperture narrow, as long as the shell. Columella with 3 plications; numerous small teeth on thickened outer lip. Common in shallow water all around the island. This is *lacrimula* Gould and *Gibberulina ovuliformis* Orbigny (American Seashells, p. 259).

GENUS *Persicula* Schumacher, 1817
Subgenus *Persicula* Schumacher, 1817

Persicula pulcherrima Gaskoin, 1849   Decorated Marginella
                                                                    Plate 23 o
Florida Keys and the West Indies.

¼ inch in length. Beautifully decorated with alternating spiral bands of white dots on a buff background and bands of vertical (axial) brown lines. The rows are separated by 4 spiral lines of brown dashes. Apex flattened; from top view it appears as a brown callus. Outer lip with many fine teeth; inner lip with 4 or 5 teeth below and a few indistinct ones above. Very common in drift sand and shallow dredgings. In *P. catenata* Montagu, 1803, the brown lines are in the shape of arrowheads pointing towards the outer lip. In *P. fluctuata* C. B. Adams, 1850, the arrow-heads are pointing away from the outer lip. The latter is commonly found in Cuba and rare in the Bahamas.

Subgenus *Gibberula* Swainson, 1840

Persicula lavalleeana Orbigny, 1842   Snowflake Marginella
                                                                    Plate 23 d
South half of Florida and the West Indies.

⅛ inch in length, color transparent white. Outer lip with many small teeth; columella has 3 to 4 oblique folds. Spire short, shoulder of body whorl squarish. Common in shallow dredgings. This is *P. minuta* Pfeiffer 1840, not Gray 1826.

GENUS *Prunum* Herrmannsen, 1852
Subgenus *Leptegouana* Woodring, 1928

Prunum apicinum Menke, 1828   Common Atlantic Marginella

Florida and the West Indies.

Reported from Mayagüez by Dall and Simpson. Rare in Puerto Rico but common in Florida.

GENUS *Hyalina* Schumacher, 1817
Subgenus *Volvarina* Hinds, 1844

Hyalina albolineata Orbigny, 1842   White-lined Marginella
Plate 23 i

Caribbean.

About ¼ inch in length. Very similar to *avena* but smaller in size, with a short spire, and the color is amber with 2 white bands. There are 4 white folds on the lower portion of the columella. A shallow-water species.

Hyalina avena Kiener, 1834   Orange-banded Marginella
Plate 23 h

Southeast U. S. and the West Indies.

¼ to ½ inch in length and slender. Color white to tan, sometimes with 3 to 5 orange-tan spiral bands. Outer lip thickened, smooth and inturned; columella with 4 slanting teeth. The animal is flesh-colored, flecked with bright-orange and white granules. A very common shallow-water species found under rocks.

Hyalina tenuilabra Tomlin, 1917   Pale Marginella
Plate 23 f

Florida to the West Indies.

½ to ¾ inch in length, subcylindrical, with an almost flat apex, with a rather open aperture, and a thin, sharp outer lip. Lower part of columella arching and with 3 or 4 spiral folds. Color milky-white or straw-colored. This is *Marginella pallida* Linné reported by Dall and Simpson. Common in Puerto Rico.

Other Marginellidae reported from Puerto Rico by Dall and Simpson, 1901:

Marginella striata Sowerby, 1846. Mayagüez, Puerto Rico.
Marginella evadne Dall and Simpson, 1901. Mayagüez, Puerto Rico.
Marginella torticula Dall, 1881. Mayagüez, Puerto Rico.
Marginella fusca Sowerby, 1846. Arroyo, Puerto Rico.
Marginella subtriplicata Orbigny, 1845. Culebra, Puerto Rico.
Marginella interrupte-lineata Mühlfeld, 1818. Mayagüez (Gundlach).

Family CONIDAE
GENUS *Conus* Linné, 1758

Conus regius Gmelin, 1791   Crown Cone
Plate 24 i

Florida, southern Mexico, the Bahamas, and south to Brazil.

2 to 3 inches in length, solid and strong. The color pattern is variable, usually reddish brown or chocolate-brown with irregular patches of white. Spire rather low, with low, irregular knobs or tubercles. Sculpture consists of many spiral threads which are usually beaded. Animal blood-red in color. It occurs along rocky reefs in shallow water. Dead shells are very common on the beaches all around Puerto Rico.

Conus cardinalis Hwass, 1792   Cardinal Cone

Florida to the West Indies.

Has knobby spire like *regius* but is smaller in size (rarely exceeds ¾ inch) and colored reddish orange or rose. In addition, the aperture of *cardinalis* is always tinted with rose or lavender, while that of *regius* is generally white. This species has not yet been reported from Puerto Rico, but it has been found in the Bahamas and the Virgin Islands.

Conus mus Hwass, 1792   Mouse Cone
                                                                  Plate 24 k
Southern Florida and the West Indies.

1 to 1½ inches in length. Color grayish with olive and brown mottling. Fresh specimens are covered with a rather thick periostracum. Spire somewhat elevated with irregular white knobs at the whorl's shoulder. This is what has erroneously been called *Conus citrinus* Gmelin. Animal dark purple-red in color. One of the most common reef cones in Puerto Rico and throughout the West Indies. It has been collected on coral reefs and under rocks at low tide.

Conus jaspideus Gmelin, 1791   Jasper Cone
                                                                  Plate 24 f
South half of Florida and the Caribbean.

½ to ¾ inch in length. Color white with irregular patches of brownish red. Spire high. Sculpture consists of several rather regularly spaced spiral lines which sometimes extend from the base to the shoulder of the body whorl. Animal yellow, speckled with black. A common shallow-water, sand-loving cone.

Conus verrucosus Hwass, 1792   Warty Cone
                                                                  Plate 24 e
Southeast Florida and the West Indies.

¾ to 1¼ inches in length. Similar to *C. jaspideus,* but can usually be differentiated by the spiral rows of small pustules or knobs on the body whorl. Common just off-shore. This is probably a genetic form of *C. jaspideus.* See Abbott, 1958.

Conus spurius Gmelin, 1791   West Indian Alphabet Cone
                                                                  Plate 24 h
Bahamas and south through the Greater Antilles.

1½ to 2½ inches in length, solid. Color white with many spiral rows of orange or reddish brown spots or irregular squares, merging into occasional patches of solid color. Spire slightly elevated and concave. Tops of whorls smooth, except for minute growth striae. Animal cream-colored. Fairly common in shallow waters of Puerto Rico.

Conus daucus Hwass, 1792   Carrot Cone
                                                                Plate 24 - 1
Florida and the West Indies.

1 to 2 inches in length, solid. Spire short; top of whorls with 4 or 5 small spiral threads. Color solid-orange to yellowish brown; aperture purplish pink within. Animal bright-orange in color. Not a common species; it prefers fairly deep water.

Conus centurio Born, 1778   Centurion Cone
                                                                Plate 24 j, m
Santo Domingo, Puerto Rico, and the Virgin Islands.

1½ to 2 inches in length. Color white with 3 bands of zigzag orange-brown lines. In addition, there are a few zigzag lines between the bands. Sculpture consists of 12 to 15 rather strong, spiral threads towards the base of the shell. This is one of the most beautiful and rarest species in this area. Most of the specimens found in Puerto Rico came from the northwest end of the island. A. and M. Hayes have recently sent us specimens of this species from St. Croix, Virgin Islands.

Conus juliae Clench, 1942   Julia's Cone
                                                                Plate 24 d
Southeast Florida and Puerto Rico.

1½ to 2 inches in length. Color variable: bright pink, orange, or reddish brown. We have even found a young olive-green specimen. There is an indistinct white band at the mid-area; a few cones have a second band at the base. This is overlaid with a series of fine, spiral, brown, broken lines or dots. Spire moderately high, flat-sided. Nuclear whorls pink; remainder of spire with zigzag reddish brown streaks alternating with white areas. Aperture pinkish to purple in fresh specimens. Animal bright-orange in color. Reasonably common on west and northwest coasts of Puerto Rico.

Conus ranunculus Hwass, 1792   Atlantic Agate Cone
                                                                Plate 24 n
West Indies.

Up to 2¾ inches in length, solid and strong. Color grayish white, irregularly splotched with chocolate-brown. Whorls moderately convex and rounded over the shoulder. Sculpture consists of numerous fine, somewhat wavy, spiral threads which are strongest towards the base.

Spire with 4 or 5 spiral threads on each whorl, which are crossed by fine growth lines. Appears to be reasonably common on Mona Island (40 miles west of Puerto Rico). M. McDowell secured a beautiful live specimen from the reefs there, and we have received at least 20 beach-worn specimens from that same locality.

Conus granulatus Linné, 1758   Glory of the Atlantic Cone
                                                                        Plate 24 g
Southeast Florida and the West Indies.

1 to 1¾ inches in length, solid and fairly slender. Color pinkish white to orange-red or bright-red, flecked with brown, especially in the mid area of the body whorl and on the spire. Top of whorls rounded and with many fine spiral and axial threads. Sculpture consists of numerous, coarse spiral threads and fine axial lines. Several persons have reported finding fresh specimens on Mona Island, and beach-worn specimens are not uncommon there. It is a rare species in Puerto Rico.

Family TEREBRIDAE
GENUS *Terebra* Bruguière, 1789

Terebra taurinus Solander, 1786   Flame Auger
                                                                        Plate 3 i
Southeast Florida and the West Indies.

4 to 6 inches in length, elongate and slender. Color cream overlaid with axial reddish brown flames. Upper whorls axially ribbed and commonly lacking color. Each whorl is divided in 2 parts. The upper part is about 2/3 the length of the whorl; it is swollen and inscribed with a single incised line. This shell has been found living in about 35 feet of water. Animal colored yellow. *T. flammea* Lamarck is this species. Common on the northwest coast of Puerto Rico.

Terebra hastata Gmelin, 1791   Shiny Atlantic Auger
                                                                        Plate 25 a
Southeast Florida and the West Indies.

1¼ to 1½ inches in length. Color bright-yellow or light-brown with a white band below the suture. Sculptured with axial ribs which extend from suture to suture; there is no spiral sculpture. Obtained from shallow dredgings. Specimens are sometimes thrown up on the beaches in Puerto Rico.

Terebra dislocata Say, 1822   Atlantic Auger
                                                                        Plate 25 d
Southeastern U. S., Texas and the West Indies.

1½ to 2 inches in length, slender. Color grayish or yellowish orange. Sculptured with about 25 axial ribs per whorl. These are divided ⅓ to

½ their length by a deep, impressed, spiral line. There are spiral cords between the ribs. Uncommon in Puerto Rico but abundant in Florida.

Terebra cinerea Born, 1778   Gray Auger
Plate 25 b
Southeast Florida and the West Indies.

1 to 2 inches in length. Color cream or light bluish brown. Sculptured with many (40 to 50 per whorl) small axial riblets which are prominent near the suture, but do not extend more than ⅓ to ½ way down the whorl. Surface covered with microscopic punctations. Apex sharp, pointed and white. Operculum light-brown, horny. A common shallow-water species.

Terebra salleana Deshayes, 1859   Sallé's Auger

North Florida to Texas and Colombia.

1 to 2 inches in length. Similar to *T cinerea* but dark bluish gray to chocolate-brown in color, and with a dark blunt apex. Reasonably common in shallow water. This may be only a form of *T. cinerea.*

Terebra juanica Dall and Simpson, 1901   San Juan Auger
Plate 29 r
Puerto Rico.

Less than ¼ inch. Color brown with a paler band just below the suture. Highly polished. Sculptured with rather strong axial ribs which run from suture to suture. Rare. Dall and Simpson reported and described this beautiful little *Terebra* from San Juan, Puerto Rico. We have found only 2 specimens in drift sand at Arecibo.

Terebra protexta Conrad, 1845   Fine-ribbed Auger
Plate 25 c
North Carolina to Texas, and the West Indies.

Shell ¾ to 1 inch in length, with 13 to 15 whorls. Color tan to brown. Sculptured with 16 to 22 fine axial ribs which run from suture to suture; these are crossed by 7 to 9 weak spiral lines. The uppermost line is about ¼ the way down the whorl. Common from shallow dredgings.

Terebra nassula Dall, 1889

Puerto Rico.

Reported from Mayagüez, Vieques, and Culebra by Dall and Simpson.

Terebra limatula var. *acrior* Dall, 1889

Plate 29 n
Puerto Rico.
Reported from Mayagüez by Dall and Simpson.

Family TURRIDAE
Subfamily TURRINAE
GENUS *Polystira* Woodring, 1928

Polystira albida Perry, 1811   White Giant Turret
Plate 26 u

South Florida, the Gulf of Mexico, and the West Indies.

3 to 4 inches in length, spindle-shaped with a high sharply-pointed spire and a long open canal. Color white, covered with a thin light-brown periostracum. There is a distinct notch on the upper part of the outer lip. Sculptured with fine revolving threads; in addition, each whorl has 3 strong ridges, the central one the strongest. Operculum clawlike, brown. Common. Listed as *Pleurotoma albida* Perry by Dall and Simpson. *Turris virgo* Wood is also this species.

Polystira florencae Bartsch, 1934   Florence's Turret
Plate 26 x

Puerto Rico.

About 1¼ inches in length, spindle-shaped. Color cream with brown clouding. Spiral sculpture similar to that of *P. albida;* in addition, there are a great many oblique lines between the spiral ridges. These oblique lines meet at an angle at the central cord of each whorl. The type locality of this species is northern Puerto Rico. We obtained our specimens from dredgings in 20 to 60 feet.

Subfamily COCHLESPIRINAE
GENUS *Ancistrosyrinx* Dall, 1881

Ancistrosyrinx radiata Dall, 1889   Common Star Turret
Plate 26 q

South Florida, the Gulf of Mexico, and the West Indies.

About ½ inch in length, delicate. Highly ornamented with sharp triangular spines on the shoulder of each whorl. Glossy, translucent. Aperture narrow, elongate. Uncommon from shallow dredgings. Reported from Mayagüez by Dall and Simpson.

Subfamily CLAVINAE
GENUS *Crassispira* Swainson, 1840
Subgenus *Crassispirella* Bartsch and Rehder, 1939

Crassispira fuscescens Reeve, 1843   Ebony Turret
Plate 25 w

Florida Keys to the West Indies.

About ¾ inch in length, solid. Color reddish brown to chocolate-brown. Whorls about 10, including the 2 smooth nuclear ones. Each whorl is sculptured with 17 to 20 short, oblique, axial ribs; between the ribs there are numerous, fine revolving threads. There is a strong spiral cord below the suture, below which is a granulose concave area. Notch on upper part of outer lip U-shaped. Reasonably common in shallow dredgings. This is *Drillia solida* C. B. Adams, 1850 reported by Dall and Simpson and *Clathrodrillia ebenina* Dall, 1890.

Crassispira nigrescens C. B. Adams, 1845   Black Turret
                                                              Plate 25 m
    West Indies.

About ¼ inch in length. All brown to black in color, with a strong, smooth, revolving cord below the suture. Surface strongly beaded; the beads are joined by spiral and axial cords, thus giving a neat reticulate appearance to the shell. Varix thick and bulbous with deep rounded notch. Uncommon from shallow dredgings.

Subgenus *Compsodrillia* Woodring, 1928

Crassispira leucocyma Dall, 1883   White-knobbed Turret
                                                              Plate 25 q
    South half of Florida and the West Indies.

⅓ inch in length, light- to dark-brown with white nodules. The nodules are divided by one or two spiral lines. A common shallow-water species.

GENUS *Clathrodrillia* Dall, 1918

Clathrodrillia melonesiana Dall and Simpson, 1901
                                                              Plate 25 o
    Puerto Rico.

Between ¼ and ½ inch in length, solid, brown to black with prominent yellowish white, elongated nodules. The surface between the nodules is microscopically reticulate. Notch short. Obtained from shallow dredgings.

GENUS *Drillia* Gray, 1838

Drillia coccinata Reeve, 1845   Scarlet-stained Drillia
                                                              Plate 25 h
    Greater Antilles.

About ½ inch. Smoothish except for microscopic spiral lines below the sutures. Body whorl with about 14 sharp, smooth axial ribs. The white ribs with bright scarlet-rose between them help to separate this species from the others. It is rare in Puerto Rico and in the Virgin Islands.

Subgenus *Neodrillia* Bartsch, 1943

Drillia cydia Bartsch, 1943   Cydia Drillia
                                                                  Plate 25 s
Florida and the West Indies.

About ¾ inch in length, elongate, stout, heavy. Color white, often
with small brown spots. Sculptured with prominent axial ribs (about
9 on body whorl) ; these are crossed by slender, closely-spaced spiral
threads. The spiral threads are crossed by finer axial sculpture giving the
surface a microscopic reticulation. Aperture large, channeled anteriorly
and posteriorly. Two specimens were obtained from shallow dredgings
at Mayagüez.

GENUS *Carinodrillia* Dall, 1919
Subgenus *Buchema* Corea, 1934

Carinodrillia liella Corea, 1934   Puerto Rican Turret
                                                                  Plate 26 v
Puerto Rico.

About ½ inch in length, elongate-conic, yellowish. Sculptured with
heavy, hump-like axial ribs; these are crossed by strong spiral cords and
finer spiral lirations. Base well-rounded, short. Aperture moderately
short, deeply channeled anteriorly and posteriorly. Obtained by dredging.

GENUS *Leptadrillia* Woodring, 1928

Leptadrillia splendida Bartsch, 1934   Splendid Turret
                                                                  Plate 25 j
West Indies.

About ⅜ inch in length, elongate. Unicolored white to salmon pink,
shiny. Body whorl sculptured with about 12 smooth, well-rounded axial
ribs. Spiral threads present only at the base of the body whorl. Reasonably common from shallow dredgings.

Subfamily *MANGELIINAE*
GENUS *Mangelia* Risso, 1826

Mangelia melanitica Dall, 1885   Brown-stained Mangelia
                                                                  Plate 25 r
West Indies.

⅛ to ¼ inch in length with a rather slender spire and short base.
Color white, stained with brown, especially at base of aperture. Sculpture on last 3 whorls cancellate. Notch large, deep, oval-rounded. Aperture much wider above than below. Obtained from shallow dredgings on
the south and west coasts of Puerto Rico.

Mangelia fusca C. B. Adams, 1845   Brown Mangelia
Plate 25 e
West Indies.

About ¼ inch in length. Dark reddish brown, sometimes with lighter spiral bands. 8 or 9 prominent, smooth, longitudinal ribs on the body whorl; spiral threads between the ribs. Common in shallow water.

Mangelia biconica C. B. Adams, 1850   Double-crowned Mangelia
Plate 25 k
West Indies.

About ¼ inch in length with 5 slightly shouldered whorls. Color all-white or banded with brown. Body whorl with about 10 rounded longitudinal ribs, and fine spiral sculpture. Reasonably common from shallow dredgings.

Mangelia bartletti Dall, 1889   Bartlett's Mangelia
Plate 25 f
Southern Florida and the West Indies.

About ¼ inch in length, with elongate body whorl and aperture. Color white to tan, touched with brown, especially at the suture. Sculptured with many broadly rounded longitudinal ribs overlaid by minute spiral threads. A common shallow-water species.

Mangelia trilineata C. B. Adams, 1845   Three-lined Mangelia
Plate 25 - 1
West Indies.

About ¼ inch, slender, elongate. White with 3 evenly-spaced, narrow, orange-brown spiral bands on the body whorl. There is a similar color band at the sutures and in the mid-area of the other whorls. Sculptured with many strong, well-beaded axial ribs and spiral cords. Uncommon.

Mangelia quadrilineata C. B. Adams, 1850   Four-lined Mangelia
Plate 25 v
West Indies.

About ¼ inch in length, elongate. Yellowish white with several fine spiral lines of brown along the suture, and four similar lines just below the periphery of the last whorl. Reasonably common.

GENUS *Ithycythara* Woodring, 1928

Ithycythara lanceolata C. B. Adams, 1850   Spear Turret
Plate 26 r
Florida and the West Indies.

¼ to ½ inch in length, elongate, slender. Color tan with spiral

bands of opaque white and brown, the darkest band being at the suture.
Whorls 8, scarcely convex, with a lightly impressed suture. Sculptured
with 6 or 7 prominent, narrow, longitudinal ribs per whorl which are
barely interrupted by the suture; the ribs have a slight nodule at the
middle of the whorl. Aperture narrow, finely toothed within. Reasonably common from shallow dredgings.

Ithycythara parkeri Abbott, 1958   Parker's Turret
                                                                       Plate 26 s

West Indies.

Similar to *I. lanceolata* but smaller, mostly snow-white and overlaid with fine spiral threads. Aperture smooth within. Lives in shallow
water. Named after John Dyas Parker, former President of the Philadelphia Shell Club, who discovered this species at Grand Cayman Island.

Ithycythara psila Bush, 1885

Puerto Rico.

Reported from Mayagüez by Dall and Simpson.

GENUS *Vitricythara* Fargo, 1953

Vitricythara metria Dall, 1903   Metria Turret
                                                                      Plate 25 u

West Indies.

About ¼ inch, slender, all-white with a striking cancellate sculpture.
Obtained from shallow dredgings.

GENUS *Glyphoturris* Woodring, 1928

Glyphoturris quadrata rugirima Dall, 1889   Frosted Turret
                                                                      Plate 26 w

Florida and the West Indies.

Less than ¼ inch, stout, white. Strongly sculptured with high axial
ribs, overridden by strong spiral cords and by microscopic, frosted spiral
threads. Common from shallow-water dredgings around Puerto Rico.

GENUS *Pyrgocythara* Woodring, 1928

Pyrgocythara coxi Fargo, 1953   Cox's Turret
                                                                      Plate 25 t

Florida and Puerto Rico.

About ¼ inch in length, slender. Grayish white. The convexly
rounded axial ribs which rise above the suture and the frosted spiral
threads covering the shell make this species easily recognizable. This
species has previously been referred to as *Mangelia balteata* Reeve; the
latter lacks spiral sculpture.

Pyrgocythara densestriata C. B. Adams, 1850   Densely-lined Turret

West Indies.

Reported from Puerto Rico by Dall and Simpson. It is similar to *P. coxi* but is larger, its ribs are wider and it has a much more elongate body whorl and aperture. Krebs in 1866 considered *P. densestriata* a white variety of the brown-banded or brown-flecked *P. badia* Reeve. Both varieties have been obtained from shallow dredgings in Puerto Rico.

GENUS *Fenimorea* Bartsch, 1934

Fenimorea janetae Bartsch, 1934   Janet's Turret
                                                          Plate 25 g
Florida and the West Indies.

Up to 1½ inches in length. Whorls 12. Top half of each whorl white, lower half chestnut-brown. Our specimen has a pink cast over it. Sculptured with 10 to 14 strong, rounded axial ribs per whorl. This beautiful little shell was first described from dredgings in 33 to 40 fathoms off Puerto Rico. Rare. We found a single specimen on the beach at Rincón, Puerto Rico.

GENUS *Monilispira* Bartsch and Rehder, 1939

Monilispira albocincta C. B. Adams, 1845   White-banded Turret

Southeast Florida and the West Indies.
About ½ inch in length, solid; short and fat compared to the other turrids. Color reddish brown to dark-brown with a white band bearing 12 or 13 knobs per whorl. Two white bands on the base of the shell. Reasonably common in shallow water under rocks.

Subfamily DAPHNELLINAE
GENUS *Daphnella* Hinds, 1844

Daphnella lymneiformis Kiener, 1840   Volute Turret
                                                          Plate 26 y
Southeast Florida and the West Indies.

½ to ¾ inch in length. The body whorl takes up about 2/3 the length of the shell. Color cream with orange-brown maculations. Whorls about 8: the 2 nuclear ones dark-brown, the next 4 with strong, beaded, axial ribs. Last 2 whorls reticulated with numerous fine spiral threads and fine axial lines. Aperture large and expanded, with a moderately large and simple sinus. Uncommon from shallow water to 25 fathoms.

Daphnella stegeri McGinty, 1955   Steger's Turret
                                                          Plate 26 t
        Florida and Puerto Rico.

        About ½ inch in length, spindle-shaped. Color dull grayish white. Notch deep, U-shaped. Spiral sculpture consists of a strong cord at the shoulder of each whorl which angulates the whorl. In addition to this, there are numerous spiral lines all over the shell. The axial sculpture is only conspicuous on the first 3 or 4 whorls. Aperture reasonably large; outer lip dentated by the spiral cords on the body whorl. Reported from fairly deep water off the Florida Coast; it is a common species from shallow dredgings in Puerto Rico.

        Other Turrid species reported from dredgings off western Puerto Rico by Dall and Simpson, 1901, are:

Drillia aepynota Dall, 1889
Drillia lissotropis Dall, 1881
Borsonia rouaulti Dall, 1889
Mangelia asarca Dall and
    Simpson, 1901   (Plate 29 o)
Mangelia morra Dall, 1881
Mangelia elata Dall, 1889
Mangelia aguadillana Dall and
    Simpson, 1901   (Plate 16 o)
Mangelia luctuosa Orbigny, 1845
Mangelia quadrata Reeve, 1845
Mangelia lavalleana Orbigny, 1845
Mitromorpha biplicata Dall, 1889

Drillia albicoma Dall, 1889
Drillia eucosmia var. *canna*
    Dall, 1889
Drillia actinocycla
    Dall and Simpson, 1901
Drillia gundlachi
    Dall and Simpson, 1901
Drillia ponciana
    Dall and Simpson, 1901
Drillia interpleura Dall and
    Simpson, 1901   (Plate 25 p)
Drillia albinodata Reeve, 1846
                      (Plate 25 n)
Drillia thea Dall, 1883 (Plate 25 i)

Subclass *OPISTHOBRANCHIA*
(Bubble-shells, Pteropods, Sea Slugs)
Order *TECTIBRANCHIA*
Family *ACTEONIDAE*

Genus *Acteon* Montfort, 1810

Acteon punctostriatus C. B. Adams, 1840   Adams' Baby-bubble
                                                          Plate 28 b
        Cape Cod to the Gulf of Mexico and the West Indies.

        3 to 6 mm. in length, solid, moderately globose. Color white to light brownish pink. Shiny and smooth except for several revolving punctate striae on the basal half of the body whorl. Columella with a single twisted fold. Uncommon from low tide to 60 fathoms.

Family *RINGICULIDAE*
Genus *Ringicula* Deshayes, 1838

Ringicula semistriata Orbigny, 1845

Plate 29 k

Southeast U. S. and the West Indies.

Reported from Mayagüez by Dall and Simpson.

Family *HYDATINIDAE*
Genus *Micromelo* Pilsbry, 1894

Micromelo undata Bruguière, 1792   Miniature Melo

Plate 27 - 1

Lower Florida Keys and the West Indies.

¼ to ½ inch in length, oval, moderately fragile. Color white or cream, overlaid by a network of reddish lines. Sculpture microscopic. Uncommon; our specimens are from the northwest coast of Puerto Rico.

Genus *Hydatina* Schumacher, 1817

Hydatina vesicaria Solander, 1786   Brown-lined Paper-bubble

Plate 27 a

South half of Florida and the West Indies.

1 to 1 ½ inches in length, globose, moderately fragile. The animal is very large. Shell white to tan, overlaid by many close-set, wavy, brown spiral lines. Reported from Puerto Rico by Gundlach as *Hydatina physis* Linné which, however, is limited to the Indo-Pacific area. Not common.

Family *BULLIDAE*
Genus *Bulla* Linné, 1753

Bulla striata Bruguière, 1792   Striated-bubble

Plate 27 e

West coast of Florida to Texas and the West Indies.

¾ to 1½ inches in length, heavy. Color brown with darker mottling. Some specimens are smooth; others are spirally grooved at the base and within the apical perforation of the shell. Columella with a large white callus, which is sometimes stained with brown. A common shell found all around Puerto Rico. Dall and Simpson's *Bulla amygdala* Dillwyn, 1817 and *B. occidentalis* A. Adams, 1850 are probably this species.

Family *ATYIDAE*
Genus *Haminoea* Turton and Kingston, 1830

Haminoea elegans Gray, 1825   Elegant Paper-bubble

Plate 27 m

Southeast Florida and the West Indies.

½ to ¾ inch, roundly oval, thin, fragile. Color brownish or green-ish yellow. Surface sculptured with numerous, fine, spiral grooves. Outer lip arising from left side of perforation. (To determine on which side of the apical perforation the lip arises, hold the shell with the apex towards you and the aperture lip facing to right.) Obtained from shallow dredg-ings; it is a common species all around Puerto Rico.

Haminoea succinea Conrad, 1846   Conrad's Paper-bubble
                                                                                    Plate 27 n
Texas to Florida and the West Indies.

A little less than ½ inch in length, fragile, usually translucent-white. Surface sculptured with minute, wavy spiral striae. Aperture long, nar-row, wider below. The lip is inserted on the right side of the perforation; in *H. elegans* the lip is inserted on the left side of the perforation. Rea-sonably common in shallow water, especially on the southwest coast of Puerto Rico.

Haminoea petiti Orbigny, 1841   Petit's Paper-bubble
                                                                                    Plate 27 p
Florida to the West Indies.

Between ¼ and ½ inch in length. Color light yellowish green. Sur-face sculptured with indistinct growth lines but lacking visible spiral lines. Columella is straighter than in any other West Indian *Haminoea*. Reasonably common on the southwestern part of Puerto Rico.

Haminoea antillarum Orbigny, 1841   Antillean Paper-bubble
                                                                                    Plate 27 o
West Florida to the West Indies.

½ to ¾ inch in size, thin but rather solid; compressed above, swollen below. Color greenish yellow. Surface having irregular growth wrinkles; fine, wavy spiral striae are seen under a strong lens. Columella extremely concave with a very narrow white callus. Not uncommon all around Puerto Rico.

GENUS *Atys* Montfort, 1810

Atys guildingi Sowerby, 1869   Guilding's Paper-bubble
                                                                                    Plate 27 k
West Indies.

¼ to ½ inch in size, thin, ovate. Color grayish white. Surface spirally striated and slightly longitudinally wrinkled, especially at the ends where it is sometimes reticulated. Uncommon.

Atys riiseana Mörch, 1875   Riise's Paper-bubble
                                                                                    Plate 27 i
Florida to the Lesser Antilles.

¼ to ½ inch in length, oblong-oval, somewhat more compressed above than below, moderately thick. Translucent-white in color. Center of shell smoothish; the ends with about a dozen, fine, spiral incised grooves. Reasonably common from shallow dredgings in Puerto Rico.

Atys caribaea Orbigny, 1841   Caribbean Paper-bubble
Plate 27 q
Southeast Florida and the West Indies.

About ¼ inch in length. Similar to *A. riiseana* but differs in being smaller, narrower, more fragile, and in having microscopic spiral lines on the center of the shell in addition to numerous microscopic axial threads at the upper end. Reasonably common on the west and north coasts of Puerto Rico.

Atys lineata Usticke, 1959   Lined Paper-bubble
Plate 27 j
Caribbean.

About ¼ inch in length, slender, white. Easily recognized by the colorless spiral lines and the lack of incised spiral lines or grooves found in the other *Atys* species. Obtained from shallow dredgings. Uncommon.

Atys sandersoni Dall, 1881   Sanderson's Paper-bubble

Puerto Rico.

Reported from Mayagüez by Dall and Simpson.

Family RETUSIDAE
GENUS *Retusa* Brown, 1827

Retusa candei Orbigny, 1841   Channeled Barrel-bubble
Plate 27 g
West Indies.

3 to 5 mm. in length, with a moderately elevated spire. Color glossy-white to cream. Surface smooth, except for microscopic growth lines. Suture channeled; nucleus, when present, very small and pimple-like. Columellar fold moderate. A common shallow-water species found all around Puerto Rico.

Retusa bullata Kiener, 1834   Striate Barrel-bubble
Plate 27 f
Florida Keys, Bermuda, and the West Indies.

5 to 8 mm. in length, cylindrical, solid. Color white. Sculptured with numerous, minute, wavy, spiral lines. Columellar plication strong. Reasonably common from shallow dredgings.

Retusa caelata Bush, 1885   Engraved Barrel-bubble

Puerto Rico.

Reported from Mayagüez by Dall and Simpson.

GENUS *Rhizorus* Montfort, 1810

Rhizorus oxytatus Bush, 1885   Southern Spindle-bubble
                                                                Plate 27 d
Southeast U. S. and the West Indies.

3 to 4 mm. in length, elongate, with a sharp long apex. Color glossy-white. Sculptured with 4 or 5 fine spiral lines at each end. Umbilicus narrow, cracklike. Reasonably common in shallow dredgings all around Puerto Rico. Reported by Dall and Simpson as *Volvula oxytata* Bush.

Rhizorus acutus Orbigny, 1842   Pointed Spindle-bubble

Southeast U. S. and the West Indies.

Reported from Mayagüez by Dall and Simpson.

Family ACTEOCINIDAE
GENUS *Cylichna* Lovén, 1846

Cylichna krebsi Mörch, 1874   Krebs' Barrel-bubble
                                                                Plate 27 b
West Indies.

2 to 3 mm. in length, similar to *C. auberi* but with strong, regular spiral striae; in addition, there are growth striae. Relatively rare, obtained from dredgings down to 75 ft. on the south and west coasts of Puerto Rico.

Cylichna auberi Orbigny, 1841   Auber's Barrel-bubble

West Indies.

2 to 3 mm. in length, ovate cylindrical, obliquely truncate at the ends. Dull-white, delicately spirally striated below. Somewhat resembling *C. bidentata* but without the fold on the columella. Columella strongly angulate. Common in shallow-water dredgings from the south coast of Puerto Rico.

Subgenus *Cylichnella* Gabb, 1872

Cylichna bidentata Orbigny, 1841   Orbigny's Barrel-bubble
                                                                Plate 27 c
North Carolina, Florida, to Texas, and the West Indies.

About 3 mm. in length, oval, with flat sides. Color glossy-white. Apex with a dished, shallow depression. Columella with a distinct fold and a less conspicuous nodule below. Common in shallow dredgings from the west and south coasts of Puerto Rico.

Family PHILINIDAE
GENUS *Philine* Ascanius, 1772

Philine sagra Orbigny, 1841   Crenulated Paper-bubble
Plate 27 h

Southeast U. S. and the West Indies.

⅛ to ¼ inch in length, oblong, fragile, white, with a large aperture. Characterized by numerous spiral lines of microscopic rings placed end to end and its crenulated lip. Not uncommon on the south coast from shallow dredgings down to 15 fathoms.

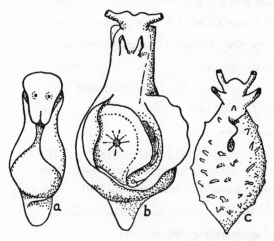

TEXT FIG. 21. Animals of some Tectibranchs. a, *Bulla;* b, *Aplysia;* c, *Bursatella* (after Abbott, *American Seashells,* 1954).

Superfamily APLYSIACEA
Family APLYSIIDAE
GENUS *Aplysia* Linné, 1767

Many shell-less mollusks are found in Puerto Rico but no attempt was made to collect them for this present study. The omission of some of the common West Indian tectibranchs or all of the nudibranchs must not be considered significant. The several opisthobranchs of Puerto Rico will be described in a separate report. The following species are reported by Dall and Simpson:

Aplysia protea Rang, 1828   West Indian Sea Hare

Reported from Ponce Reefs, San Antonio Bridge, San Juan, Mayagüez, Guanica, Vieques, Culebra Island. This is the commonest sea-hare in Puerto Rico. It gives off a harmless purple ink.

Aplysia cervina Dall and Simpson, 1901

Mayagüez, Puerto Rico.

Aplysia parvula (Guilding) Mörch, 1863

Caballo Blanco Reef, Vieques Island.

Subfamily DOLABRIFERINAE
GENUS *Dolabrifera* Gray, 1847

Dolabrifera ascifera Rang, 1828

Guanica, Ponce, Culebra, Vieques Island, Puerto Rico.

Dolabrifera sowerbyi "Guilding" Sowerby, 1868

Hucares, Puerto Rico.

GENUS *Bursatella* Blainville, 1817

Bursatella pleii Rang, 1828

Text fig. 21 c

Boqueron, Puerto Rico.

Family PLEUROBRANCHIDAE
GENUS *Pleurobranchus* Cuvier, 1804

Pleurobranchus lacteus Dall and Simpson, 1901

Ensenada Honda, Culebra Island, Puerto Rico.

Pleurobranchus amarillius Mattox, 1953

Isla de la Gata, off Parguera, Puerto Rico.

Family PYRAMIDELLIDAE
GENUS *Pyramidella* Lamarck, 1799

Pyramidella dolabrata Linné, 1758   Giant Atlantic Pyram
Plate 28 c

Bahamas and the West Indies.

¾ to 1¼ inches in length, solid, pyramidal in shape. Highly polished, white, with 2 or 3 spiral brown lines. Columella large and with 2 or 3 strong plicae. Outer lip usually smooth but sometimes toothed. A not-too-common sand-dweller found on all coasts of Puerto Rico.

Pyramidella subdolabrata Mörch, 1854   False Giant Pyram

Puerto Rico.

Similar to *P. dolabrata* but it has a duller color, lighter suture, and less strongly developed columellar folds; the bands of color are wider and less distinct than in *dolabrata*. Reported from Fajardo by Dall and Simpson.

Pyramidella fusca C. B. Adams, 1839   Brown Pyram
                                                             Plate 26 m
Canada to Florida and the West Indies.

About ¼ inch in length, conical, rather elongate. Color light-brown and shining. Whorls about 6; suture well-impressed. Aperture large, oval. Operculum thin, light-brown. Uncommon.

Pyramidella candida Mörch, 1875   Brilliant Pyram
                                                             Plate 28 d
North Carolina to the Gulf of Mexico and the West Indies.

½ inch in length, color glossy-white, with about 12 flat whorls. Suture crenulated. Columella with 3 plaits. Found in reasonably shallow water, and is common in drift all around Puerto Rico.

GENUS *Triptychus* Mörch, 1875

Triptychus niveus Mörch, 1875   Three-corded Pyram
                                                             Plate 28 e
Florida to the West Indies.

A little over ¼ inch in length, with about 11 flattened whorls. Color white. Whorls sculptured with 3 distinct spiral cords; the upper two are nodulous and the lowest one plain. Columella plaited. Reasonably common in shallow dredgings and drift sand all around Puerto Rico.

GENUS *Odostomia* Fleming, 1817

Odostomia laevigata Orbigny, 1842   Smooth Odostome
                                                             Plate 26 k
Southeast U. S. to the Lesser Antilles.

3 to 5 mm. in length, elongate-ovate. White, smooth, polished. Suture and columella tooth weak. A quite variable, common shallow-water species.

Odostomia solidula C. B. Adams, 1850   Solid Odostome
                                                             Plate 26 n
West Indies.

5 to 8 mm. in length, elongate, thick, smoothish. Color tan. Whorls moderately convex with a distinct suture. Columella plait oblique. Reasonably common in beach drift.

Odostomia canaliculata C. B. Adams, 1850   Channeled Odostome
                                                           Plate 26 · 1
West Indies.

About 3 mm. in length, with about 6 flat whorls. White, smooth. Suture channeled. Columella plait nearly transverse. Rare.

Subgenus *Chrysallida* Carpenter, 1856

Odostomia seminuda C. B. Adams, 1839   Half-smooth Odostome
                                                           Plate 26 e
Nova Scotia to Gulf of Mexico and the West Indies.

3 to 4 mm. in length, elongate-conic, white. Sutures distinct. About 2 smooth nuclear whorls; succeeding whorls cancellate. Body whorl with about 4 broad, indented, revolving ridges. Reasonably common from shallow dredgings at La Parguera, Puerto Rico.

Odostomia gemmulosa C. B. Adams, 1850   Nodulose Odostome
                                                           Plate 26 f
West Indies.

About 5 mm. in length, elongate, all white. Sculptured with about 3 prominent, nodulose spiral ridges per whorl. Aperture ovate; columellar plait prominent. Rare.

GENUS *Cingulina* A. Adams, 1860

Cingulina babylonia C. B. Adams, 1845   Babylon Pyram
Bermuda and the West Indies.

About 2 mm. in length, dull white. There are 4 whorls in addition to the smoothish nuclear whorls. Sculpture consists of 3 to 4 prominent spiral cords on the body whorl and 2 similar cords on the other whorls. Spaces between the cords concave. Obtained from shallow dredgings. *Odostomia* (*Miralda*) *judithae* Usticke, 1959 undoubtedly is this species.

GENUS *Turbonilla* Risso, 1826

Turbonilla elegans Orbigny, 1842   Elegant Turbonilla
                                                           Plate 26 b
West Indies.

3 to 4 mm. in length, with 9 slightly angular whorls. Color white. The vertical ribs are rounded and smooth. Below the angulation of the whorl there are 3 or 4 distinct spiral threads between the vertical ribs. Columella with a slight fold. Obtained from shallow dredgings.

Turbonilla pupoides Orbigny, 1842   Fat Turbonilla
                                                           Plate 26 d
West Indies.

About 3 mm. in length, strong, with about 8 flat whorls. Color white or yellowish brown. Base spirally striated. Its squat, fat appearance helps to separate this species from the others. Uncommon from 50-75 feet dredgings.

Turbonilla unilirata Bush, 1899   Single-lined Turbonilla

Southeast U. S. to the West Indies.

About 3 mm. in length, with 9 gradually tapering whorls. Color white. The single spiral thread a little distance below the suture separates this species from all others. Rare.

Turbonilla haycocki Dall and Bartsch, 1911   Haycock's Turbonilla
Plate 26 g

Bermuda and the West Indies.

About 4 mm. in length, elongate, whitish in color. Suture deep. Whorls 10-12, flat-sided, bearing numerous slightly curved, smooth vertical ribs (about 30 on body whorl). Spiral sculpture between the ribs consists of numerous microscopic incised lines. There is a single nude spiral area just above the midway point between the sutures. Base of shell with many wavy, spiral lines. Uncommon from shallow water.

Turbonilla abrupta Bush, 1899   Abrupt Turbonilla
Plate 26 c

West Indies.

About 4 mm. in length with 9 flattened whorls and deep sutures. Color all white. The vertical ribs (about 20) rounded, oblique, separated by wider, deep, smooth, flat-bottomed spaces, which terminate just above the suture in very square-cut ends. Base well-rounded, smooth. Obtained from shallow dredgings.

Turbonilla interrupta Totten, 1835   Interrupted Turbonilla
Plate 26 a

Maine to the West Indies.

5 to 6 mm. in length, slender, white to yellow in color. Sculpture consists of 20 to 24 smooth vertical ribs and 11 to 14 spiral lines between them. Base short, well-rounded, with strong spiral lines. Common from shallow dredgings.

Turbonilla reticulata C. B. Adams, 1850   Reticulate Turbonilla

West Indies.

Reported from Mayagüez by Dall and Simpson.

Turbonilla portoricana Dall and Simp., 1901   Puerto Rican Turbonilla
Plate 29 i

Puerto Rico.

Type described from specimen found at Mayagüez.

Turbonilla insularis Dall and Simpson, 1901   Island Turbonilla

Plate 29 s

Puerto Rico.

Type described from specimens found at Mayagüez.

Order *SACOGLOSSA*
Family *OXYNOEIDAE*
GENUS *Oxynoe* Rafinesque, 1819

Oxynoe antillarum Mörch, 1863   Antillean Oxynoe

West Indies.

Shell about ¼ inch in length, fragile, vitreous. Aperture large, narrow at the top. Smooth except for a few growth lines. Common on the alga, *Caulerpa racemosa*.

GENUS *Lobiger* Krohn, 1847

Lobiger souverbii Fischer, 1856   Souverbie's Lobiger

Plate 28 a

West Indies.

About 10 mm. in length and 6 mm. wide, fragile and transparent, with numerous wrinkled growth lines. Aperture very large, semi-oval. This species was originally described from Guadeloupe, and as far as we know, this is the first time it has been reported from Puerto Rico. This strikingly beautiful animal is greenish brown in color; the two pairs of natatory appendages are orange on the inside. The black striations of the mantle are seen through the transparent shell. Found on the alga *Caulerpa racemosa*.

Order *PTEROPODA*
Suborder *THECOSOMATA*
Family *CAVOLINIDAE*

These are small pelagic species whose dead shells are glassy and fragile. They are sometimes washed ashore or brought up in dredges. Probably all of the 24 known species, as illustrated in the accompanying text figure (from Abbott's *American Seashells*), are represented in waters near Puerto Rico.

Eight species were listed from Mayagüez by Dall and Simpson:

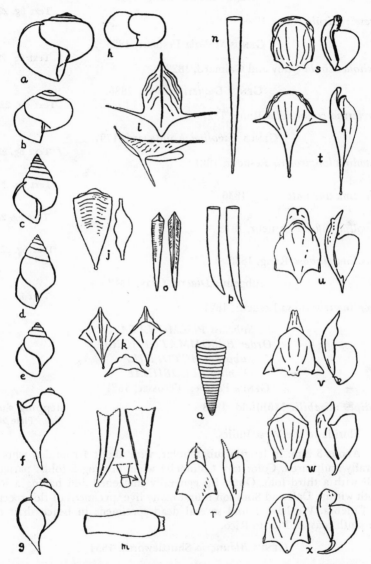

TEXT FIG. 22. Shells of *Pteropods* (after Abbott, *American Seashells,* 1954).

GENUS *Creseis* Rang, 1828

Creseis acicula Rang, 1828   Text fig. 22 n

GENUS *Styliola* Lesueur, 1825

Styliola subula Quoy and Gaimard, 1827   Text fig. 22 o

GENUS *Cuvierina* Boas, 1886

Cuvierina columnella Rang, 1827   Text fig. 22 m

GENUS *Cavolina* Abildgaard, 1791

Cavolina longirostris Lesueur, 1821   Text fig. 22 v

Cavolina uncinata Rang, 1836   Text fig. 22 x

Cavolina inflexa Lesueur, 1813   Text fig. 22 r

Cavolina gibbosa Rang, 1836   Text fig. 22 w

Subgenus *Diacria* Gray, 1842

Cavolina trispinosa Lesueur, 1821   Text fig. 22 t

Subclass *PULMONATA*
Order *BASOMMATOPHORA*
Suborder *ACTOPHILA*
Family *ELLOBIIDAE*
GENUS *Pedipes*, Férussac, 1821

Pedipes mirabilis Mühlfeld, 1818   Stepping shell
                                                                 Plate 28 j

Florida to the West Indies.

About 3 mm. in length, subglobular, with about 4 rounded whorls, spirally sculptured. Color tan. Columella wide, bearing 2 folds; parietal wall with a third fold. Outer lip generally thickened and having a low tooth within. Dall and Simpson found many live specimens of this species on Culebra. We have found several dead specimens in beach drift on the south coast of Puerto Rico.

GENUS *Blauneria* Shuttleworth, 1854

Blauneria heteroclita Montagu, 1808

Southeast U. S. to the West Indies.

Reported from Puerto Rico by Dall and Simpson.

GENUS *Tralia* Gray, 1840

Tralia ovula Bruguière, 1789   Egg Tralia
Plate 28 m

Bermuda, Florida to the West Indies.

About ½ inch in length, oval to elongate in shape. Color tan to dark-brown. Parietal wall with a white glaze, bearing 2 folds; in addition there is a single fold on the columella. Outer lip inflected at the center and with a single revolving ridge inside. Reasonably common above tide line.

GENUS *Melampus* Montfort, 1810

Melampus coffeus Linné, 1758   Coffee Melampus
Plate 28 p

Florida to the West Indies.

½ to ¾ inch in length, cone-shaped. Color brown, usually with 3 narrow light-colored revolving bands: the upper one on the shoulder of the body whorl. Outer lip with numerous small white teeth. Columella with a single fold; higher up on the parietal wall there is a double fold. A very common shell on the salt marshes and in the mangrove swamps.

Subgenus *Pira* H. and A. Adams, 1855

Melampus monile Bruguière, 1789   Yellowish Melampus
Plate 28 n

Florida to the West Indies.

Similar to *Melampus coffeus,* but yellowish and usually with a single columella fold and one fold on the parietal wall. Reasonably common on salt flats. *Melampus flavus* Gmelin, 1791 is a synonym.

GENUS *Detracia* Gray, 1840

Detracia bullaoides Montagu, 1808   Bulla Melampus
Plate 28 o

Florida to the West Indies.

About ½ inch in length, tapering at both ends. Grayish brown with white revolving bands. The specimens we have collected tend to be darker towards the spire end. The aperture short, extending less than half way up the length of the shell. Not common; found above tide line.

Suborder PATELLIFORMIA
Family TRIMUSCULIDAE
GENUS *Trimusculus* Schmidt, 1832

Trimusculus goesi Hubendick, 1946   Goes' False Limpet
Plate 28 i

West Indies.

¼ to ½ inch in size, conic in shape, with an almost round base. Color white. Interior glossy with a small channel. Sculptured with numerous bumpy radial lines. These animals live on rocks along the shore. Reasonably common.

Family SIPHONARIIDAE
GENUS *Williamia* Monterosato, 1884

Williamia krebsi Mörch, 1877   Krebs' False Limpet
Plate 28 f

Florida Keys and the West Indies.

About ¼ inch or less in length, limpet-like (*Acmaea*) in shape. Color brown, usually rayed with tan. Apex to the side and hooked. Sculpture microscopic. Reasonably common on the northwest end of Puerto Rico.

GENUS *Siphonaria* Sowerby, 1824

Siphonaria pectinata Linné, 1758   Striped False Limpet

Florida to Texas and the West Indies. Old World.

1 inch in length, resembling the limpet, *Acmaea*. Color whitish with brown lines. Exterior with numerous, fine, radial threads, or smoothish. Muscle scar with 3 swellings; the gap is located on one side of the shell. Compare with *Acmaea* which has the gap located at the front end of the shell. Lives along the shores on rocks. This species has not been recorded from Puerto Rico as yet.

CHAPTER V

Scallops,
Oysters and other Clams

Class *PELECYPODA*

Order *PROTOBRANCHIA*
Family *SOLEMYACIDAE*
GENUS *Solemya* Lamarck, 1818
SUBGENUS *Petrasma* Dall, 1908

Solemya occidentalis Deshayes, 1857   West Indian Awning Clam

Plate 30 b

West coast of Florida and the West Indies.

¼ inch in length, very fragile, with a weak, toothless hinge; gaping at both ends; and covered by a delicate, shiny, brown periostracum. A slender ridge or rib borders the chondrophore. Uncommon in shallow-water dredgings. Reasonably common in the stomach contents of the bonefish (*Albula vulpes*).

Superfamily *NUCULACEA*
Family *NUCULIDAE*
GENUS *Nucula* Lamarck, 1799

Nucula aegeënsis Jeffreys, 1879   West Indies Nut Clam

Text fig. 23

Southeast U. S. and the West Indies.

Less than ⅓ inch in length, ovate. Exterior white; interior pearly. Surface sculptured with fine concentric lines. Hinge with few chevron-shaped teeth. Ventral margin minutely crenulate. Uncommon from shallow dredgings in Puerto Rico.

155

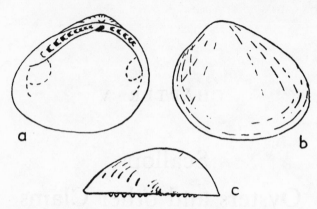

TEXT FIG. 23. *Nucula aegeensis* Jeffreys. a, interior; b, exterior; c, end view.

GENUS *Nuculana* Link, 1807
Subgenus *Saccella* Woodring, 1925

Nuculana acuta Conrad, 1831   Pointed Nut Clam
                                                                              Plate 30 a

Cape Cod to the West Indies.

¼ to ⅜ inch in length, moderately elongate, posterior end pointed. When not covered by the thin light-yellow periostracum the shell is shiny-white. Sculptured with many concentric lines. Live specimens are common from shallow dredgings and dead shells have been found on beaches all around Puerto Rico.

GENUS *Yoldia* Möller, 1842
Subgenus *Adrana* H. and A. Adams, 1858

Yoldia perprotracta Dall, 1912   Long Yoldia
                                                                              Plate 30 c

Canal Zone and Puerto Rico.

About 1 inch in length, elongate, rather bluntly pointed at the posterior, and more rounded at the anterior end. Glossy-white with a thin, brown periostracum, showing regular concentric striae. Hinge with about 38 anterior and 48 posterior teeth, separated by a small, sub-triangular pit. Described as a fossil from the Canal Zone; live specimens are reasonably common in shallow dredgings from mud bottoms on the west and southwest coasts of Puerto Rico. (For gross anatomy see Warmke and Abbott, 1953).

Family *MALLETIIDAE*
Genus *Tindaria* Bellardi, 1875
Subgenus *Neilonella* Dall, 1881

Tindaria corpulenta Dall, 1886

West Indies.

Dall and Simpson report finding two opposite worn valves of this species at Mayagüez.

Order *FILIBRANCHIA*
Suborder *TAXODONTA*
Superfamily *ARCACEA*
Family *ARCIDAE*
Subfamily *ARCINAE*
Genus *Arca* Linné, 1758

Arca zebra Swainson, 1833   Turkey Wing

Plate 30 - 1

North Carolina to the Lesser Antilles; Bermuda.

2 to 3 inches in length, one-half as high. Color tan with reddish brown, zebra-stripe markings. Sculptured with low ribs of irregular size. Periostracum brown, matted. A very abundant and widespread species found attached by its byssus to rocks. Formerly *A. occidentalis* Philippi, 1847.

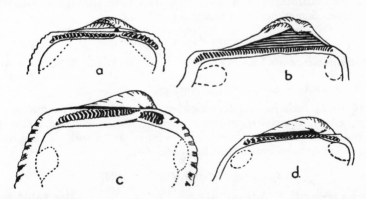

TEXT FIG. 24. Various types of Ark hinges. a, *Arcopsis adamsi* W. H. Dall, ligament limited to a very small triangle between the umbones; b, *Arca imbricata* Bruguière, long, narrow hinge line with numerous small teeth; wide ligament area between the beaks; c, *Anadara ovalis* Bruguière, ligament very narrow and depressed; beaks close together; d, *Barbatia domingensis* Lamarck, very narrow, long, ligament posterior to beaks.

Arca imbricata Bruguière, 1789   Mossy Ark
                                                                        Plate 30 e
North Carolina to the West Indies.

1 to 2½ inches in length, irregular in shape, brown. Can easily be separated from *A. zebra* by its large byssal opening, finely beaded ribs, and absence of the zebra-like stripes. Periostracum quite heavy and foliated. Common all around Puerto Rico. Found attached to underside of rocks in shallow water. Formerly *A. umbonata* Lamarck, 1819.

GENUS *Barbatia* Gray, 1847
Subgenus *Barbatia* Gray, 1847

Barbatia candida Helbling, 1779   White Bearded Ark
                                                                        Plate 30 i
North Carolina to Brazil.

1 to 2 inches in length, fairly thin. All white, covered with a brown periostracum. Sculptured with numerous, slightly beaded ribs, those on the posterior dorsal area very strongly beaded. Relatively common; attached to rocks in shallow water.

Barbatia cancellaria Lamarck, 1819   Red-brown Ark
                                                                        Plate 30 j
South Florida and the West Indies.

1 to 1½ inches in length, rather compressed. Characterized by its fine beaded sculpturing and dark, red-brown color throughout. A common species. Sometimes listed as *B. barbata* Linné.

Subgenus *Acar* Gray, 1857

Barbatia domingensis Lamarck, 1819   White Reticulated Ark
                                                                        Plate 30 d
Southeast U. S. and the Lesser Antilles.

½ to ¾ inch in length, somewhat irregular in shape but easily recognized by its coarsely reticulated surface. Color white to cream. A reasonably common shallow-water species found under rocks. This species was listed as *Arca reticulata* Gmelin by McLean.

Subgenus *Fugleria* Reinhart, 1937

Barbatia tenera C. B. Adams, 1845   Doc Bales' Ark
                                                                        Plate 30 g
Southern half of Florida to Texas and the Caribbean.

1 to 1½ inches in length, thin, rather fat. White, sculptured with numerous fine, thread-like ribs, covered with a thin brown periostracum. Dead specimens frequently are found on the beaches in Puerto Rico.

GENUS *Arcopsis* von Koenen, 1885

Arcopsis adamsi Dall, 1886   Adams' Miniature Ark
                                                            Plate 30 f
North Carolina to Brazil.

¼ to ⅓ inch in length, moderately inflated, almost rectangular in
form. Color white. Easily recognized by its small size and finely cancellate
surface. Ligament limited to a very small triangular area between the
umbones. Reasonably common under rocks all around Puerto Rico.

Subfamily *ANADARINAE*
GENUS *Anadara* Deshayes, 1830
Subgenus *Larkinia* Reinhart, 1935

Anadara notabilis Röding, 1798   Eared Ark
                                                            Plate 30 h
Florida to the Caribbean and Brazil.

1½ to 3½ inches in length. About 26 ribs, crossed by fine, concentric threads which are also prominent between the ribs. Young
specimens (2 inches or less) are easily recognized by their quadrate
shape and the prominent posterior dorsal wing, but mature specimens
become more elongate and the posterior dorsal wing is less conspicuous.
A very common species which lives in shallow water on mud and grass
bottoms. This was listed as *A. auriculata* Lam. by McLean and as *A.
deshayesi* Hanley by Dall and Simpson.

Anadara lienosa floridana Conrad, 1869   Cut-ribbed Ark
                                                            Plate 30 k
Southeast U. S., Texas and the Greater Antilles.

2½ to 5 inches in length, elongate. This species is easily separated
from the others by the grooves in its numerous, square ribs. Common
in western Puerto Rico. This is what McLean listed as *Arca secticostata*
Reeve, 1844.

Anadara transversa Say, 1822   Transverse Ark
Eastern U. S. and Texas. West Indies.

½ to 1½ inches in length. The left valve overlaps the right valve.
Ligament fairly long, moderately narrow, rough or pustulose. Ribs on
left valve usually beaded, rarely so on right valve; 30 to 35 ribs per
valve. Periostracum grayish brown. Uncommon in mud below low tide.

Subgenus *Lunarca* Gray, 1847

Anadara ovalis Bruguière, 1789   Blood Ark
                                                            Plate 30 m
Cape Cod to the West Indies and the Gulf States.

1½ to 2 inches in length. Distinguished by its roundish to ovate shape. Ribs 26 to 35 in number, square and smooth. Ligament very narrow; beaks close together. Periostracum dark-brown. Dead shells are common on the beaches of Puerto Rico. Previously listed as *Arca campechiensis* Gmelin, 1791.

Subgenus *Cunearca* Dall, 1898

Anadara brasiliana Lamarck, 1819   Incongruous Ark
                                                                    Plate 30 n

Southeast U. S., the West Indies to Brazil.

1 to 2½ inches in length, almost as high as long; inflated. Hinge line short, beaks well-separated. Ribs 26 to 28, broad, with many concentric grooves. Periostracum thin, light-brown. Found all around Puerto Rico.

Anadara chemnitzi Philippi, 1851   Chemnitz's Ark
                                                                    Plate 30 o

Florida, Texas and the West Indies.

Similar to *A. brasiliana* but thick-shelled, less than 1 inch, and the beaks are slightly forward of the center of the ligament area. Uncommon.

Family *GLYCYMERIDIDAE*
GENUS *Glycymeris* da Costa, 1778

Glycymeris decussata Linné, 1758   Decussate Bittersweet
                                                                    Plate 31 b

Southeast Florida and the West Indies.

2 inches in length, heavy. Cream to white, splotched with chestnut-brown. Sculptured with numerous radial lines. Hinge curved, with numerous small, slanted teeth. This species is much larger and more inflated than *G. pectinata*. Sometimes listed as *G. pennaceus* Lam., 1819. Dead shells have been found on the beaches of Puerto Rico.

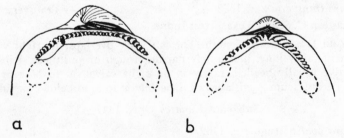

a   b

TEXT FIG. 25. Arrangement of teeth, beak and ligament in a, *Glycymeris decussata* Linné; b, *G. pectinata* Gmelin.

Glycymeris undata Linné, 1758   Atlantic Bittersweet
    Southeast U. S. and the West Indies.

    2 inches in length, similar to *G. decussata,* but differs in having the
beaks centrally located, and pointing toward each other. In *decussata,* the
beaks point posteriorly. In *undata* the ligament is centrally located.
G. lineata Reeve is a synonym.

Glycymeris sericata Reeve, 1843   Silky Bittersweet
    West Indies.

    Reported by McLean from Ponce, Puerto Rico; St. Thomas; Tor-
tola; St. Croix, Virgin Islands.

Glycymeris pectinata Gmelin, 1791   Comb Bittersweet
                                                        Plate 31 a
    Southeast U. S. and the West Indies.

    ½ to 1 inch in length, oval. Color grayish, often splotched with
brown or purplish brown. Sculptured with 20 to 40 raised, radial ribs.
Commonly taken alive in shallow water dredgings.

Suborder *ANISOMYARIA*
Superfamily *MYTILACEA*
Family *MYTILIDAE*
GENUS *Crenella* Brown, 1827

Crenella divaricata Orbigny, 1842   Divaricate Crenella
                                                        Text fig. 26
    Southeast U. S. and the West Indies.

    Less than ⅛ inch in length, oval, inflated, white all over. Sculptured
with numerous fine, beaded radiating ribs which often branch. Commonly dredged from shallow water.

TEXT FIG. 26. *Crenella divaricata* Orbigny, ⅛ inch.

GENUS *Modiolus* Lamarck, 1799

Modiolus americanus Leach, 1815   Tulip Mussel
                                                           Plate 31 k
North Carolina to the West Indies.

1 to 4 inches in length, smooth under the heavy, hairy, brown periostracum. Beautifully colored with deep-rose or light-purple rays. A common shallow-water mussel. Formerly listed as *M. tulipa* Lam. or *Volsella americana.*

GENUS *Brachidontes* Swainson, 1840
Subgenus *Brachidontes* Swainson, 1840

Brachidontes citrinus Röding, 1798   Yellow Mussel
                                                           Plate 31 c
Southern Florida and the West Indies.

1 to 1½ inches in length, elongate. Its elongate shape and conspicuous yellow periostracum make it easy to recognize. Sculptured with numerous, fine radial markings. Anterior end has four minute white teeth. Bordering the ligament are about 30 very small, equal-sized teeth on the edge of the shell. Fresh specimens are commonly washed ashore in Puerto Rico.

Subgenus *Hormomya* Mörch, 1853

Brachidontes exustus Linné, 1758   Scorched Mussel
                                                           Plate 31 f
Southeast U. S. to the West Indies.

¾ inch in length, yellowish brown to dark-brown outside and mottled with a metallic purple and white inside. Sculptured with numerous, fine radial ribs. This species is smaller, broader, and darker in color than *B. citrinus.* This common little mussel adheres to rocks in clusters.

Subgenus *Ischadium* Jukes-Brown, 1905

Brachidontes recurvus Rafinesque, 1820   Hooked Mussel
                                                           Plate 31 g
Cape Cod to the West Indies.

1 to 2 inches in length, almost triangular in outline, flattish, broad, obliquely curved at the anterior end. Color grayish brown to black outside and purplish to rosy brown inside. Sculptured with numerous, wavy radial ribs. Clusters of individuals are found attached to mangrove roots, on oysters, and on dock pilings. Common in Puerto Rico.

GENUS *Amygdalum* Mühlfeld, 1811

Amygdalum dendriticum Mühlfeld, 1811   Paper Mussel
Plate 31 n
West Indies.

1 to 1¼ inches in length, elongate, smooth, glistening, thin. Shell cream with a glossy thin, greenish or yellowish periostracum. Interior iridescent-white. Posterior slope beautifully marked with dark, cobwebby streaks. This is a rare and exceedingly delicate and beautiful species. Called *Modiolus arborescens* Dillwyn, 1817 by Dall and Simpson.

GENUS *Musculus* Röding, 1798

Musculus lateralis Say, 1822   Lateral Musculus
Plate 31 c
Southeast U. S. and the West Indies.

⅜ inch in length, oblong, fragile. Color variable: light-brown, greenish, or pinkish; interior iridescent. Sculptured with minute radial ribs at both ends; center area with concentric growth lines only. Common from shallow dredgings in Puerto Rico.

GENUS *Botula* Mörch, 1853

Botula fusca Gmelin, 1791   Cinnamon Chestnut Mussel
Plate 31 d
Southeast U. S. and the West Indies.

About ¾ inch in length, elongate, grayish. Recognized by the strongly impressed periodic growth lines; rarely entirely smooth. Beaks anterior, umbones prominent. Uncommon; a rock borer. *B. cinnamomea* Lamarck, 1819 is an absolute synonym.

GENUS *Lioberus* Dall, 1898

Lioberus castaneus Say, 1822   Say's Chestnut Mussel
Plate 31 h
Florida and the West Indies.

½ to 1 inch in length, oval-elongate, inflated, and thin. Exterior chestnut-brown and glossy. Posterior end usually covered by periostracum. Interior bluish white and iridescent. A moderately common shallow-water species.

GENUS *Lithophaga* Röding, 1798

Lithophaga nigra Orbigny, 1842   Black Date Mussel
Plate 31 m
Southeast Florida and the West Indies.

1 to 2 inches in length, elongate, cigar-shaped. Black-brown outside and iridescent inside. Anterior part of each valve with strong, vertical markings; remainder of shell smoothish, except for irregular growth lines. This is a common coral-boring species.

Lithophaga antillarum Orbigny, 1842   Antillean Date Mussel
     Southern Florida and West Indies.

Is very similar to *L. nigra* but larger, lighter in color, and has most of its surface marked with numerous diagonal lines which are divaricate on the posterior end. Reported by Dall and Simpson from Guanica, Puerto Real and Arroyo, Puerto Rico. Do not confuse with *Coralliophaga coralliophaga*. See page 174.

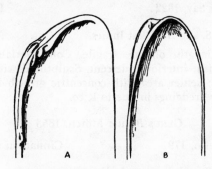

TEXT FIG. 27. *Coralliophaga* and *Lithophaga* hinges. a, *Coralliophaga coralliophaga* Gmelin, with teeth; b, *Lithophaga antillarum* Orbigny, no teeth.

Subgenus *Diberus* Dall, 1898

Lithophaga bisulcata Orbigny, 1842   Mahogany Date Mussel
                                                       Plate 31 j
     North Carolina, the Gulf of Mexico, and the West Indies.

1 to 1½ inches in length, elongate, cylindrical and coming to a point at the posterior end. A sharp, oblique, indented line divides each valve into two sections. Mahogany-brown in color, but commonly encrusted with calcareous deposits which may project beyond the margins. This is a common rock-boring species.

GENUS *Gregariella* Monterosato, 1884

Gregariella coralliophaga Gmelin, 1791   Ridged Mussel
                                                       Plate 31 - 1
     West Indies.

About ¾ inch in length, inflated, with a high posterior ridge from which radiating striae curve backward and downward. Brown outside and iridescent inside. The beaks, placed at the extreme anterior end, curve inward and forward. The inner edges of the shell are finely serrate. Periostracum heavy on the posterior dorsal area. This species is a rock-borer. Reasonably common. Previously placed in the genus *Modiolaria* by some workers. *Botulina* Dall, 1889 is a synonym of *Gregariella*.

Superfamily PTERIACEA
Family ISOGNOMONIDAE
GENUS *Isognomon* Solander, 1786

Isognomon alatus Gmelin, 1791   Flat Tree Oyster
Plate 32 c

South half of Florida and the West Indies.

2 to 3 inches in length, more or less fan-shaped, with very flat valves. Dull gray or purplish in color; interior pearly. Hinge has 8 to 12 close-set parallel grooves. Exterior with many growth lines. This common bivalve usually lives in colonies attached to mangrove roots.

Isognomon bicolor C. B. Adams, 1845   Two-toned Tree Oyster
Florida Keys, Bermuda and Caribbean.

Similar to *I. alatus* but smaller, heavier and with stronger lamellations on the outside. McLean states that the most characteristic feature of this species is the raised pallial line which marks off the body portion of the shell from the distal portion. Commonest on the south coast of Puerto Rico.

Isognomon radiatus Anton, 1839   Lister's Tree Oyster
Plate 32 a

Southeast Florida and the West Indies.

1 to 2 inches in length, elongate. Yellowish in color with irregular, reddish brown radial markings. Hinge short, with 4 to 8 widely-spaced grooves. Inside pearly. This common species lives attached to rocks in shallow water. Formerly *I. listeri* Hanley, 1843.

Family PTERIIDAE
GENUS *Pteria* Scopoli, 1777

Pteria colymbus Röding, 1798   Atlantic Wing Oyster
Plate 31 i

Southeast U. S. and the West Indies.

1½ to 3 inches in length. The elongate posterior wing makes this species easy to recognize. Exterior dark-brown with broken, radial lines of a lighter color. Pearly inside. A common pearly oyster, found attached by its byssus to sea whips and sea fans.

GENUS *Pinctada* Röding, 1798

Pinctada radiata Leach, 1814   Atlantic Pearl Oyster
                                                                Plate 32 b
South half of Florida and the West Indies.

1½ to 3 inches in length, moderately inflated to flattish, rather thin and brittle. Color variable: tan, reddish brown to green. Interior pearly. The surface is often covered with thin, overlapping scales which are delicately spiny in young specimens. A common pearly oyster found attached to rocks in shallow water. It rarely produces a pearl of gem quality.

Family *PINNiDAE*
GENUS *Pinna* Linné, 1758

Pinna rudis Linné, 1758   Red Pen Shell
Puerto Rico south to Trinidad and Tobago. Eastern Atlantic.

5½ to 7 inches in length, wedge-shaped. Color red-orange to dark reddish brown. Sculptured with 5 to 8 strong, spiny, radiating ribs. This large, robust species is rare in Puerto Rico. According to Turner and Rosewater (Johnsonia, 1958) the few specimens of this species in the West Indies probably have been introduced by mechanical transport from the western Mediterranean or West Africa.

Pinna carnea Gmelin, 1791   Amber Pen Shell
                                                                Plate 34 i
Southeast Florida and the West Indies.

4 to 11 inches in length, elongate, wedge-shaped, fragile, with a central radial ridge which is most conspicuous at the pointed end. Color light- or dark-orange. Sculpture consists of about 10 longitudinal ridges, smooth or spiny. Fresh specimens are commonly thrown up on the beaches after storms. They live buried in the soft sand with the broad end projecting just above the bottom.

GENUS *Atrina* Gray, 1840
Subgenus *Servatrina* Iredale, 1939

Atrina seminuda Lamarck, 1819   Spiny Pen Shell
                                                                Plate 34 k
Eastern U. S. to Brazil.

5 to 9 inches in length, wedge-shaped. Color dark- to light-brown. Sculptured with 5 to 16 spiny, longitudinal ridges; rarely smoothish. The spines are usually tubular and slightly recurved. This species attaches itself by a large and powerful byssus. A common species in Puerto Rico.

Atrina serrata Sowerby, 1825   Saw-toothed Pen Shell
North Carolina to the West Indies.

Similar in size and shape to *A. seminuda,* but covered with more numerous and smaller spines; also it is usually lighter in color and thinner-shelled. In *serrata* the spines are low and imbricated. Uncommon.

Superfamily *PECTINACEA*
Family *PLICATULIDAE*
GENUS *Plicatula* Lamarck, 1801

Plicatula gibbosa Lamarck, 1801   Kitten's Paw
Plate 34 g
Southeast U. S., the Gulf States, and West Indies.

1 inch in length, solid, shaped somewhat like a cat's paw. Usually light in color and marked with red or brown. Sculptured with 5 to 9 radial ribs, which make the margins of the valves fluted. Hinge with 2 strong, equal-sized teeth. A common intertidal species found attached to stones, coral or dead shells. *P. spondyloidea* Meuschen is this species.

Family *PECTINIDAE*
GENUS *Pecten* Müller, 1776
Subgenus *Amusium* Röding, 1798

Pecten laurenti Gmelin, 1791   Laurent's Scallop
Plate 32 d, g
West Indies.

2½ to 3½ inches in size, rather thin, smooth, glossy; exterior without ribs. Interior with about 30-40 very fine ribs, which are commonly arranged in pairs. Upper (left) valve flat, lower valve moderately convex. Flat valve reddish brown with light and dark flecks. Convex valve cream to tan, sometimes with light-brown radial lines. Rare. Our few specimens found came from the Mayagüez area of Puerto Rico.

Subgenus *Euvola* Dall, 1898

Pecten ziczac Linné, 1758   Zigzag Scallop
Plate 4 a; 32 h
Southeast U. S. and the West Indies.

2 to 4 inches in size. Upper valve flat, lower valve very deep and convex. There are 18-22 broad, very low ribs on the deep valve. Flat valve maroon-red in color, mottled with white and brown. Deep valve tan to brownish red. Single valves are fairly common on the beaches of Puerto Rico.

Pecten raveneli Dall, 1898   Ravenel's Scallop
Plate 32 f
North Carolina to the Gulf of Mexico, and the West Indies.

Similar to *P. ziczac,* but smaller in size (1 to 2 inches). In *P. raveneli* the deep valve has 25 very distinct ribs which are whitish in color with tan or pink between them. The ribbing on the flat valve is also more pronounced. Dall and Simpson reported 2 young valves of this species from Mayagüez. It is rare in Puerto Rico.

Pecten chazaliei Dautzenberg, 1900   Chazalie Scallop
                                                            Plate 32 c

Southern Florida, the Gulf of Mexico, and Puerto Rico.

1 inch in size, quite fragile. Upper left valve (flat) with about 20 small, narrow ribs; lower valve moderately deep, with low ribs. Color tan, flecked with reddish brown. Rare. Mrs. A. Phares found a single lower valve of this beautiful little species at Rincón, Puerto Rico. This was listed as *P. tereinus* Dall, 1925 in "American Seashells," and is a synonym.

GENUS *Chlamys* Röding, 1798

Chlamys sentis Reeve, 1853   Sentis Scallop
                                                            Plate 33 c

Southeast U. S. and the West Indies.

1 to 1½ inches in length, similar to *C. ornata* but with about 50 ribs of varying sizes; usually there are 2 to 4 smaller ribs between the slightly larger ones. Color purple-red, vermillion, orange, white or mottled near the beaks. Appears to be a relatively shallow-water species.

Chlamys ornata Lamarck, 1819   Ornate Scallop
                                                            Plate 33 a

Southeast Florida to the West Indies.

1 to 1¼ inches in length, with rather flat valves. One hinge ear small, the other twice as large. Color usually cream with strong maroon maculations. Sculpture consists of 18 groups of 3 closely-spaced scaly riblets, the center ribs usually being the largest in each group. Common shallow-water species. Compare with the less abundant *C. sentis* Reeve.

Chlamys benedicti Verrill and Bush, 1897   Benedict's Scallop
                                                            Plate 33 b

Florida, the Gulf of Mexico and Puerto Rico.

About ½ inch in length. Color pink, red, orange, light purple, lemon yellow or with chalk-white zigzag stripes. Sculptured with about 22 strong ribs alternating with weaker ribs, total about 45. Not common; obtained from shallow dredgings.

Chlamys imbricata Gmelin, 1791   Little Knobby Scallop
                                                            Plate 33 j

Southeast Florida and the West Indies.

1 to 1¾ inches in length. White, variously mottled and spotted with red or brown. Characterized by prominent, cup-shaped, delicate scales on the 8 to 10 ribs. There are smaller cords between the main ribs. Not common in Puerto Rico.

Subgenus *Palliolum* Monterosato, 1884

Chlamys nana Verrill and Bush, 1897   Tiny Smooth Scallop
Eastern U. S. and Puerto Rico.

About 5 mm. in size, thin, nearly orbicular, compressed. It is translucent, commonly clouded with milky-white. Interior smooth; exterior appears smooth, but bears fine concentric striae and minute radial riblets. Of the 5 specimens found, all showed the concentric sculpture, but the radial sculpture was absent. Rare. Our specimens were obtained from dredgings in about 12 fathoms; however this species has been reported from 43 to 294 fathoms.

GENUS *Leptopecten* Verrill, 1897

Leptopecten bavayi Dautzenberg, 1900   Bavay's Scallop
                                                Plate 33 d
West Indies.

Usually less than ½ inch in size, open-fan-shaped, thin, fragile. Color white, commonly streaked with pale-yellow, orange or brown. Sculptured with about 20 sharp ribs; there are numerous microscopic wavy growth lines between the ribs. This rare and beautiful little shell is relatively common from shallow dredgings in the Mayagüez area of Puerto Rico.

GENUS *Lyropecten* Conrad, 1862

Lyropecten antillarum Récluz, 1853   Antillean Scallop
                                             Plate 33 f
South Florida and the West Indies.

½ to ¾ inch in length and width. Valves fragile, both nearly flat. Color either white, light-yellow, pastel orange or light-brown, frequently mottled, flecked or striped with white. Surface sculpture consists of 10-15 moderately rounded ribs; growth lines exceedingly fine. Not common in shallow water.

Subgenus *Nodipecten* Dall, 1898

Lyropecten nodosus Linné, 1758   Lion's Paw
                                          Plate 4 b; 33 g
Southeast U. S. and the West Indies.

3 to 6 inches in size, rather heavy and robust. Color varies from

purplish red, maroon, to bright-orange. The entire surface is sculptured with numerous riblets; in addition there are 7 to 9 large, nodulous ribs. In Puerto Rico, single valves are commonly found on the beaches after storms.

GENUS *Aequipecten* P. Fischer, 1886
Subgenus *Aequipecten* P. Fischer, 1886

Aequipecten muscosus Wood, 1828   Rough Scallop
                                                              Plate 33 e
Southeast U. S. and the West Indies.

¾ to 1¼ inches in size, both valves fairly inflated. A very colorful species, either bright yellow, orange, red, orange-brown, or sometimes mottled. Sculptured with 18 to 20 ribs. The center part of each rib bears erect, concave scales, and on each side there are 2 rows of much smaller scales. Dead shells are common on the beaches all around Puerto Rico.

Aequipecten lineolaris Lamarck, 1819   Wavy-lined Scallop
                                                              Plate 33 h
Florida Keys to the Lesser Antilles.

About 1 inch in size, with moderately inflated valves. Surface highly glossy. Bottom valve white; top valve rosy-tan with numerous characteristic, thin, wavy lines of pink-brown running concentrically. There are about 18 ribs; in fresh specimens these are quite angular at the summit, but rounded in worn specimens. *A. mayaguezensis* Dall & Simpson is this species. Uncommon in water less than 50 feet.

Subgenus *Argopecten* Monterosato, 1889

Aequipecten gibbus Linné, 1758   Calico Scallop
                                                              Plate 33 i
Eastern U. S., the Gulf of Mexico, and the West Indies.

1 to 2 inches, both valves quite inflated. Bottom valve whitish; upper valve may be mottled with pink, purple or brown on white background. Ribs about 20, smooth, except for fine concentric laminations over the whole surface. Common on the beaches after storms and from shallow dredgings.

Family *SPONDYLIDAE*
GENUS *Spondylus* Linné, 1758

Spondylus americanus Hermann, 1781   Atlantic Thorny Oyster
                                                              Plate 4 e; 34 a, b
Florida and the West Indies.

3 to 4 inches in size, heavy. This is a variable species both in color

and sculpture. Color ranges from all white, or white with yellow or orange-red umbones, to all orange or all red. Some adults have many beautiful, long spines (see plate 4 e) ; others are much less spinose. The young are frilly and have the appearance of a *Chama* (plate 34 b) but can easily be distinguished from it by the characteristic ball-and-socket type hinge of *Spondylus*. Attached to rocks, coral or other hard objects. It is quite common all around Puerto Rico.

Family *LIMIDAE*
GENUS *Lima* Bruguière, 1797
Subgenus *Lima* Bruguière, 1796

Lima lima Linné, 1758   Spiny Lima
                                                          Plate 34 f
Southeast Florida and the West Indies.

1 to 1½ inches in height, all white. Sculpture consists of numerous, even, spinous, radial ribs. On beach specimens, the spines are usually worn off. This species is easily recognized by its oblique hinge line; also, the anterior ear is much smaller than the posterior one. A relatively common shallow-water species.

Subgenus *Limaria* Link, 1807

Lima pellucida C. B. Adams, 1846   Antillean Lima
                                                          Plate 34 e
Southeast U. S. and the West Indies.

¾ to 1 inch in height, elongate, oblique, thin, inflated, semi-translucent, white. Sculptured with many fine radial ribs of uneven size and distribution. Common in shallow dredgings. Previously listed from Puerto Rico as *Lima inflata* Lamarck and *Lima hians* Gmelin.

Subgenus *Ctenoides* Mörch, 1853

Lima scabra Born, 1778   Rough Lima
                                                          Plate 34 c
Southeast Florida and the West Indies.

1 to 3 inches in height. Coarsely sculptured with irregular, radial rows of short, bar-like ribs. Periostracum dark- to light-brown. A common species under or between rocks in shallow water. The animal is bright orange in color.

Lima scabra form *tenera* Sowerby, 1843 (plate 34 d) is similar in shape but is more delicate and more finely ribbed, having an almost satiny sheen. Common under rocks in shallow water.

GENUS *Limatula* S. Wood, 1839

Greenland to Puerto Rico. Alaska to Mexico.
Limatula subauriculata Montagu, 1808   Small-eared Lima

½ inch in height, ovate-oblong, inflated. Equivalve and nearly equilateral. Sculptured with numerous small radial riblets. Inside, at the middle of the valve, there are 2 prominent, radial riblets. Easily separated from *Lima* because it lacks the obliquity that is typical of *Lima*. This species is moderately common in cooler waters but rare in Puerto Rico. *L. henderson* Olsson and McGinty, 1958 is very close to this species.

Superfamily ANOMIACEA
Family ANOMIIDAE
GENUS *Anomia* Linné, 1758

Anomia simplex Orbigny, 1842   Common Jingle Shell
                                                                        Plate 34 h
Eastern U. S., the Gulf of Mexico, and the West Indies.

1 to 2 inches in size, irregular in shape. Color translucent-yellow, silvery or orange. The right or lower valve is flat with a large notch, through which the byssus passes. The other valve has 1 large and 2 small muscle scars. A common species attached to rocks, logs or shells. On one occasion several were found attached to a live trumpet shell (*Charonia*).

GENUS *Pododesmus* Philippi, 1837

Pododesmus rudis Broderip, 1834   False Jingle Shell
                                                                        Plate 34 j
Florida and the West Indies.

1 to 4 inches in size, irregular, compressed. Color whitish to grayish brown. The top or holeless valve has only 2 muscle scars. Surface of valves sculptured with irregular, broken ridges, crossed by scaly growth lines. Fairly abundant all around Puerto Rico.

Superfamily OSTREACEA
Family OSTREIDAE
GENUS *Ostrea* Linné, 1758

Ostrea equestris Say, 1834   Crested Oyster
                                                                        Plate 35 c
Southeast U. S., the Gulf States, and the West Indies.

1 to 2 inches in length, more or less oval. The heavily crenulated margins help to identify this species. It lacks the series of clasping projections found in *O. frons*. Interior dull-gray with a greenish brown stain. Abundant at Crashboat Landing on the northwest coast of Puerto Rico. Reported from the south coast as *Ostrea cristata* Born by Dall and Simpson in 1901 and by McLean in 1951.

Ostrea frons Linné, 1758   'Coon Oyster
Plate 35 e

Southeast U. S. and the West Indies.

1 to 2 inches in size. The clasping projections by which the shell attaches to branches or roots help to identify this species. The radial plicate sculpture and corresponding sharply folded valve margins are also characteristic. Color is usually purplish brown. Common all around Puerto Rico usually attached to sea fan stems or mangrove roots.

GENUS *Crassostrea* Sacco, 1897

Crassostrea rhizophorae Guilding, 1828   Caribbean Oyster
Plate 35 b

Caribbean.

2 to 6 inches in length, variable in shape. Upper valve flat and fitting well down into the deep-cupped lower valve; margins straight and smooth. This is the common edible oyster found attached to mangrove roots. According to N. T. Mattox (1949), it has been estimated that from 25 to 30 thousand pounds of these oysters are harvested annually in Puerto Rico. *C. virginica* Gmelin previously reported from Puerto Rico is a closely related northern relative of this species.

Order *EULAMELLIBRANCHIA*
Suborder *HETERODONTA*
Superfamily *ASTARTACEA*
Family *CRASSATELLIDAE*
GENUS *Crassinella* Guppy, 1874

Crassinella lunulata Conrad, 1834   Lunate Crassinella
Plate 35 k

Southeast U. S. and the West Indies.

¼ to ⅓ inch in length, as high, quite compressed, solid, subtriangular. Dorsal margins straight and about 90 degrees to each other; the anterior margin slightly longer and with a wider, sunken area. The valves are peculiarly askew, so that the posterior dorsal margin of the left valve is more obvious than that of the right valve. Color whitish or pinkish brown; interior commonly brown. Sometimes faintly rayed. Sculptured with 15 or more concentric ribs. A common shell on the beaches and from shallow dredgings.

Crassinella martinicensis Orbigny, 1842   Martinique Crassinella

West Indies.

About 1/16 inch in length, relatively triangular, somewhat inflated. Dorsal margins equal in length; the anterior and posterior slopes are at right angles to each other. Color white, shaded with brown. Surface

with 8-15 smooth, rounded concentric ribs. It can be separated from
C. guadalupensis by its shape, and from *C. lunulata* by its size and the
inflation of valves. Uncommon.

Crassinella guadalupensis Orbigny, 1842   Guadeloupe Crassinella
                                                            Plate 35 m
     West Indies.

     Less than ¼ inch in length, compressed, irregular in outline. Dorsal
margins unequal in length, with high, sharp beaks. Shell rounded
anteriorly and more or less attenuate behind. White or variously shaded
with reddish brown. Sculptured with about 10 sharp, concentric ridges.
Common from shallow dredgings.

Superfamily CARDITACEA
Family CARDITIDAE
GENUS *Cardita* Bruguière, 1792

Cardita gracilis Shuttleworth, 1856   West Indian Cardita
                                                            Plate 35 d
     Mexico to the West Indies.
     1 to 1½ inches in length, elongate-quadrate. Color whitish, shaded
with brown. Surface sculptured with about 17 flattened, wrinkled ribs
which become more elevated and almost spinose on the posterior slope.
Common all around Puerto Rico.

Family TRAPEZIIDAE
GENUS *Coralliophaga* Blainville, 1824

Coralliophaga coralliophaga Gmelin, 1791   Coral Clam
                                                            Plate 35 g
     Florida, Texas, and the West Indies.

     ½ to 1¾ inches in length, elongate, with the umbones at the
anterior end. Color yellowish white. Sculptured with fine radial threads
and periodic concentric ridges. This shell is very similar in appearance
to *Lithophaga antillarum,* but can be distinguished by the presence of
distinct teeth in the hinge. (See p. 164, fig. 27). This species is found
living in the burrows of other rock-boring mollusks.

Superfamily DREISSENACEA
Family DREISSENIDAE
GENUS *Mytilopsis* Conrad, 1857

Mytilopsis domingensis Récluz, 1852   False Mussel
                                                            Plate 35 a
     West Indies.

     ¾ to 1¼ inches in length, mussel-like in shape, grayish white in
color, covered with a dark-brown periostracum. Interior splotched with

dark-gray. This bivalve attaches itself by its short byssus to rocks and branches. It is found in brackish to fresh water.

Superfamily *LUCINACEA*
Family *DIPLODONTIDAE*
GENUS *Diplodonta* Bronn, 1831

Diplodonta punctata Say, 1822   Common Atlantic Diplodon
Plate 35 h, i
Southeast U. S. and the West Indies.

Up to ¾ inch in length, well-inflated. Color white. Its larger size and rounded, subquadrate shape help to separate this species from the other *Diplodonta*. Sculpture consists of numerous, fine concentric lines and coarse growth lines. Common from shallow-water dredgings.

Diplodonta nucleiformis Wagner, 1852   Wagner's Diplodon
Plate 35 j
Southeast U. S. to Puerto Rico.

Less than ½ inch in length and about the same width, subglobose, moderately heavy. Color white. Surface with very fine concentric sculpture only. Uncommon.

Subgenus *Phlyctiderma* Dall, 1899

Diplodonta semiaspera Philippi, 1836   Pimpled Diplodon
Plate 35 - l
Southeast U. S., Texas, and the West Indies.

Rarely over ½ inch in length, inflated, almost orbicular. Chalky-white, with distinct pustulose sculpture. We found this species embedded in coral. Fairly common in shallow dredgings.

Diplodonta gabbi Dall, 1900   Gabb's Diplodon

West Indies.

Reported from San Juan, Puerto Rico by Dall and Simpson as *D. puncturella* Dall, 1900.

Diplodonta notata Dall & Simpson, 1901   Flattened Diplodon
Plate 35 l
Florida to Puerto Rico.

Between ¼ and ½ inch in length, suborbicular, compressed. Color white. The umbones are nearly central. Surface minutely pitted. There are 2 cardinal teeth in each valve; the left anterior and right posterior ones are bifid. Common from shallow dredgings.

Subfamily THYASIRINAE
GENUS *Thyasira* Lamarck, 1818

Thyasira trisinuata Orbigny, 1842   Atlantic Cleft Clam
Plate 36 f

Nova Scotia to Florida and the West Indies.

¼ to ½ inch in length, oblong, fragile, white. Posterior slope with 2 deep, distinct, radial grooves. Hinge without teeth, except for a long, weak posterior lateral. Surface sculptured with fine concentric lines. Moderately common in shallow dredgings.

Thyasira conia Dall & Simpson, 1901   Granulated Cleft Clam

Puerto Rico.

Differs from the above by its smaller size (¼ inch), finely granular surface, and single radial groove of posterior slope. Rare deep-water species reported by Dall and Simpson from San Juan, Puerto Rico.

Family LUCINIDAE
GENUS *Lucina* Bruguière, 1797

Lucina pensylvanica Linné, 1758   Pennsylvania Lucina
Plate 36 a

Southeast U. S. and the West Indies.

1 to 2 inches in length, usually quite inflated. Color pure-white with a thin yellowish periostracum. The deep furrow from the beak to the posterior ventral edge of the valve makes it easy to identify. Moderately common all around Puerto Rico, and very abundant in the Cabo Rojo Lighthouse area.

Lucina phenax Dall and Simpson, 1901   Mock Lucina
Puerto Rico.

About ½ inch in length, inflated, thin. Color white, with a grayish, papery periostracum. Resembling young *L. pensylvanica* but thinner and lacking hinge teeth. Uncommon from shallow dredging.

Subgenus *Carilinga* Chavan, 1937

Lucina blanda Dall and Simpson, 1901   Three-Ridged Lucina
Plate 36 d

West Indies.

¼ to ½ inch in length, obliquely triangular in outline. Color white, sometimes yellow or salmon. The surface is evenly sculptured with numerous concentric ridges, interspersed with three or four deeper concentric grooves. Found on the beach and in shallow dredgings. The Miocene fossil, *L. trisulcata* Conrad, is very similar.

GENUS *Phacoides* Gray, 1847

Phacoides pectinatus Gmelin, 1791   Thick Lucina
Plate 36 b

Southeast U. S., Texas, and the West Indies.

1 to 2½ inches in length, ovate, compressed, white or flushed with bright-orange. Sculptured with numerous sharp, concentric ridges. Lunule strongly raised. A reasonably common shallow-water species found all around Puerto Rico.

Subgenus *Lucinisca* Dall, 1901

Phacoides muricatus Spengler, 1798   Spinose Lucina
Plate 36 i

Florida Keys, and the West Indies.

½ inch in length, pure white. This beautiful little species is easily recognized by its spinous radial ribs. Reasonably common in shallow dredgings from muddy bottoms.

Subgenus *Callucina* Dall, 1901

Phacoides radians Conrad, 1841   Dosinia-like Lucina
Plate 36 j

Southeast U. S. and Puerto Rico.

About ¾ inch in length, solid, nearly orbicular, superficially resembling the white clam, *Dosinia*. Color white. Surface covered with regular, fine concentric lines cut by faint radiating threads. Beaks high, turned forward over a deep lunule. Ventral margin crenulated. Moderately common just offshore in Puerto Rico.

GENUS *Myrtea* Turton, 1822

Myrtea pristiphora Dall and Simpson, 1901   Lamellated Lucina
Plate 29 c

Puerto Rico.

Less than ½ inch in length, white. Easily recognized by the pronounced concentric sculpture which is raised into lamellated projections along the dorsal border of the shell. Obtained from dredgings in 30 and 45 fathoms.

GENUS *Anodontia* Link, 1807

Anodontia alba Link, 1807   Buttercup Lucina
Plate 36 c

Southeast U. S. and the West Indies.

1½ to 2 inches in length, more or less circular in shape, inflated. Interior tinted with yellow-orange. Hinge without distinct teeth. Sculptured with weak, irregular concentric growth lines. A very common species found on beaches all around Puerto Rico. This was formerly known as *Lucina chrysostoma* Philippi.

Anodontia philippiana Reeve, 1850   Chalky Buttercup

Southeast U. S. and the West Indies.

2 to 4 inches in length, very similar to *A. alba,* but larger, all-white, with a more chalky shell, and the interior is usually pustulose. Unlike *A. alba,* the anterior muscle scar is not parallel to the pallial line but diverges at an angle of about 30 degrees. This species was formerly known as *A. schrammi* Crosse, 1876. Uncommon.

GENUS *Codakia* Scopoli, 1777
Subgenus *Codakia* Scopoli, 1777

Codakia orbicularis Linné, 1758   Tiger Lucina
                                                                      Plate 36 g
Florida to Texas and the West Indies.

2½ to 3½ inches in length, compressed, circular. Color white, frequently flushed with yellow or rose at ends of the hinge and at the margins of the valves. Roughly sculptured by numerous coarse radial threads which are crossed by finer concentric threads. A very common species all around Puerto Rico.

Subgenus *Ctena* Mörch, 1860

Codakia costata Orbigny, 1842   Costate Lucina
                                                                      Plate 36 k
Southeast U. S. and the West Indies.

½ inch in length, quite fat, usually circular in shape. Color white to yellow. Sculptured with fine radial threads crossed by finer concentric threads. A common shallow-water species found on sandy bottoms.

Codakia portoricana Dall, 1901   Puerto Rican Lucina

Puerto Rico.

Similar to *C. costata* but smaller (8 mm. or less) more finely and evenly sculptured, and more inflated. Reported by Dall and Simpson from San Juan and Mayagüez. Uncommon.

Codakia orbiculata Montagu, 1808   Dwarf Tiger Lucina
                                                                      Plate 36 h
Southeast U. S. and the West Indies.

1 inch or less in length, very similar to *orbicularis,* but small, pure-white, with stronger radial sculpture, and with strong posterior lateral teeth. A common shallow-water species.

Codakia pectinella C. B. Adams, 1852   Tiny Lucina
                                                           Plate 36 c
Jamaica, Puerto Rico, and Argentina.

¼ inch or less, quite inflated, subcircular in shape. Color white. The concentric sculpture is stronger than the radial ribs in the umbonal region. Relatively common in shallow dredgings from sandy or muddy bottoms.

GENUS *Divaricella* von Martens, 1880

Divaricella quadrisulcata Orbigny, 1842   Cross-hatched Lucina
                                                        Plate 36 - 1
Eastern U. S. and the West Indies.

½ to 1 inch in length, almost circular in outline, inflated. Color pure-white and glossy. Easily recognized by the divaricate or criss-cross sculpture. Inner margins are finely fluted or crenulate. Often washed ashore. *D. dentata* Wood, 1815 is probably only a form of this species.

Family *CHAMIDAE*
GENUS *Chama* Linné, 1758

Chama macerophylla Gmelin, 1791   Leafy Jewel Box
                                                     Plate 4 c; 37 b
Southeast U. S. and the West Indies.

1 to 3 inches in length. Color variable: white, yellow, or purple, or a combination of these colors. Surface with numerous foliations. The inner margin is crenulated. Attached by the left valve to coral, stones, or dead shells. Very common all around Puerto Rico.

Chama congregata Conrad, 1833   Little Corrugated Jewel Box
                                                         Plate 37 g
Southeast U. S. and the West Indies.

½ to 1½ inches in length. Color dull-white, usually with radial rows of reddish brown specklings. Sculpture reduced to wavy cords and low axial corrugations. The unattached valve may have a few short, flat spines. A common shallow-water species found attached to any hard surface; often attached to shells of the same species.

Chama sarda Reeve, 1847   Red Jewel Box
                                                         Plate 37 d
Florida Keys and the West Indies.

About 1 inch in length, with the attached valve often deeply cupped. Color mostly red, internally and externally. Sculpture consists of irregular foliations; internal margin crenulated. A common species found attached to coral and dead shells.

Chama florida Lamarck, 1819   Florida Jewel Box
                                                         Plate 37 c
South Florida to the West Indies.

About 1 inch in length, subcircular. Ground color white, with several radial rows of deep pink. The interior of both valves white, the upper pink stained. Interior margins crenulated. Single valves are very common on beaches all around Puerto Rico.

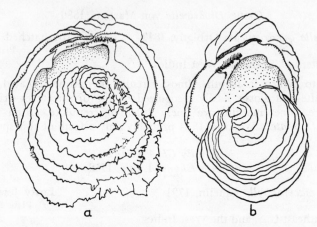

TEXT FIG. 28. *Pseudochama* is a mirror image of *Chama*. a, *Chama macerophylla* Gmelin; b, *Pseudochama radians* Lamarck.

GENUS *Pseudochama* Odhner, 1917

Pseudochama radians Lamarck, 1819   Atlantic Left-handed Jewel Box
                                                         Plate 37 c
Southern Florida and the West Indies.

1 to 3 inches in length, heavy. Color white, shaded with brown. In shape *Pseudochama* is a mirror image of *Chama* (see text fig. 28). Attached by the right valve to various hard substances. Relatively common.

GENUS *Echinochama* P. Fischer, 1887

Echinochama arcinella Linné, 1767   True Spiny Jewel Box
                                                         Plate 37 a
West Indies to Brazil.

1 to 1½ inches in length, quadrate, with a distinct heart-shaped lunule. Exterior cream, interior white, usually flushed with reddish purple. Young specimens sometimes have the purple on the outside.

Surface pitted, sculptured with 16 to 35 spinose radial ribs. A common species found free or attached to coral, broken shells, or rocks.

Superfamily *ERYCINACEA*
Family *ERYCINIDAE* (Leptonidae)
Genus *Erycina* Lamarck, 1805

Erycina periscopiana Dall, 1899

Inequilateral Erycina
Plate 37 f

North Carolina and Puerto Rico.

¼ inch or less in length, subquadrate, with the ends bluntly rounded and the dorsal and ventral margins nearly parallel. Beaks low, valves compressed, very inequilateral, the beaks being nearly at the posterior fifth of the shell. Surface polished, smooth, or marked by minute growth lines and very obscure occasional radial lines. This species was described from Cape Lookout, North Carolina, dredged in 22 fathoms, on sandy bottom. Our specimens (5) came from shallow dredgings (20-40 feet) off Mayagüez, Boqueron and La Parguera, Puerto Rico.

Erycina emmonsi Dall, 1899

Emmons' Erycina
Plate 37 i

North Carolina and Puerto Rico.

⅓ inch in length, elongate, compressed, nearly equilateral. White or translucent. Surface concentrically and somewhat irregularly sculptured by minute lines. This species was described off Cape Lookout, North Carolina, in 12 to 31 fathoms. Our specimens were obtained from shallow dredgings.

Genus *Vesicomya* Dall, 1886

Vesicomya pilula Dall, 1881

Florida and the West Indies.

Reported from Mayagüez, Puerto Rico, by Dall and Simpson

Genus *Basterotia* Hoernes, 1859

Basterotia quadrata Hinds, 1843

Square Basterotia
Text fig. 31 a, b

West Indies.

¼ to ½ inch in length, subquadrate, inflated. Color white. Surface sculptured with concentric growth lines. Umbones prominent. Hinge with a long conical tooth. Uncommon in Puerto Rico. The form *Basterotia quadrata granatina* Dall, 1886, can be separated from the above by its distinctly granular surface and prominent umbonal ridge.

Dead specimens are reasonably common on the beaches.

Subgenus *Basterotella* Olsson and Harbison, 1953

Basterotia elliptica Récluz, 1850   Elliptical Basterotia
                                                           Text fig. 31 e
    West Indies.

Similar to *B. quadrata,* but elliptical in outline. Not common. *B. newtoniana* C. B. Adams, 1852 is a synonym.

Superfamily *CARDIACEA*
Family *CARDIIDAE*
Subfamily *TRACHYCARDIINAE*
GENUS *Trachycardium* Mörch, 1853

Trachycardium magnum Linné, 1758   Magnum Cockle
                                                           Plate 37 k
    Lower Florida Keys and the West Indies.

2 to 3½ inches in height, elongate. Interior color yellow in the umbonal area. The posterior margin is yellow, merging into reddish purple at the extreme edge. Exterior with 32 to 35 radiating ribs. The ribs on the posterior end have small, tooth-like scales. Middle ribs completely smooth and squarish. Not as common as the other two species.

Trachycardium muricatum Linné, 1758   Yellow Cockle
                                                           Plate 37 m
    Southeast U. S. and the West Indies.

About 2 inches in height, subcircular. Interior white or cream; under the umbones there is a patch of yellow, bordered by streaks of purple on either side. Exterior with 30 to 40 moderately scaly, radiating ribs. A very common shallow-water species found all around Puerto Rico.

Trachycardium isocardia Linné, 1758   Prickly Cockle
                                                           Plate 4 d; 37 - 1
    West Indies to the northern coast of South America.

2 to 3 inches in height, subelongate. Interior color consists of a wide band of salmon, shading to purple, which extends from the umbones to the ventral margin of the shell. Exterior with 31 to 37 strong, radiating ribs which possess numerous imbricated scales. A beautiful and very common shallow-water species found all around Puerto Rico.

GENUS *Papyridea* Swainson, 1840

Papyridea soleniformis Bruguière, 1789   Spiny Paper Cockle
                                                           Plate 37 j
    Southeast U. S. and the West Indies.

1 to 1¾ inches in length, fairly fragile, moderately compressed, and
gaping at both ends. Color cream, with violet or light-orange mottlings.
Sculptured with 40 to 55 fine, oblique, radiating ribs which are
minutely spinose. Posterior half of shell bears about 10 strong, elongated
serrations. Reasonably common on the beaches all around Puerto Rico.

Papyridea semisulcata Gray, 1825   Frilled Paper Cockle
                                                              Plate 37 h
Southern Florida to the West Indies.

Less than ½ inch in length, thin, delicate and inflated. Color
usually white, sometimes with a tinge of pink or orange-yellow. Sculptured with about 30 fine, oblique, radiating ribs. Posterior half of shell
markedly serrated. Reasonably common from shallow-water dredgings.

Subfamily *FRAGINAE*
Genus *Trigoniocardia* Dall, 1900

Trigoniocardia antillarum Orbigny, 1842   Antillean Strawberry Cockle
                                                              Plate 38 c
Greater Antilles.

¼ to ⅜ inch in length, subquadrate, inflated. Color white. Sculptured with 16 to 18 ribs, of which the 5 or 6 middle ones are extra large.
The concentric threads in the inter-spaces between the ribs are quite
noticeable. Commonly dredged from shallow water. This has previously
been listed as *T. ceramidum* Dall.

Genus *Americardia* Stewart, 1930

Americardia guppyi Thiele, 1910   Guppy's Strawberry Cockle
                                                              Plate 38 a
Florida, Bahamas and Caribbean.

¼ to ½ inch in length, subquadrate to subcircular in outline. Color
cream or maculated with reddish brown or purplish. Sculptured with
26 to 29 radial ribs which are about the same width over the entire shell.
Uncommon. Previously listed as *Trigoniocardia antillarum* Orb. in
Johnsonia.

Americardia media Linné, 1758   Atlantic Strawberry Cockle
                                                              Plate 38 b
Southeast U. S. and the West Indies.

1 to 2 inches in length, heavy, inflated, quadrate in outline. Color
whitish with orange-brown mottlings. Sculptured with 33 to 37 scaly
radial ribs. Posterior slope flattened and slightly concave. Margin strongly
serrated. A common shallow-water species found all around Puerto Rico.

Subfamily LAEVICARDIINAE
GENUS *Laevicardium* Swainson, 1840

Laevicardium laevigatum Linné, 1758   Common Egg Cockle
Plate 38 e

Southeast U. S. and the West Indies.

1 to 2 inches in length, elongate, polished, smooth. Exterior and interior color variable, usually yellow with orange, but may be tinted with purple or mottled with brown. Occasional specimens have brown radial lines; this latter form was described as a subspecies (*Cardium serratum multilineatum*) by Dall and Simpson in 1901. A very common shallow-water species.

Laevicardium pictum Ravenel, 1861   Ravenel's Egg Cockle

Southeast U. S. and the West Indies.

½ to 1 inch in height, obliquely triangular in shape. Color white or cream with delicate shadings of rose. Some specimens have brown zigzag lines. Umbo very low and near the anterior end. Dredged from fairly shallow to deep water. Uncommon.

Laevicardium sybariticum Dall, 1886   Dall's Egg Cockle
Plate 38 d

Southeast U. S. and the West Indies.

½ to 1 inch in height, squarish in shape, inflated, and with deep-pink umbones. Uncommon in Puerto Rico.

Subfamily PROTOCARDIINAE
GENUS *Microcardium* Thiele, 1934

Microcardium tinctum Dall, 1881   Pink Micro-cockle
Plate 38 f; 29 e

Southern Florida to the Lesser Antilles.

¼ to ⅝ inch in length, thin, inflated, and subquadrate in outline. Color white with delicate shadings of pink. Umbones pink, high and prominent. Sculpture consists of more than 150 minute radial ribs crossed by finer concentric lines. A deep-water form which occasionally comes up in shallow dredgings or on the beaches of Puerto Rico.

Microcardium peramabile Dall, 1881   Eastern Micro-cockle

Rhode Island to the West Indies.

Is similar to *M. tinctum*, but generally white, with fewer radial ribs (about 90), and has a sharp line of demarcation between the sculptures of the posterior and anterior slopes. Reported by Dall and Simpson from Mayagüez and Aguadilla, Puerto Rico. Rare.

Superfamily *VENERACEA*
Family *VENERIDAE*
Subfamily *VENERINAE*
GENUS *Antigona* Schumacher, 1817
Subgenus *Periglypta* Jukes-Brown, 1914

Antigona listeri Gray, 1838   Princess Venus
                                                       Plate 38 - 1

Southeast Florida and the West Indies.

2 to 4 inches in length, oblong-oval in shape. Exterior cream, maculated with brown. Interior cream; usually the posterior muscle scar is stained purplish brown. Sculpture consists of numerous radial riblets crossed by sharp concentric ribs, making the surface cancellate. Lives in sand in shallow water. Reasonably common on the west and south coasts of Puerto Rico.

Subgenus *Ventricolaria* Keen, 1954

Antigona rigida Dillwyn, 1817   Rigid Venus
                                                       Plate 38 m

Florida Keys to Brazil.

1½ to 2½ inches in length, almost circular in outline, inflated. Color cream with brown mottling; interior white or cream. Sculptured with numerous prominent concentric ribs between which there are 1 to 3 smaller concentric threads. Lunule heart-shaped, deeply sunk. Escutcheon on left valve marked with purplish red. Reasonably common.

Antigona rugatina Heilprin, 1887   Queen Venus

North Carolina, Gulf of Mexico to Puerto Rico.

More inflated and has 4 to 6 concentric threads between the concentric ribs. Reported from Mayagüez, Puerto Rico, by Dall and Simpson. Uncommon.

GENUS *Chione* Mühlfeld, 1811
Subgenus *Chione* Mühlfeld, 1811

Chione cancellata Linné, 1767   Cross-barred Venus
                                                       Plate 4 f; 38 o

Southeast U. S., Texas and the West Indies.

1 to 1¾ inches in length, ovate to subtriangular in outline, heavy. Color ashy, often irregularly rayed with brown. Interior white, usually with some purple. Surface sculptured with many strong, concentric ridges and numerous weaker radial ribs. A common shallow-water species found all around Puerto Rico. *C. mazycki* Dall, 1902 is probably this species.

Chione granulata Gmelin, 1791   Beaded Venus
                                                    Plate 38 i
    West Indies.

¾ to 1¼ inches in length, inflated. Color yellow, variously mottled with purple. Interior shaded with purple. Surface with numerous radiating ribs crossed by concentric ridges, giving the shell a granular or beaded appearance. A shallow-water species, reasonably common all around Puerto Rico.

Chione intapurpurea Conrad, 1849   Lady-in-waiting Venus
                                                    Plate 38 n
    North Carolina, the Gulf States and the West Indies.

1 to 1½ inches in length and height. Color white to cream, commonly maculated with brown. Interior white, usually splotched with reddish purple. Sculptured with numerous concentric ribs which are serrated on the lower edge. Not very common in Puerto Rico.

Subgenus *Timoclea* Brown, 1827

Chione pygmaea Lamarck, 1818   White Pygmy Venus
                                                    Plate 38 j
    Florida and the West Indies.

¼ to ½ inch in length, elongate-oval in shape. Color white, variously flecked and spotted with brown; beaks commonly pink. Escutcheon with 4 or 5 brown, zebra-stripes. Sculpture cancellate. Lunule white. A common shallow-water species.

Subgenus *Lirophora* Conrad, 1862

Chione paphia Linné, 1767   King Venus
                                                    Plate 38 h
    Lower Florida Keys and West Indies.

Up to 1½ inches in length, thick and solid. Color white or cream, mottled and shaded with reddish brown. Interior white with suffusion of purplish pink. Surface sculptured with 10 to 12 large concentric ribs which are thin at their ends. Not nearly as common as *C. cancellata*.

Chione latilirata Conrad, 1841   Imperial Venus

    North Carolina to Brazil.

Similar to *C. paphia* but with only 5 to 7 large, bulbous, concentric ribs which are not thin or flattened at their ends. Dall and Simpson reported finding dead valves of this species at Mayagüez, Puerto Rico.

GENUS *Anomalocardia* Schumacher, 1817

Anomalocardia brasiliana Gmelin, 1791   West Indian Pointed Venus
Plate 38 g

West Indies to Brazil.

¾ to 1½ inches in length, heavy. Color yellowish white, variously shaded and spotted with purple or brown. Surface with concentric corrugations. Inner margins of values crenulated. Reasonably common in Puerto Rico.

Subfamily *MERETRICINAE*
GENUS *Transennella* Dall, 1883

Transennella conradina Dall, 1883   Conrad's Transennella
Plate 39 g

South half of Florida to the West Indies.

Up to ⅝ inch in length, glossy, roundly triangular in shape, smooth except for fine growth lines. Exterior white or cream with fine zigzag markings of pale-brown; usually purple at the posterior end. Three cardinal teeth in each valve; middle right tooth bifid. Left posterior lateral tooth present, with opposite socket in right valve. Pallial sinus oblique. Inner ventral margin with oblique groovings. Moderately common.

Transennella stimpsoni Dall, 1902   Stimpson's Transennella
Plate 39 a

Southeast U. S., the Bahamas, and Puerto Rico.

¼ to ½ inch in length, glossy, roundly triangular in shape. Exterior white or bluish with brown streaks and chevron markings; interior white to purple. Sculpture of fine concentric grooves. Pallial sinus extends to middle of valve; inner margin obliquely grooved. Moderately common.

Transennella cubaniana Orbigny, 1842   Cuban Transennella
Plate 39 d

Florida Keys and West Indies.

About ⅜ inch in length, trigonal in shape. Shell pure-white, rarely flecked with brown. Sculptured with fine impressed concentric lines. Inner margin obliquely grooved. Moderately common.

Transennella culebrana Dall and Simp., 1901 Puerto Rican Transennella
Plate 29 b

Puerto Rico.

About ⅜ inch in length, subtrigonal in outline, with obscure surface sculpture, and a rather thick, yellowish brown periostracum. Uncommon.

GENUS *Tivela* Link, 1807

Tivela mactroides Born, 1778   Trigonal Tivela
                                                                Plate 39 e
West Indies to Brazil.

About 1½ inches in height, solid, inflated, trigonal. Variously rayed
and clouded with brown. Surface smooth; beaks central and prominent.
Common all around Puerto Rico.

Tivela abaconis Dall, 1902   Abaco Tivela
                                                                Plate 39 h
Bahamas, Caribbean and Vera Cruz, Mexico.

About ½ inch in length, subquadrate, and moderately inflated. Subtranslucent, deep rose at the beak and in the interior, becoming paler
towards the margins. Surface polished. Beaks high, pointed, subcentral.
Rare in Puerto Rico.

Subfamily PITARINAE
GENUS *Pitar* Römer, 1857
Subgenus, *Pitar* Römer, 1857

Pitar aresta Dall and Simpson, 1901   West Indian Venus
                                                                Plate 39 m
West Indies.

About 2 inches in length, solid and inflated, inequilateral, rounded
in front and somewhat rostrate behind. Color white or grayish white.
Surface with numerous irregular growth lines which are most prominent
towards the margin of the valves. Umbones prominent and incurved.
First described from Puerto Rico. Uncommonly found on the west and
south coasts of Puerto Rico.

Pitar albida Gmelin, 1791   White Venus
                                                                Plate 39 n
West Indies.

1 to 2 inches in length, nearly elliptical, less inflated than *P. aresta*.
Anterior end a little narrowed and rounded; posterior end broadly
rounded. Color usually all-white. Lunule narrow and elongate. Uncommon.

Pitar fulminata Menke, 1828   Lightning Venus
                                                              Plate 4 h; 39 c
Southeast U. S. and the West Indies.

1 to 1½ inches in length, inflated. Color white with brown, usually
in the form of zigzag markings. Surface sculptured with numerous, concentric growth lines. Lunule very large and outlined by an impressed

line. A common shallow-water species found all around Puerto Rico. Gundlach reported this from San Juan as *Pitar hebraea* Lamarck, 1818.

Subgenus *Hysteroconcha* P. Fischer, 1887

Pitar dione Linné, 1758   Royal Comb Venus
Plate 39 k
Texas to Panamá and the West Indies.

1 to 1¾ inches in length, trigonal-ovate in shape. Color whitish purple. Surface covered with thin, sharp, concentric lamellae. Characterized by 2 radial rows of long spines at the posterior end of the valve. Reasonably common wherever found, but its distribution in Puerto Rico is limited to the east end.

Pitar circinata Born, 1778   Purple Venus
Plate 39 j
West Indies.

1 to 1¾ inches in length. Color varies from all-white, white clouded with purple, to purple. Similar to *P. dione* but lacking the spines on the posterior end of the valve. Periostracum light-brown and thin. A common shallow-water species in Puerto Rico.

Subfamily *CIRCINAE*
GENUS *Gouldia* C. B. Adams, 1847

Gouldia cerina C. B. Adams, 1845   Waxy Gould Clam
Plate 38 k
Southeast U. S. and the West Indies.

About ⅓ inch in length, trigonal in shape, slightly inflated. Color yellowish white, sometimes with brown markings on the dorsal area. Occasional specimens are tinted pink interiorly just under the umbones. Surface reticulate; the concentric lines are most prominent except at the ends of the valves where the radial lines are most prominent. Umbones small and central. A common species from shallow-water dredgings.

Gouldia insularis Dall and Simpson, 1901   Insular Gould Clam
Plate 29 a
Puerto Rico.

¼ inch or less. Similar to *G. cerina* but smaller, more rounded in outline, yellowish white. This species was first described from San Juan and Mayagüez, Puerto Rico. It is common in shallow dredgings. Listed as *Circe insularis* by Dall and Simpson.

GENUS *Macrocallista* Meek, 1876

Macrocallista maculata Linné, 1758   Calico Clam
Plate 39 f
Southeast U. S. and the West Indies.

1½ and 2½ inches in length, solid, ovate, glossy-smooth. Exterior cream with checkerboard markings of reddish brown. Periostracum thin, light straw in color. Reasonably common on the west coast of Puerto Rico.

Subfamily DOSINIINAE
GENUS *Dosinia* Scopoli, 1777
Subgenus *Dosinidia* Dall, 1902

Dosinia concentrica Born, 1778   Southern Dosinia
                                                                 Plate 39 i
    Cuba south to Brazil.

2 to 3 inches in length, subcircular, compressed. Color yellowish white, glossy. Sculptured with numerous, even, concentric ridges. Common. Specimens in perfect condition are often washed ashore after a heavy blow. This species is very similar to *D. elegans* Conrad, 1846 which, however, does not extend as far south as Puerto Rico.

Subfamily GEMMINAE
GENUS *Gemma* Deshayes, 1853

Gemma purpurea Lea, 1842   Amethyst Gem Clam
                                                                 Plate 39 o
    Eastern U. S., Puerto Rico.

⅛ inch in length, trigonal, moderately inflated. Color white, polished. Sculptured with numerous, fine concentric ridges. First collected in Puerto Rico by Dr. Raymond Cable in the tidal mud flats at Cabo Rojo Lighthouse where it is very common. Possibly introduced by migrating water fowl.

GENUS *Parastarte* Conrad, 1862

Parastarte triquetra Conrad, 1846   Brown Gem Clam
                                                                 Plate 39 - 1
    Florida to the West Indies.

⅛ inch in size, very similar to *Gemma,* but higher than long. Color tan to dark-brown. Surface highly polished, smooth except for irregular growth lines. Many were found living in the mud flats at Cabo Rojo Lighthouse. Possibly introduced by water fowl.

GENUS *Cyclinella* Dall, 1902

Cyclinella tenuis Récluz, 1852   Atlantic Cyclinella
                                                                 Plate 39 b
    Eastern U. S. and the West Indies.

1 to 2 inches in length, thin, almost circular in outline. Color dull-white. Resembling *Dosinia,* but is easily separated from it by the more ventrally located anterior muscle scar. Exteriorly, *Dosinia* is glossy and sculptured with concentric ridges. *Cyclinella* is not glossy and is sculptured with numerous irregular growth lines. Reasonably common from shallow dredgings on the west and south coasts of Puerto Rico.

Family PETRICOLIDAE
Subfamily PETRICOLINAE
GENUS *Petricola* Lamarck, 1801

Petricola lapicida Gmelin, 1791   Boring Petricola
                                                                                      Plate 44 e
South half of Florida and the West Indies.

½ to 1 inch in length, ovate, inflated. Color white. Sculpture consists of numerous, branching radial lines, and concentric growth lines forming a somewhat criss-cross pattern. Upon careful examination it will be seen that this is not sculpture on the true surface of the shell but is part of a calcareous coating which has been deposited on the shell. Common in coral rock.

GENUS *Rupellaria* Fleuriau, 1802

Rupellaria typica Jonas, 1844   Atlantic Rupellaria
                                                                                      Plate 44 b
Southeast U. S. and the West Indies.

About 1 inch in length, rounded in front and more or less compressed, attenuate and gaping posteriorly. Exterior grayish white; interior stained with buff or brown. Sculptured with numerous, irregularly-spaced, coarse radial ribs. A moderately common coral borer.

Subfamily COOPERELLINAE
GENUS *Cooperella* Carpenter, 1864

Cooperella atlantica Rehder, 1943   Atlantic Cooperella

Florida and Puerto Rico.

Less than ¼ inch in length, thin, inflated, broadly oval. Translucent whitish, smooth except for growth ridges. In the left valve there are 3 thin, divergent cardinal teeth, the central one bifid; in the right valve there are 2 thin divergent cardinals. No lateral teeth are present. Ligament external, rather short and broad, and located posterior to the umbones. Uncommon from shallow-water dredgings.

Superfamily *TELLINACEA*
Family *TELLINIDAE*
Genus *Tellina* Linné, 1758
Subgenus *Tellina* Linné, 1758

Tellina radiata Linné, 1758   Sunrise Tellin
                                                              Plate 4 i; 40 p
Southeast U. S. and the West Indies.

2 to 4 inches in length, elongate, smooth, highly polished. Color white, rayed with orange-red, or white and yellow. The interior is flushed with yellow, and the umbones are usually red. This strikingly beautiful species is relatively rare in Puerto Rico, except at Mona Island. It is quite common in the Virgin Islands. *T. unimaculata* Lamarck, 1818, is merely an all-white form.

Tellina laevigata Linné, 1758   Smooth Tellin
                                                             Plate 40 o
Southern Florida and the West Indies.

2 to 3 inches in length, oval in shape. Color whitish, faintly rayed or banded with yellow or orange. Surface smooth except for microscopic growth lines. Interior polished, white to yellow. This species has seldom been found in Puerto Rico, but it is relatively common in the Virgin Islands and other parts of the West Indies.

Subgenus *Tellinella* Mörch, 1853

Tellina listeri Röding, 1798   Speckled Tellin
                                                             Plate 4 j; 40 k
Southeast U. S. and the West Indies.

2 to 3½ inches in length, elongate and somewhat attenuate behind. Color whitish, variously flecked and rayed with brown or purplish brown. Interior yellowish. Surface covered with numerous, evenly-spaced concentric threads. Relatively uncommon in Puerto Rico, but common in the Virgin Islands. *T. interrupta* Wood, 1815, is a synonym.

Subgenus *Scissula* Dall, 1900

Tellina similis Sowerby, 1806   Candy Stick Tellin
                                                             Plate 40 n
Florida and the West Indies.

About 1 inch in length, rectangular in shape, compressed, strong. Opaque-white, commonly tinted with yellow. Easily recognized by the fine, concentric threads which cross the growth lines at an oblique angle. Double valves are sometimes washed ashore after storms.

Tellina caribaea Orbigny, 1842   Caribbean Tellin
Plate 40 m

West Indies.

About 1 inch in length, elongate, moderately inflated, thin, glossy. White, pink, or tinted with yellowish orange. Minutely sculptured with low concentric growth lines and fine oblique grooves which cross the concentric sculpture at an angle. Reasonably common in Puerto Rico.

Tellina candeana Orbigny, 1842   Wedge Tellin
Plate 40 j

Florida, Bermuda and the West Indies.

About 5/16 inch in length, strong, shiny, resembling *similis,* but smaller, more truncate posteriorly, with weaker oblique sculpturing on the posterior slopes. Uncommon from shallow dredgings.

Tellina exilis Lamarck, 1818   Pink Thin Tellin
Plate 40 g

Bermuda and the West Indies.

½ to ¾ inch in length, all-pink, thin-shelled, translucent. Oblique sculpture present. On the interior of the valves there are 2 radial thickenings or weak, white internal ribs at the posterior end. This species is very close to *Tellina iris* Say found from North Carolina to Florida, but *exilis* has a longer pallial sinus which touches, or nearly touches, the anterior adductor scar. Uncommon from shallow dredgings.

Subgenus *Angulus* Mühlfeld, 1811

Tellina mera Say, 1834   Mera Tellin
Plate 40 c

Florida, the Bahamas and Puerto Rico.

½ to ¾ inch in length, rounded anteriorly and bluntly angular in back. Glossy white. Smoothish, with fine, irregular concentric lines of growth most evident near the margins. A moderately common shallow-water species. This species is closely related to *T. promera* Dall, 1900, also reported from this area; *promera* may be only a subspecies of *mera.*

Tellina sybaritica Dall, 1881   Dall's Dwarf Tellin
Plate 40 e

Southeast U. S., the Gulf of Mexico and the West Indies.

¼ to ⅓ inch in length, elongate, rounded anteriorly, somewhat truncate at the lower posterior end. Color white to crimson. Surface with numerous concentric lines. Right valve with 2 strong lateral teeth. A common shallow-water species.

Tellina consobrina Orbigny, 1842   Consobrine Tellin

West Indies.

Dall and Simpson report several valves of this species from Mayagüez, Puerto Rico.

Tellina pauperata Orbigny, 1842   White Dwarf Tellin

Tampa Bay, Florida to the West Indies.

Less than ½ inch in length, anterior border long and straight, posterior short and truncate. Color white, polished. Surface with fine concentric striations or nearly smooth. Uncommon from shallow-water dredgings.

Tellina vitrea Orbigny, 1842   Glassy Tellin

West Indies.

About 1¼ inches in length, rounded in front, truncate behind; thin, glassy, polished. Color white, often tinted with yellow and deep-pink within. Dall and Simpson reported this species from Mayagüez and Boqueron, Puerto Rico.

Subgenus Scrobiculina Dall, 1900

Tellina magna Spengler, 1798   Great Tellin

Southeast U. S. and the West Indies.

3 to 4½ inches in length, compressed and glossy-smooth. Left valve glossy white, rarely yellowish; right valve glossy orange to pinkish. Lois and Ted Arnow found this beautiful species at Playa de Vega Baja on the north coast of Puerto Rico. Rare.

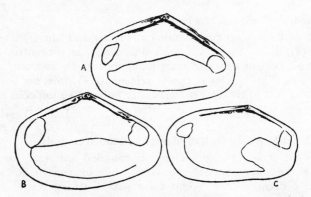

TEXT FIG. 29. Tellinidae showing hinge and pallial sinus scars. a, *Tellina alternata* Say, pallial sinus does not touch the anterior muscle scar; b, *Tellina punicea* Born, pallial sinus just touches the anterior muscle scar; c, *Macoma tageliformis* Dall, no lateral teeth.

Subgenus *Eurytellina* P. Fischer, 1887

Tellina alternata Say, 1822   Alternate Tellin
Plate 40 h

Southeast U. S., the Gulf States and the West Indies.

2 to 3 inches in length, elongate and compressed. Glossy-white flushed with pink and some yellow. Surface with distinct and regular concentric sculpture. A common shallow-water species found all around Puerto Rico. (See text fig. 29a).

Tellina lineata Turton, 1819   Rose Petal Tellin
Plate 40 - 1

Florida and the West Indies.

1 to 1½ inches in length, moderately elongate, solid, with a fairly strong twist to the right at the posterior end. Color all-white or flushed with pink. There is an all-pink form, but it has not been found in Puerto Rico. Surface glossy, iridescent, with numerous minute concentric striae. Uncommon.

Tellina punicea Born, 1778   Watermelon Tellin
Plate 4 g; 40 d

Florida Keys and the West Indies.

1 to 2¼ inches in length, elongate, and compressed. Similar to *T. alternata* but bright watermelon-red or purplish red inside and outside. Can easily be separated from *alternata* and *angulosa* because in *punicea* the pallial sinus just touches the anterior muscle scar, which it does not in the other two species. (See text fig. 29 b). A very common shallow-water species.

Tellina georgiana Dall, 1900   Georgia Tellin
Plate 40 a

Southeast U. S. to the West Indies.

Up to 1 inch in length, elongate, and compressed. Reddish orange, shiny. Surface covered with fine concentric sculpture. Resembling *T. alternata* and *T. punicea*, but can be separated from them by its color and smaller size. Also, in the right valve of *georgiana*, the strong anterior lateral tooth is some distance from the cardinals. The pallial sinus nearly touches the anterior muscle scar. Uncommon in Puerto Rico.

Tellina persica Dall and Simpson, 1901   Puerto Rican Tellin
Plate 29 g

Puerto Rico.

About ¾ inch in length, ½ inch in height, compressed. White, suffused with apricot-yellow, paler on the umbones. Surface sculptured by numerous, narrow, rounded concentric ridges. Interior brilliantly polished. Pallial sinus free from the pallial line below, except for a very short distance. Dredged from 20 to 30 fathoms, sand bottom. Rare.

Tellina vespusiana Orbigny, 1842   Vesper Tellin

West Indies.

Less than ½ inch in length, elongate, and has a flexure of the posterior end of the valves. Surface with fine concentric lines; color pinkish or red, lighter at the beaks. Dall and Simpson reported finding one valve of this species at Mayagüez, Puerto Rico.

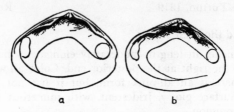

TEXT FIG. 30. Small Tellinas, showing interior scars. a, *Tellina aequistriata* Say, the sinus is wholly confluent below; b, *Tellina martinicensis* Orbigny, the sinus is only partly confluent below.

Subgenus *Merisca* Dall, 1900

Tellina cristallina Spengler, 1798   Crystal Tellin
                                                                Plate 40 b
South Carolina to the West Indies.

About 1 inch in length; thin, transparent; color white. Sculptured with conspicuous, widely spaced concentric ridges. Posterior end forming a projection beyond the margin. This last characteristic makes it easy to identify. Uncommon. This is *crystallina* Wood, 1815 and *schrammi* Récluz, 1853.

Tellina aequistriata Say, 1824   Striated Tellin
                                                                Plate 40 f
Southeast U. S. to northern Brazil.

⅜ to ¾ inch in length, rostrate behind, dull-white in color. The surface is marked with pronounced concentric sculpturing. The pallial sinus nearly reaches the anterior adductor and is wholly confluent below. (See text fig. 30 a). Reasonably common from shallow dredgings.

Tellina martinicensis Orbigny, 1842   Martinique Tellin
                                                                Plate 40 i
Florida and the West Indies.

About ⅜ inch in length. This species is similar in shape, color, and sculpture to *T. aequistriata* but is more inflated, with more conspicuous umbones. The umbonal region is smoothish. The sinus is only partly confluent below and free from adductor scar. (See text fig. 30 b). Reasonably common from shallow dredgings.

GENUS *Arcopagia* Brown, 1827

Arcopagia fausta Pulteney, 1799   Faust Tellin
                                                          Plate 41 - 1
Southeast U. S. and the West Indies.

2 to 4 inches in length, roundish oval in shape. Moderately inflated, heavy. Color whitish on the outside; inside glossy-white with a yellow flush. In young specimens the yellow shows through to the outside. Surface smooth except for irregular, concentric growth lines. The thin yellow-brown periostracum usually peels off. Ligament strong. A moderately common species all around Puerto Rico.

GENUS *Strigilla* Turton, 1822

Strigilla carnaria Linné, 1758   Large Strigilla
                                                        Plate 41 d; 29 f
Southeast U. S. to the Caribbean.

¾ to 1 inch in length, roundish oval, moderately compressed. Color deep-pink inside and outside; some specimens are pinkish white on the outside and the deep-pink inside. Surface sculptured by oblique radial lines in the central and posterior regions of the valves; at the anterior region the oblique lines are wavy and run in the opposite direction. A very common species found all around Puerto Rico.

Strigilla rombergi Mörch, 1853   Romberg's Strigilla
                                                           Plate 29 d
Southeast Florida, the Bahamas to Lesser Antilles.

Very similar to *carnaria,* but in this species the pallial sinus does not reach the anterior adductor muscle. In *carnaria* the upper border of the pallial sinus is joined to the anterior adductor scar. Uncommon. Reported by Dall and Simpson from San Juan, Puerto Rico.

Strigilla pisiformis Linné, 1758   Pea Strigilla
                                                           Plate 41 e
Florida Keys, the Bahamas and the West Indies.

⅓ to ½ inch in length, similar to *S. carnaria* but smaller and more inflated. White with pink umbones. Only the deepest part of the inside of the shell is colored pink, whereas in *carnaria* the entire inside is pink. A common species all around Puerto Rico.

Strigilla mirabilis Philippi, 1841   White Strigilla

Southeast U. S., Texas and the West Indies.

⅓ inch in length, oval, inflated, similar to *S. pisiformis* but all-white. The pallial line from the posterior muscle scar does not reach the anterior muscle scar as it does in *pisiformis*. Sometimes listed as *Strigilla flexuosa* Say. Uncommon in Puerto Rico.

GENUS *Quadrans* Bertin, 1878

Quadrans lintea Conrad, 1837   Lintea Tellin
                                                                    Plate 41 j
Southeast U. S. and the West Indies.

Two worn valves of this species were reported from Mayagüez by Dall and Simpson. It closely resembles *Tellina aequistriata*, but is larger and not as densely sculptured. Uncommonly dredged from shallow water.

GENUS *Macoma* Leach, 1819

Macoma constricta Bruguière, 1792   Constricted Macoma
                                                                    Plate 41 k
Florida to Texas and the West Indies.

1 to 2½ inches in length. Dull-white covered with a thin, gray periostracum. Sculptured with fine concentric growth lines. Anterior and ventral margins rounded; posterior end twisted slightly to the right. Single valves are reasonably common on the beaches all around Puerto Rico. The Macomas have the appearance of Tellins but lack lateral teeth.

Macoma tageliformis Dall, 1900   Tagelus-like Macoma
                                                                    Plate 41 i
West Indies.

1 to 2 inches in length, oblong. It resembles *M. brevifrons* but differs in being heavier, higher, less attenuate behind, and in having a stronger truncation. Color dull-white; fresh specimens have a thin, brown periostracum which is most noticeable near the margins. Common around Mayagüez, Puerto Rico. (See text fig. 29 c).

Macoma pseudomera Dall and Simpson, 1901   Puerto Rico Macoma
                                                                    Plate 41 f; 29 h
Puerto Rico.

½ to ¾ inch in length, heavy, moderately inflated. All-white. Characterized by its small size, heaviness, and the short, truncate posterior end. The pallial sinus is short and scarcely confluent with the pallial line below. Reasonably common from shallow dredgings.

Macoma tenta Say, 1834 Tenta Macoma
Plate 41 c

Cape Cod to Florida and the West Indies.

½ to 1 inch in length, fragile, elongate, smooth. White with a delicate iridescence; this latter character helps to separate it from the other Macomas. Obtained from shallow dredgings in mud bottoms. *M. souleyetiana* Récluz is this species.

Macoma aurora Hanley, 1844 Hanley's Macoma
Plate 41 a

Florida to Brazil.

½ to ¾ inch in length, smooth and polished. The posterior end of the shell is rather short. Color white with a characteristic orange flush. Obtained from shallow dredgings; not common.

Macoma brevifrons Say, 1834 Short Macoma
Plate 41 h

New Jersey south to Brazil.

About 1½ inches in length, oblong, polished. Color white with a characteristic orange flush on the umbones; this region is also iridescent. Below the smooth umbones the shell has numerous close-set growth lines, covered by a light-brown periostracum. The anterior end is short and rounded; the posterior end is truncate. Sparsely distributed all around Puerto Rico.

Subgenus *Cymatoica* Dall, 1889

Macoma orientalis hendersoni Rehder, 1939 Atlantic Undulated Macoma
Plate 41 b

Florida south to Puerto Rico.

¼ to ⅜ inches in length, rather thin, fragile. Dull-white in color. Surface sculptured with concentric undulations. The posterior end is rostrate and slightly up-turned. The characteristic shape and sculpture make it easy to separate this species from all others. Reasonably common from shallow dredgings on the south and west coasts of Puerto Rico.

GENUS *Apolymetis* Salisbury, 1929

Apolymetis intastriata Say, 1826 Atlantic Grooved Macoma
Plate 41 g

South half of Florida and the Caribbean.

2 to 3 inches in length, irregular in shape, rounded or subquadrate, thin. Color white. Easily recognized by the strong radial rib at the posterior end of the right valve; the left valve has a radial groove at that

end. Dead shells are commonly washed ashore, especially around Cabo Rojo lighthouse area of Puerto Rico.

Family SEMELIDAE
GENUS *Semele* Schumacher, 1817

Semele proficua Pulteney, 1794   White Atlantic Semele
Plate 42 e
Southeast U. S. and the West Indies.

½ to 1½ inches in length, rounded in outline. Color yellowish white exteriorly; interior glossy, usually yellow, sometimes speckled with purple or brown. The surface bears concentric lines and microscopic radial striations. A shallow-water species, reasonably common all around Puerto Rico. A color form, *radiata* Say, has a few pink, radial rays.

Semele purpurascens Gmelin, 1791   Purplish Semele
Plate 42 c
Southeast U. S. and the West Indies.

1 to 1½ inches in length, oblong. Color orange or purplish, heavily speckled with these colors. The surface is smooth, except for fine concentric growth lines and microscopic oblique lines. A reasonably common shallow-water species in Puerto Rico.

Semele bellastriata Conrad, 1837   Cancellate Semele
Plate 42 a
Southeast U. S. and the West Indies.

½ to ¾ inch in length, oblong. Color yellowish white with reddish flecks. Its strongly cancellate surface makes it easy to separate from the other species. Mayagüez and vicinity is the only location where we have found this species in Puerto Rico. Reasonably common in shallow dredgings.

Semele nuculoides Conrad, 1841   Tiny Semele
Plate 42 b
Southeast U. S. and the West Indies.

About ¼ inch in length, oblong, beaks near the anterior end. Color usually white, occasionally yellow or orange. Surface sculptured with fine, regular concentric lines. A common shallow-water species found all around Puerto Rico.

GENUS *Cumingia* Sowerby, 1833

Cumingia antillarum Orbigny, 1842   Southern Cumingia
Text fig. 31 c, d
Lower Florida Keys and the West Indies.

¼ to ½ inch in length, irregular in outline, fairly thin. Color grayish white. Surface sculptured with strong concentric threads and microscopic radial threads between them. The spoon-shaped pit below the beaks in each valve and the elongate lateral teeth help to identify this species. We have found specimens embedded at the base of sea fans and in coral. *C. coarctata* Sowerby, 1833, is an Eastern Pacific species.

GENUS *Abra* Lamarck, 1818

Abra aequalis Say, 1822   Common Atlantic Abra
Plate 42 i

Southeast U. S., Texas and the West Indies.

¼ inch in size, rounded. Color all-white; smooth, glossy. Anterior margin of right valve grooved. A common shallow-water species in Puerto Rico.

Abra lioica Dall, 1881   Dall's Little Abra

Eastern U. S. and the West Indies.

¼ inch in size, similar to *aequalis,* but the beaks are nearer the anterior end, the shell is thinner, transparent, and more elongate. Anterior margin of right valve not grooved. A common shallow-water species in Puerto Rico.

Abra longicallis americana Verrill and Bush, 1898   Elongate Abra

Arctic Ocean to West Indies (deep water) .

Can be separated from the other two species by its large size (about 1 inch) and its elongate, subtriangular shape. It is smoothish, shining, straw-colored. Reported from Mayagüez by Dall and Simpson.

Family DONACIDAE
GENUS *Donax* Linné, 1758

Donax denticulatus Linné, 1758   Common Caribbean Donax
Plate 4-1; 42 d

Caribbean.

About 1 inch in length, wedge-shaped. The zigzag lines on the posterior slope of each valve make it easy to separate this common, colorful species from the other two *Donax.* The surface is radially grooved; these grooves are minutely pin-pointed. This species lives in the sand and can easily be obtained between tides. It is delicious in chowder or served with rice.

Donax tumidus Philippi, 1849   Fat Little Donax
Plate 42 f

Gulf of Mexico to West Indies.

⅓ to ½ inch in length. The small size and the heavily beaded radial threads on the posterior slope are characteristic of this species. Uncommon.

Donax striatus Linné, 1767   Striate Donax
Plate 42 h

West Indies.

About 1 inch in length. The flat to slightly concave posterior slope bears numerous, fine radial threads. Uncommon in Puerto Rico.

GENUS *Iphigenia* Schumacher, 1817

Iphigenia brasiliensis Lamarck, 1818   Giant False Donax
Plate 42 m

South half of Florida and the West Indies.

2 to 2½ inches in length, rather solid, almost triangular in shape. Color cream, with the beak area stained purple or occasionally orange. Periostracum thin, glossy, brown. Surface smooth except for irregular growth lines. A moderately common shallow-water species in Puerto Rico.

Family SANGUINOLARIIDAE
GENUS *Sanguinolaria* Lamarck, 1799

Sanguinolaria cruenta Solander, 1786   Atlantic Sanguin
Plate 4 k; 42 g

South Florida, the Gulf States and the West Indies.

1½ to 2 inches in length, slightly inflated, thin, ovate and somewhat attenuate posteriorly. Color white, flushed with pink on the umbones and the upper part of the shell. Previously listed as *Sanguinolaria sanguinolenta* Gmelin, 1791. It is uncommon in Puerto Rico.

GENUS *Asaphis* Modeer, 1793

Asaphis deflorata Linné, 1758   Gaudy Asaphis
Plate 42 k

Southeast Florida and the West Indies.

1½ to 2½ inches in length, inflated. Color yellowish white stained or rayed with rose or purple. Surface sculptured with numerous, coarse radial threads. Reasonably common on the south coast of Puerto Rico.

GENUS *Tagelus* Gray, 1847

Tagelus divisus Spengler, 1794   Purplish Tagelus
Plate 42 - l

Eastern U. S., the Gulf States and the Caribbean.

1 to 1½ inches in length, elongate, fragile, smooth. Color whitish purple with a prominent purple radial streak. The thin, glossy, brown periostracum covers most of the shell. The weak internal median rib under the umbones helps to identify this species. A reasonably common shallow-water species in Puerto Rico.

Tagelus plebeius Solander, 1786   Stout Tagelus
Plate 42 n

Cape Cod to Florida and the West Indies.

2 to 3⅓ inches in length, elongate, rather inflated. Color white. Surface sculptured with small, irregular concentric growth lines. Compared to *T. divisus,* this species is larger, heavier, and lacks the internal ribs. Previously listed as *T. gibbus* Spengler. Found all around Puerto Rico in shallow areas.

GENUS *Heterodonax* Mörch, 1853

Heterodonax bimaculatus Linné, 1758   Small False Donax
Plate 42 j

South half of Florida and the West Indies.

½ to 1 inch in length, oval and truncate anteriorly. Color most variable: white, yellow, orange, red, purple, or flecked or rayed with any combination of these. Exterior smooth, except for fine growth lines. Reasonably common on the south coast of Puerto Rico.

Suborder *ADAPEDONTA*
Superfamily *SOLENACEA*
Family *SOLENIDAE*
GENUS *Solen* Linné, 1758

Solen obliquus Spengler, 1794   Antillean Jackknife Clam
Plate 43 i

West Indies.

4 to 6 inches in length, elongate, with the dorsal and ventral margins parallel. Umbones anterior. Color dull-white, faintly rayed with light-brown, covered with a pronounced brown periostracum. One cardinal tooth in each valve. Double valves are common on the beaches around Mayagüez, Puerto Rico.

GENUS *Solecurtus* Blainville, 1825

Solecurtus cumingianus Dunker, 1861   Corrugated Razor Clam
Plate 43 h

Southeast U. S. and the West Indies.

1 to 2 inches in length, gaping at both ends. Color all-white, with a dull, yellowish-brown periostracum. Surface sculptured with coarse, concentric growth lines crossed by oblique, wavy threads. Uncommon.

Solecurtus sanctaemarthae Orbigny, 1842   St. Martha's Razor Clam
Plate 43 f
    Southeast U. S. and the West Indies.

    Similar to *S. cumingianus,* but smaller, fatter and having stronger sculpture. Uncommon.

Superfamily MACTRACEA
Family MACTRIDAE
GENUS *Mactra* Linné, 1767

Mactra alata Spengler, 1802   Winged Mactra
Plate 43 k
    Caribbean to Brazil.

    2 to 4 inches in length, ovate-trigonal in outline, moderately thin and inflated. Color white, usually covered with a thin, flaky, yellowish periostracum. Posterior slope flattened, with a distinctly elevated ridge. Moderately common all around Puerto Rico.

Mactra fragilis Gmelin, 1791   Fragile Atlantic Mactra
Plate 43 g
    Southeast U. S., Texas and the West Indies.

    2 to 3 inches in length, oval, moderately thin, flattened. Color white and usually covered by a thin, grayish brown periostracum. Posterior slope rounded, with 2 radial lines, one of which is very close to the dorsal margin of the valve. Moderately common in Puerto Rico.

GENUS *Mulinia* Gray, 1837

Mulinia portoricensis Shuttleworth, 1856   Puerto Rican Surf Clam
Plate 43 d
    Puerto Rico.

    1 to 1½ inches in length, trigonal, with prominent central beaks. Color white or cream, sometimes stained orange; covered by a fairly thick, brown periostracum. Surface smooth, except for irregular growth wrinkles. Reasonably common in shallow dredgings.

GENUS *Labiosa* Möller, 1832

Labiosa. anatina Spengler, 1802   Smooth Duck Clam
Plate 43 j
    Eastern U. S. and Puerto Rico.

    2 to 3 inches in length, ¾ as high, fairly thin but strong. White to tan in color. Moderately smooth, except for irregular growth lines. Posterior end with a distinct radial rib. Shell gapes with flaring edges. Uncommon in Puerto Rico. Formerly *lineata* Say, 1822.

Family MESODESMATIDAE
GENUS *Ervilia* Turton, 1822

Ervilia nitens Montagu, 1806   Common Ervilia
                                                  Plate 43 b

Southeast U. S. and the West Indies.

About ¼ inch in length, smoothly oval. Color white, usually shaded with pink. Sculptured with numerous, fine concentric ridges. When present, the radial threads are strongest on the ends of the valves. Common just offshore and in shallow dredgings.

Ervilia concentrica Gould, 1862   Concentric Ervilia

Southeast U. S. to the West Indies.

Similar to *E. nitens,* but smaller and with more prominent umbones. Reported from San Juan and Mayagüez by Dall and Simpson.

Ervilia rostratula Rehder, 1943   Rostrate Ervilia

Florida and the West Indies.

About 3/16 inch, stout, subtrigonal, rather inflated, white or yellowish; posterior end slightly rostrate; sculpture consisting of strong concentric riblets, crossed posteriorly by fine radial lines. Rare in Puerto Rico.

Family HIATELLIDAE
GENUS *Saxicavella* Fischer, 1870

Saxicavella sagrinata Dall and Simpson, 1901   Puerto Rican Saxicavella
                                                  Text fig. 31 f

Puerto Rico.

About ¼ inch, rounded-triangular, compressed, fragile. The surface is irregularly, concentrically undulated and is minutely granular. Shell substance translucent; interior polished. This species was described from a specimen found in 30 fathoms off Mayagüez, Puerto Rico. Our specimens were dredged from 5 to 15 fathoms. Uncommon.

Superfamily MYACEA
Family MYACIDAE
GENUS *Sphenia* Turton, 1822

Sphenia antillensis Dall and Simpson, 1901   Antillean Sphenia
                                                  Plate 43 e

Puerto Rico.

⅛ to ¼ inch in length, subquadrate, thin, irregular in shape. Inequilateral, right valve a little larger than the left. There is a single small tooth in front of the resilium pit. All-white, covered with a yellowish periostracum. Surface dull, sculptured with concentric growth lines. Reasonably common from shallow dredgings on the west and south coasts of Puerto Rico.

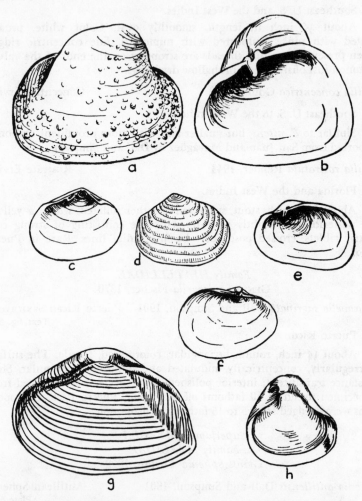

TEXT FIG. 31. Miscellaneous Small Clams. a and b, *Basterotia quadrata granatina* Dall; c and d, *Cumingia antillarum* Orbigny, e, *Basterotia elliptica* Recluz; f, *Saxicavella sagrinata* Dall and Simpson; g, *Corbula aequivalvis* Philippi; h, *Notocorbula operculata* Philippi.

Family *CORBULIDAE*
Genus *Notocorbula* Iredale, 1930

Notocorbula operculata Philippi, 1848   Oval Corbula
Text fig. 31 h

Southeast U. S., Gulf of Mexico and the West Indies.

Usually less than ¼ inch in length, almost as high. Glossy-white, sometimes tinted with rose. The absence of a distinct umbonal ridge makes it easy to separate this species from the others in this group. This is *Corbula disparilis* Orbigny. Live specimens are relatively common from shallow dredgings. The genus *Varicorbula* Grant and Gale, 1931, is a synonym of *Notocorbula*.

Genus *Corbula* Bruguière, 1792

Corbula aequivalvis Philippi, 1836   Equal-valved Corbula
Text fig. 31 g

West Indies.

Up to ½ inch in length, nearly equilateral and equivalve, with a strong, sharp posterior ridge. Color whitish. Surface sculptured with strong, regular, rounded concentric ridges. Single valves are reasonably common on the beach and in shallow dredgings.

Corbula caribaea Orbigny, 1842   Caribbean Corbula
Plate 43 c

Eastern U. S. and the West Indies.

½ to ⅝ inch in length, solid and greatly inflated when fully adult. Subtriangular, drawn out into a decided point behind. The right valve encloses the left, and throughout its posterior portion it projects widely over the left. Color whitish; surface sculptured with rather strong, irregular concentric ridges. Very common from shallow sandy-mud dredgings. For the present we are following McLean's arrangement by including *Corbula swiftiana* C. B. Adams as a synonym of *C. caribaea*.

Corbula contracta Say, 1822   Contracted Corbula
Plate 43 a

Eastern U. S. and the West Indies.

¼ to ½ inch in length, anterior border short and rounded; posterior extremity rostrate. The posterior ventral margin of the right valve overlaps the left. Color white. Surface with numerous concentric ridges. The left valve has a V-shaped notch in the hinge just anterior to the beak. A common shallow-water species.

Corbula dietziana C. B. Adams, 1852   Dietz's Corbula

Southeast U. S. to the West Indies.

Reported from Mayagüez by Dall and Simpson. May be separated from *C. contracta* by its distorted shape and the presence of bright-red coloring. The inside of the valves is pinkish; the ventral margins are rayed with carmine-rose.

Family GASTROCHAENIDAE
GENUS *Gastrochaena* Spengler, 1783

Gastrochaena hians Gmelin, 1791   Atlantic Gastrochaena
Plate 44 k

North Carolina to Texas and the West Indies.

½ to ¾ inch in length, thin, chalky in substance. Valves rather spathulate, with low, fine concentric ridges. Posterior end large and rounded. The entire anterior-ventral end is widely open to accommodate the foot. Found in soft, coral rocks, sometimes at the base of seafans. Listed as *Gastrochaena cuneiformis* Spengler by Dall and Simpson.

GENUS *Spengleria* Tryon, 1861

Spengleria rostrata Spengler, 1793   Spengler Clam
Plate 44 g

Southeast Florida and the West Indies.

About one inch in length, elongate, truncate at the posterior end. The elevated, triangular, lamellose area which radiates from the beaks to the posterior end is very characteristic of this species. This coral borer is uncommon in Puerto Rico.

Superfamily ADESMACEA
Family PHOLADIDAE
GENUS *Cyrtopleura* Tryon, 1862

Cyrtopleura costata Linné, 1758   Angel Wing
Plate 44 m

Eastern U. S., Texas, and the West Indies.

4 to 8 inches in length, moderately fragile, chalky-white. Surface sculptured with about 30 strong, beaded or scaly radial ribs. Easily recognized by its size and form. Found living in mud. The fishermen have been seen digging for these at low tide on the mud flats at Guayanilla on the south coast of Puerto Rico. We also have specimens from Guanica (Mrs. Oliver) and Mayagüez, but it does not appear to be very common.

GENUS *Barnea* Risso, 1826
Subgenus *Anchomasa* Leach, 1852

Barnea truncata Say, 1822   Fallen Angel Wing

Maine to Brazil.

2 to 2½ inches in length, fragile, whitish in color. It resembles the Angel Wing, *C. costata,* but is widely gaping at both ends, truncate at the posterior end, and with an elongate, narrow accessory plate over the beak area. The internal condyle is long and thin. This species bores into clay, soft rock, or wood. Donald Arnow found several valves of this species at Boca de Cangrejos, on the northeast coast of Puerto Rico.

GENUS *Martesia* Blainville, 1824

Martesia cuneiformis Say, 1822   Wedge-shaped Martesia
                                                   Plate 44 - 1

Southeast U. S., Texas, and the West Indies.

½ to ¾ inch in length, similar to *striata,* but smaller and fatter. The calcareous plate in this species is shaped like the head of a spear. A common wood-boring species.

Martesia striata Linné, 1767   Striate Martesia
                                                     Plate 44 j

West Florida to Texas and the West Indies.

¾ to 1¼ inches in length, elongate, moderately fragile, gaping at the posterior end, and whitish in color. It is separated from *M. cuneiformis* by its larger size and by the broadly rounded, somewhat heart-shaped, calcareous plate over the umbones. Commonly found boring in wood.

Family TEREDINIDAE

This is the family of shipworms which is very common in the West Indies and which is of great economic importance. A full and technical account of *Bankia* is given by Clench and Turner in Johnsonia (1946). The following are the species reported from this area by McLean (1951) : *Teredo dominicensis* Bartsch, 1921 (St. Thomas, Virgin Islands). *Teredo thomsoni* Tryon, 1863 (St. Thomas, Virgin Islands). *Bankia gouldi* Bartsch, 1908 (San Juan, Puerto Rico). *Bankia caribbea* Clench and Turner, 1946 (Fajardo, Puerto Rico). *Bankia fimbriatula* Moll and Roch, 1931 (San Juan, Puerto Rico).

Suborder *ANOMALODESMACEA*
Superfamily *PANDORACEA*
Family *LYONSIIDAE*
GENUS *Lyonsia* Turton, 1822

Lyonsia beana Orbigny, 1842   Pearly Lyonsia
                                                     Plate 44 c

Southeast U. S. and the West Indies.

½ to 1¼ inches in length, irregular in shape, inequilateral, gaping both anteriorly and posteriorly. Shell pearly inside and outside, covered by a thin periostracum. Umbones anterior, small, and close together. This species has been found living with sponges. We have also found it on the byssus of *Pinctada radiata*. Reasonably common.

Lyonsia hyalina floridana Conrad, 1849   Florida Glassy Lyonsia
Plate 44 f

Florida to Texas and to Puerto Rico.

¼ to ½ inch in length, thin and fragile, semitranslucent. Periostracum very thin, with numerous raised radial lines and marginal folds. Umbones small and pointing; hinge without teeth. Uncommon from shallow dredgings.

Family PANDORIDAE
GENUS *Pandora* Chemnitz, 1795

Pandora bushiana Dall, 1886   Southern Pandora
Plate 44 a

Florida to the West Indies.

About ½ inch in length, compressed, inequivalve. Smooth except for growth lines. Shiny-white exteriorly with pearly interior. Right valve flat; left valve convex. Short and rounded anteriorly, prolonged posteriorly. Umbones minute and inconspicuous. Reasonably common from shallow dredgings.

Family THRACIIDAE
GENUS *Cyathodonta* Conrad, 1849

Cyathodonta semirugosa Reeve, 1859   Wavy Caribbean Thracia
Plate 44 h

Puerto Rico and the lower Caribbean.

¾ to 1 inch in length, subovate, very thin and fragile, white. Sculptured with concentric undulations. Posterior end gapes with flaring edges. Obtained from shallow dredgings in mud bottoms. Not common.

Order SEPTIBRANCHIA
Family VERTICORDIIDAE
GENUS *Verticordia* Sowerby, 1844
Subgenus *Trigonulina* Orbigny, 1846

Verticordia ornata Orbigny, 1842   Ornate Verticord
Plate 44 i

Eastern U. S. and the West Indies.

¼ inch in length, oval to round, compressed and with about a dozen strong, sharp, curved radial ribs which extend beyond the margin.

Exterior dull-white and finely beaded; interior pearly. Uncommon from shallow dredgings.

Family *CUSPIDARIIDAE*
Genus *Cardiomya* A. Adams, 1864

Cardiomya perrostrata Dall, 1881   West Indian Cuspidaria
                                                              Plate 44 d

West Indies.

¼ to ⅜ inch in length, with a long, narrow rostrum. Sculptured with about 20 radial ribs which alternate in size, every other one being slightly larger than the intervening one. This beautiful little bivalve is reasonably common from shallow dredgings.

Cardiomya ornatissima Orbigny, 1842   Ornate Cuspidaria

Southeast U. S. to the West Indies.

Similar to *C. perrostrata* but has seven to nine prominent radial ribs with broad interspaces. Reasonably common.

Cardiomya costellata Deshayes, 1837   Ribbed Cuspidaria

Southeast U. S. to the West Indies.

Reported from Mayagüez in 30 fathoms by Dall and Simpson. Rare.

CHAPTER VI

Squids,
Chitons and Tusk Shells

Class *CEPHALOPODA*

Subclass *COLEOIDEA*
Order *DECAPODA*
Family *SPIRULIDAE*
GENUS *Spirula* Lamarck, 1799

Spirula spirula Linné, 1758

Common Spirula
Plate 42 b

Worldwide.

About 1 inch in diameter, coiled in a flat spiral. Shell white, fragile. Interior of shell chambered; each small chamber is divided from the other by a concave, nacreous-white septum. There is a small siphonal tube running back into the shell and piercing the septa. This species has a worldwide distribution in warm seas. Many shells are cast up on the beaches in Puerto Rico. The squid-like animal lives at great depths, but the dead shell floats to the surface.

Class *AMPHINEURA*

Order *LEPIDOPLEURIDA*
Family *LEPIDOPLEURIDAE*
GENUS *Lepidopleurus* Risso, 1826

Lepidopleurus pergranatus Dall, 1889

Granular Chiton

Puerto Rico and Dominica.

About ½ inch in length, elongated, slightly elevated, without a jugum. Entire shell waxen or white. The whole surface of the shell is covered with close, granular sculpture. Girdle wide, covered with delicate scales. This species was not found in the present study, but it is being included since it was reported by Dall and Simpson off San Juan, Puerto Rico, in 138 fathoms.

Order CHITONIDA
Family LEPIDOCHITONIDAE
GENUS *Lepidochitona* Gray, 1821

Lepidochitona liozonis Dall and Simp., 1901   Puerto Rican Red Chiton

Puerto Rico.

About 10 mm. in length, and about 7 mm. in width. Colored dark-red, flecked with gray. Surface of valves nearly smooth, minutely granulose. Girdle naked, leathery, brown. First described from Culebra Island, Puerto Rico. Rare.

Family MOPALIIDAE
GENUS *Ceratozona* Dall, 1882

Ceratozona squalida C. B. Adams, 1845   Rough Girdle Chiton
                                                     Text fig. 33 c

Southeast Florida to the West Indies.

1 to 2 inches in length. Surface commonly eroded, gray with blue-green mottling. Surface roughly sculptured. Girdle leathery, yellowish brown, with numerous spines. When the animal is alive, the foot is bright orange. Interior of valves bluish green. Reasonably common on rocky shores. This was listed as *Ceratozona rugosa* Sowerby in "American Seashells" (not Gray, 1826).

Family CRYPTOPLACIDAE
GENUS *Cryptoconchus* Burrow, 1815

Cryptoconchus floridanus Dall, 1889   White-barred Chiton
                                                     Text fig. 32 b

Southeast Florida to Puerto Rico.

About 1 inch in length, broadly oval. Characterized by the naked, black-brown girdle which extends over the valves, except along the narrow mid-dorsal area. The exposed portions of the valves are beaded and white when not incrusted with algae. On each side of the valves there is a minute pore bearing short bristles. The gills begin halfway back along the side of the foot. Uncommon.

GENUS *Acanthochitona* Gray, 1821

Acanthochitona pygmaea Pilsbry, 1893   Dwarf Glass-haired Chiton
                                                     Text fig. 32 c

West coast of Florida to the West Indies.

½ to ¾ inch in length, elongate, with the girdle covering most of

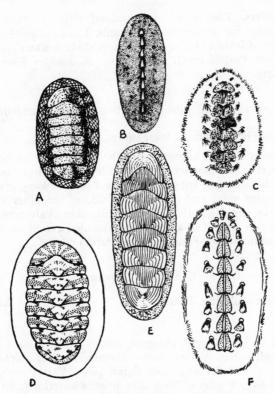

TEXT FIG. 32. Some of the smaller chitons found in Puerto Rico. a, *Ischnochiton papillosus* C. B. Adams, ½ inch; b, *Cryptoconchus floridanus* Dall, 1 inch or less; c, *Acanthochitona pygmaea* Pilsbry, ½ to ¾ inch; d, *Tonicia schrammi* Shuttleworth, 1 inch; e, *Ischnochiton limaciformis* Sowerby, 1 to 2 inches; f, *Acanthochitona hemphilli* Pilsbry, about 1 inch.

each valve. Colored cream, green, brown, or variegated with these colors. Girdle with 18 tufts of long, glassy bristles. Dorsal ridge triangular, cut by longitudinal grooves. Lateral areas of valves and end valves pustulous. Found on rocks at low tide.

Acanthochitona spiculosa Reeve, 1847   Glass-haired Chiton

Southeast Florida and the West Indies.

1 to 1½ inches in length, elongate, with the girdle covering most of each valve. Color bluish green variegated with gray. There are 4 clumps of glassy bristles near the anterior valve and one on each side of

the other valves. The dorsal, longitudinal ridge is raised, narrow, smoothish except for microscopic pin-points. Lower edge of girdle with a dense fringe of brown or bluish bristles. A shallow-water species found living on dead *Porites* coral. Uncommon. *A. astriger* Reeve is probably a synonym.

Acanthochitona hemphilli Pilsbry, 1893   Red Glass-haired Chiton
                                                                     Text fig. 32 f
Key West, Florida and the West Indies.

A little over 1 inch in length, with the girdle covering most of each valve. Color red, occasionally spotted with white. Girdle rusty-brown, lower edge with spiculose fringe. There are 4 tufts of long, glassy bristles near the anterior valve and one on each side of the other valves. The tufts are set in cup-like collars of the girdle skin. Valves heart-shaped, covered with tiny, round, sharply raised pustules, except on the narrow dorsal longitudinal ridge. Found on dead *Porites* coral.

GENUS *Choneplax* Carpenter, 1882

Choneplax lata Guilding, 1829   Lata Chiton

Antilles.

About 1 inch in length, elongate, narrow, with a wide girdle and relatively small valves. Valves almost diamond-shaped, greenish brown, papillose, except for the smoothish dorsal ridge. Valves usually eroded. Girdle velvet-like; 4 tufts of long silky bristles anteriorly, and one tuft on each side between the valves (18 tufts in all). This is probably the first record of this species in Puerto Rico. It is found in the crevices of dead *Porites* coral.

Family *ISCHNOCHITONIDAE*
GENUS *Calloplax* Thiele, 1909

Calloplax janeirensis Gray, 1828   Rio Janeiro Chiton
                                                                     Text fig. 33 d
Lower Florida Keys, the West Indies and Brazil.

½ to ¾ inch in length, gray to greenish brown, or speckled with red. Very strongly sculptured. Lateral areas with 3 to 4 very coarse, large, beaded ribs; anterior valve with 12 to 18 ribs. Central ridge (or jugal tract) with longitudinal rows of fine beads; apex elevated, smooth and rounded. Central area with about 12 sharp, granulose, longitudinal ribs. Interior of valves white. Girdle with occasional short delicate hairs. Found under rocks in shallow water.

GENUS *Ischnochiton* Gray, 1847
Subgenus *Stenoplax* Carpenter, 1878

Ischnochiton papillosus C. B. Adams, 1845   Mesh-pitted Chiton
                                                          Text fig. 32 a

Tampa to the Lower Florida Keys and the West Indies.

About ½ inch in length, oval. Color whitish with heavy mottling
of browns or greens. Surface moderately granulose throughout. Without very distinct lateral areas. End valves with concentric rows of fine,
low beads. Girdle narrow, with tiny varicolored scales. A very common,
shallow-water species, usually found under rocks.

Ischnochiton limaciformis Sowerby, 1832   Slender Chiton
                                                          Text fig. 32 e

Florida Keys, West Indies, Central America and Peru.

1 to 2 inches in length, elongate and narrow. Color buff, gray, or
green and marbled with darker color. Sculpture of the central areas
consisting of fine, smooth, longitudinal riblets. These continue on the
lateral areas, becoming broader and flat. End valves with somewhat
wavy, flattened, concentric ridges. Girdle scales minute. Common on
wave-swept rock shores. *Ischnochiton purpurascens* C. B. Adams, 1845,
is a synonym.

Ischnochiton floridanus Pilsbry, 1892

One small specimen reported from Ensenada Honda, Culebra, by
Dall and Simpson.

Ischnochiton striolatus Gray, 1828

Reported from Arroyo and Ponce, Puerto Rico, and Ensenada
Honda, Culebra, by Dall and Simpson.

Ischnochiton reticulatus Reeve, 1847
Reported from eastern Puerto Rico by Gundlach.

GENUS *Callistochiton* Carpenter, 1882

Callistochiton shuttleworthianus Pilsbry, 1893   Rusty Chiton

Key West, Florida, to the West Indies.

About ½ inch in length, and ⅓″ in width, oval. Easily recognized
by the rust color of both shell and girdle. Pilsbry suggests that this

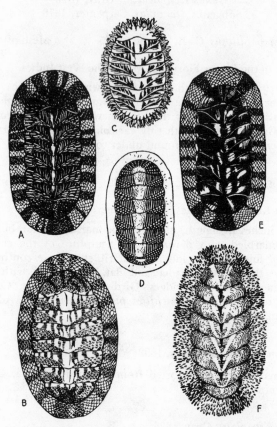

TEXT FIG 33. a, *Chiton tuberculatus* Linné, 2 to 3
inches in length; b, *Chiton squamosus* Linné, 2 to 3
inches; c, *Ceratozona squalida* C. B. Adams, 1 to 2
inches; d, *Calloplax janeirensis* Gray, ½ to ¾ inch
in length; e, *Chiton marmoratus* Linné, 2 to 3 inches;
f, *Acanthopleura granulata* Gmelin, 2 to 3 inches.

color may be due to iron oxide under the rocks. Lateral area of valves
with two strong tubercular ribs. The central areas have coarse net-like
sculpture. Girdle covered by minute imbricating scales. This species has
not yet been found in Puerto Rico; however since it is reasonably common under rocks at St. Croix, Virgin Islands, we include it for comparison.

Family CHITONIDAE
Subfamily CHITONINAE
GENUS *Chiton* Linné, 1758

Chiton tuberculatus Linné, 1758   Common West Indian Chiton
                                                     Text fig. 33 a
West Indies.

2 to 3 inches in length. Color grayish green to olive-green. Girdle
with alternating zones of whitish and dark-green scales. Lateral areas
with about 5 irregular radiating cords. Central areas smooth at the top
with many long, strong, wavy, longitudinal ribs on the sides. End valves
with irregular, wavy radial cords. Under side of valves blue-green. A
very common species under rocks at tide level.

Chiton tuberculatus form *assimilis* Reeve, 1847

Fawn-colored, with white dots on the lateral areas; girdle light-
green; central area sculptured with fine close riblets. Reported from
Guanica by Dall and Simpson.

Chiton squamosus Linné, 1764   Squamous Chiton
                                                     Text fig. 33 b
Southeast Florida and the West Indies.

2 to 3 inches in length. Color yellowish tan with irregular, brown
markings. Posterior edges of valves marked with alternating yellow and
brown areas. Girdle with alternating stripes of grayish green and grayish
white scales. Posterior valve with minutely beaded ribs. Lateral areas of
middle valves with 6 to 8 rows of small beads between which are microscopic pin-holes. Central areas smooth except for five transverse
scratches. Under side of valves blue-green. Common on rocky shores;
usually found quite high up on the rocks.

Chiton viridis Spengler, 1797   Spengler's Chiton

West Indies.

2 to 3 inches in length. Color variable, mottled with various
shades of green and brown. Similar to *C. squamosus,* but the margins
of the central areas have 6 to 11 very short, wavy ribs, and the lateral
areas have 3 or 4 strong pustulous ribs. Interior of valves white. Reasonably common in Puerto Rico.

Chiton marmoratus Gmelin, 1791   Marbled Chiton
                                                     Text fig. 33 e
West Indies.
2 to 3 inches in length. Color variable; dark-brown, olive, or gray,

variously marked with lighter blotches and longitudinal lines. Easily recognized because the entire surface of the valves is smooth, except for a microscopic, silky texture. Girdle with alternating gray and dark-green scales. Under side of valves blue-green. A very common species found on rocky shores.

Subfamily *ACANTHOPLEURINAE*
Genus *Acanthopleura* Guilding, 1829
Subgenus *Maugeria* Gray, 1857

Acanthopleura granulata Gmelin, 1791   Fuzzy Chiton
                                                                              Text fig. 33 f
South half of Florida and the West Indies.

2 to 3 inches in length. Easily identified by its thick, white and black, fuzzy girdle. Surface brownish, granulated all over. Sculpture indistinct because the valves are usually eroded. Under side of valves colored dark-brown in the center and light-green on the edge. Foot dull-orange. Very abundant on and under rocks just below high tide line.

Genus *Tonicia* Gray, 1847

Tonicia schrammi Shuttleworth, 1856   Schramm's Chiton
                                                                              Text fig. 32 d
Southeast Florida and the West Indies.

About 1 inch in length, colored brownish red to buff with darker mottling and speckles. Easily recognized by its naked girdle and numerous microscopic eyes on upper surface of valves. Lateral areas separated from the smooth central areas by a strong, rounded rib. The central area has a peppering of about 75 tiny, black eyes. Head valves smooth except for 8 to 10 broad rays of tiny black eyes. Interior of valves white with a red stain in the center. Moderately common on *Porites* coral.

Class *SCAPHOPODA*

Family *SIPHONODENTALIIDAE*
Genus *Cadulus* Philippi, 1844
Subgenus *Polyschides* Pilsbry and Sharp, 1897

Cadulus quadridentatus Dall, 1881   Four-toothed Cadulus
                                                                              Text fig. 34 c
Southeast U. S. and the West Indies.

5 to 10 mm. in length, smooth, swollen behind the aperture. Apex with 4 well-defined slits. Shell circular in cross-section. Found in shallow dredgings.

Cadulus tetrodon Pilsbry and Sharp, 1897   Fusiform Cadulus

Southeast U. S. to the West Indies.

5 mm. in length, slender. Apex is cut by four triangular slits. Shell gradually tapers at the two ends, making it fusiform in shape. Rare. Only one specimen has been found in dredgings in Puerto Rico.

Subgenus *Platyschides* Henderson, 1920

Cadulus portoricensis Henderson, 1920   Puerto Rican Cadulus

Puerto Rico.

About 7 mm. in length, moderately curved, smooth, without central swelling. Apex with 4 shallow slits. First described from Mayagüez, Puerto Rico. Found in dredgings down to 25 fathoms.

Cadulus elephas Henderson, 1920

Emerson (1952) reports this species off Punta Cerro Gordo, in 240-300 fathoms and off Punta Picua, in 180-280 fathoms.

Cadulus simpsoni Henderson, 1920

Dall and Simpson reported a large number of specimens of this species from Mayagüez in 25 fathoms. It is listed as *Cadulus carolinensis bushii* Dall in their report.

Cadulus vulpidens Watson, 1879

Off Culebra Island in 390 fathoms. Reported by Henderson.

Cadulus nitidus Henderson, 1920

The type of this species was selected from a lot of 40 specimens collected at Mayagüez, Puerto Rico, in 25 fathoms. *Cadulus amiantus* Dall, listed in Dall and Simpson, is this species.

Subgenus *Gadila* Gray, 1847

Cadulus acus Dall, 1889   Slender Cadulus

Text fig. 34 d

West Indies.

7 to 10 mm. in length, exceedingly slender, slightly curved. Apical end sculptured with fine growth lines. Surface usually variegated by opaque bands of varying widths. Apex simple. A very abundant shallow-to deep-water species.

Cadulus rastridens Watson, 1879

Reported off Culebra Island, in 390 fathoms, by Henderson.

Cadulus minusculus Dall, 1889

One shell reported from Mayagüez by Dall and Simpson.

Cadulus iota Henderson, 1920

Henderson reports this species from Mayagüez Harbor in 25 fathoms.

Subgenus *Cadulus* Philippi, 1844

The following deep-water species were reported by Henderson as having been dredged off Culebra Island, in 390 fathoms, bottom of Pteropod ooze.

Cadulus curtus Watson, 1879   *Cadulus congruens* Watson, 1879
Cadulus ampullaceus Watson, 1879   *Cadulus exiguus* Watson, 1879
Cadulus obesus Watson, 1879

GENUS *Entalina* Monterosato, 1872

Entalina platamodes Watson, 1879

Henderson reported this deep-water species from off Culebra Island in 390 fathoms.

GENUS *Siphonodentalium* Sars, 1859

Siphonodentalium tytthum Watson, 1879

Henderson reports this species was taken north of Culebra Island in 390 fathoms by the Challenger at Station No. 24.

Family DENTALIIDAE
GENUS *Dentalium* Linné, 1758
Subgenus *Dentalium* Linné, 1758

Dentalium gouldi portoricense Henderson, 1920   Puerto Rican Tusk
                                                    Text fig. 34 e
Puerto Rico.

About 1⅝ inches in length, hexagonal, vitreous. The ribs are narrow and rod-like, separating broad flat spaces. Our specimens show numerous growth lines over the whole surface of the shell. Described from Mayagüez Harbor in 25 to 30 fathoms, on sand, mud, and shell bottom. Uncommon from shallow dredgings.

Subgenus *Graptacme* Pilsbry and Sharp, 1897

Dentalium calamus Dall, 1889   Slit Plug Tusk
                                                    Text fig. 34 h
Southeast U. S. and the Greater Antilles.

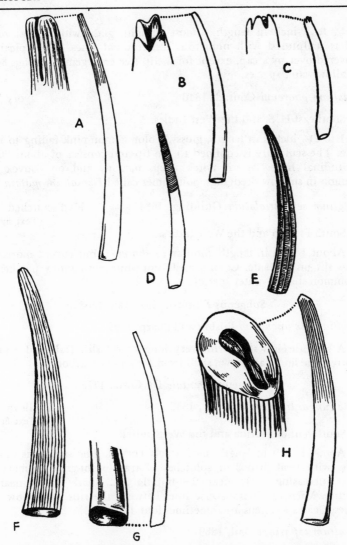

TEXT FIG. 34. Tusk Shells found in Puerto Rico. a, *Dentalium semistriolatum* Guilding, 1 inch, showing an enlargement of the apical slit; b, *Dentalium liodon* Pilbry and Sharp, 1 inch, showing an enlargement of apical notch; c, *Cadulus quadridentatus* Dall, ¼ to ½ inch, with enlarged apex; d, *Cadulus acus* Dall, up to ½ inch; e, *Dentalium gouldi portoricense* Henderson, 1⅝ inches; f, *Dentalium antillarum* Orbigny, 1 inch; g, *Dentalium didymum* Watson, 1 inch, showing enlarged anterior end; h, *Dentalium calamus* Dall, ¾ to 1 inch, showing enlargement of apical end.

¾ to 1 inch in length, almost straight, glassy-white. Most of the shell is sculptured with numerous longitudinal lines. The apical end is covered over by a cap, except for a slit (see enlargement in fig. 34 h). A shallow-water species.

Dentalium eboreum Conrad, 1846   Ivory Tusk

Southeast U. S. and the West Indies.

1 to 2½ inches in length, glossy. Color salmon-pink fading to ivory-white. The sculpture is confined to the tip and consists of about 20 fine longitudinal lines. Apical notch deep, narrow, and on convex side. Common in shallow dredgings. Sometimes called *Dentalium matara* Dall.

Dentalium semistriolatum Guilding, 1834   Half-scratched Tusk
                                                                 Text fig. 34 a
South Florida and the West Indies.

About 1 inch in length. Similar to *eboreum,* but curved more, with apical slit on the side. Color translucent-white with milky patches. An uncommon shallow-water species.

Subgenus *Fustiaria* Stoliczka, 1868

Dentalium stenoschizum Pilsbry and Sharp, 1897

A sculptureless shell with very long apical slit. Dall and Simpson reported one fine, half-grown shell from Mayagüez Harbor.

Subgenus *Dentale* Da Costa, 1778

Dentalium antillarum Orbigny, 1842   Antillean Tusk
                                                                 Text fig. 34 f
South half of Florida and the West Indies.

About 1 inch in length, moderately curved. The surface is opaque-white, with weak bands or splotches of translucent-gray. Primary ribs 9 but increasing to 12 near the middle and finally to 24 near the aperture. Microscopic transverse lines between the ribs. A shallow-water species. Dead specimens are sometimes found in sand.

Dentalium taphrium Dall, 1889

Reported from Mayagüez by Dall and Simpson.

Dentalium ceratum Dall, 1881   Reticulated Tusk

Florida to the Lesser Antilles.

1 to 2 inches in length. Color yellow, becoming white on the anterior half of the shell. The texture is glassy, with a polished surface. Sculpture consists of 9 primary ribs at the apex, which soon increase to 18.

These become fainter and finally disappear, leaving the anterior half of the shell perfectly smooth. Characterized by delicate, microscopic reticulations between the ribs at the apical end. There is no definite apical notch or slit. Many young dead specimens have been found on the beaches and in shallow dredgings. Adult specimens are rare in Puerto Rico.

Dentalium disparile Orbigny, 1842

Reported by Dall and Simpson from Mayagüez.

Subgenus *Episiphon* Pilsbry and Sharp, 1897

Dentalium sowerbyi Guilding, 1834

Dentalium filum Sowerby reported from Mayagüez by Dall and Simpson is this species.

Dentalium johnsoni Emerson, 1952

Emerson gives the type locality for this species as off Puerto Rico, Station 25, 18° 32′ 15″ N., 66° 22′ 10″ W., 240-300 fathoms.

Subgenus *Bathoxiphus* Pilsbry and Sharp, 1897

Dentalium didymum Watson, 1879   Flattened Tusk
                                                          Text fig. 34 g
Yucatan, Puerto Rico, Barbados.

About 1 inch in length, attenuate, slightly curved. Color white; shiny, porcellanous. Easily recognized because it is slightly flattened laterally, especially toward the convex side. This is one of the most abundant species and occurs from shallow water to 390 fathoms. Although no apical features were noted in Watson's description, we noticed a "pipe" projection in several of our specimens.

Subgenus *Compressidens* Pilsbry and Sharp, 1897

Dentalium pressum Pilsbry and Sharp, 1897

Reported by Henderson from off Culebra Island, 390 fathoms.

Dentalium ophiodon Dall, 1881

Emerson (1952) reports this species off Punta Maldonado in 200-300 fathoms. Also off Punta Cerro Gordo in 240-300 fathoms.

Subgenus *Laevidentalium* Cossmann, 1888

Dentalium liodon Pilsbry and Sharp, 1897   Smooth Tusk
                                                          Text fig. 34 b
West Indies.

About one inch in length, moderately curved, rather slender. Color white, semi-transparent to opaque with the surface brilliantly polished. It is sculptureless, except for occasional circular growth lines. Apical notch is narrow and V-shaped. Uncommon; a shallow to moderately deep-water species.

Dentalium callipeplum Dall, 1889

Gulf of Mexico and West Indies.

Reported by Dall and Simpson. Dredged off Mayagüez (Puerto Rico, in 25 fathoms. Emerson (1952) also reports this species off Punta Cerro Gordo, Puerto Rico, in 240-350 fathoms.

Selected Bibliography

Although this list of marine mollusk papers on the tropical Western Atlantic is by no means complete, it contains very useful and, in most cases, readily available references. More extensive bibliographies are found in Abbott's "American Seashells" and Keen's "Marine Shells of Tropical West America" (see below). Research workers should consult the Mollusca Section of the "Zoological Record" which is published by the Zoological Society of London, Regent's Park, London, N.W. 1.

ABBOTT, R. TUCKER. 1954. *American Seashells*. 541 pp., 40 pls. (24 in color), numerous text figs. D. Van Nostrand Co., Inc., Princeton, N.J.

ABBOTT, R. TUCKER. 1958. *The Marine Mollusks of Grand Cayman Island, West Indies*. 138 pp., 5 pls. Monograph 11, Academy Natural Sciences, Philadelphia 3, Pa.

CLENCH, WILLIAM J., editor. *Johnsonia. Monographs of the Marine Mollusca of the Western Atlantic*. Vols. 1 through 4 and continued. Department of Mollusks, Museum of Comparative Zoölogy, Cambridge 38, Mass. The leading scientific publication on West Indian marine mollusks. Excellent illus., descriptions, ranges, etc.

CLENCH, W. J. and R. D. TURNER. 1950. *The Western Atlantic Marine Mollusks Described by C. B. Adams*. Occasional Papers on Mollusks, vol. 1, no. 15, pp. 233-404, illus. Department of Mollusks, Museum Comparative Zoölogy, Cambridge 38, Mass.

DALL, WILLIAM H. 1886 and 1889. *Reports on the results of dredging . . . Steamer 'Blake'*. Report on the Mollusca. Pt. 1 (1886) on Brachiopoda and Pelecypoda; pt. 2 (1889) on Gastropoda and Scaphopoda, Bulletin Museum Comparative Zoölogy, 12, pp. 171-318, pls. 1-9; Bull. 18, pp. 1-492, pls. 10-40.

DALL, WILLIAM H. 1900. *Synopsis of the Family Tellinidae and of the North American species*. Proc. U. S. National Museum, vol. 23, pp. 285-326, pls. 2-4.

DALL, WM. H. and CHAS. T. SIMPSON. 1901. *The Mollusca of Porto Rico*. U. S. Fish Commission Bulletin for 1900, vol. 20, pp. 351-524, pls. 53-58.

DESJARDIN, MAX. 1949. *Les Rissoina de l'Ile de Cuba*. Journal de Conchyliologie, Paris, vol. 89, pp. 193-208.

EMERSON, WILLIAM K. 1952. *The Scaphopod Mollusks Collected by the First Johnson-Smithsonian Deep-sea Expedition*. Smithsonian Miscellaneous Collections, vol. 117, no. 6, pp. 1-14.

GUNDLACH, DON JUAN. 1883. *Apuntes para la Fauna Puerto-Riquena*. Anales de la Soc. Espan. de Hist. Nat., vol. 12, pp. 5-58 and 441-484.

HEILPRIN, ANGELO. 1888. *Contribution to the Natural History of the Bermuda Islands*. Proc. Acad. Natural Sciences Philadelphia for 1888, pp. 302-328, pls. 14-16.

HENDERSON, JOHN B. 1920. *A Monograph of the East American Scaphopod Mollusks*. U. S. National Museum Bulletin 111, pp. 1-177, pl. 1-20.

JOHNSON, CHARLES W. 1934. *List of Marine Mollusca of the Atlantic Coast from Labrador to Texas*. Proc. Boston Soc. Nat. Hist., vol. 40, no. 1, pp. 1-204.

JOHNSTONE, KATHLEEN YERGER. 1957. *Sea Treasure. A guide to Shell Collecting*. 242 pp., 8 colored plates. Houghton Mifflin Co., Boston.

KEEN, MYRA. 1958. *Marine Shells of Tropical West America*. 624 pp., numerous illustration. Stanford University Press, California.

KREBS, H. 1864. *The West Indian Marine Shells with Some Remarks*. (a republication by Clench, W. J., C. G. Aguayo and R. D. Turner, 1947, in Revista de la Sociedad Malacologica "Carlos de la Torre", Habana, vols. 5 and 6).

MATTOX, N. T. 1948. *Observations on Some Uses for Marine Gastropods in Puerto Rica*. Turtox News, vol. 26, no. 7, July.

MATTOX, N. T. 1953. *A New Species of Pleurobranchus from the Caribbean (Tectibranchiata)*. Nautilus, Philadelphia, vol. 66, no. 4, pp. 109-114.

McLEAN, RICHARD A. 1951. *The Pelecypoda or Bivalve Mollusks of Porto Rico and the Virgin Islands*. Scientific Survey of Porto Rico and the Virgin Islands, (New York Academy of Sciences), vol. 17, pt. 1, pp. 1-183, 26 pls.

MORCH, O. A. L. 1874-1877. *Synopsis molluscorum marinorum Indiarum occidentalium*. Malakozoologische Blätter, vol. 22, pp. 142-184; vol. 24, pp. 14-66.

OLSSON, AXEL A. and ANNE HARBISON. 1953. *Pliocene Mollusca of Southern Florida.* Monograph 8, Academy Natural Sciences, Philadelphia 3, Pa., 457 pp., 65 pls.

OLSSON, AXEL A. and THOMAS L. McGINTY. 1958. *Recent Marine Mollusks from the Caribbean Coast of Panama with Descriptions of Some New Genera and Species.* Bull. American Paleontology, vol. 39, pp. 1-58.

ORBIGNY, ALCIDE D'. 1843-1852 (plates, 1842). *Mollusques.* In R. Sagra's Histoire . . . de l'Ile de Cuba. 2 vols. and Atlas. Spanish edition published in 1845.

SMITH, E. A. 1885. *Report on the Lamellibranchiata collected by H.M.S. 'Challenger' during the years 1873-76.* Challenger Report, Zoology, vol. 13, pt. 35, pp. 1-341, pls. 1-25.

USTICKE, G. W. N. 1959. *A Check List of the Marine Shells of St. Croix, U. S. Virgin Islands with Random Annotations.* Privately printed. 90 pp., 4 pls.

VERRILL, A. E. and K. J. BUSH. 1900. *Additions to the Marine Mollusca of the Bermudas.* Trans. Connecticut Academy, vol. 10, pp. 513-544, pls. 63-65.

WATSON, R. B. 1885-1886. *Report on the Scaphopoda and Gastropoda collected by H. M. S. 'Challenger' during the years 1873-76.* Challenger Reports, Zoology, vol. 15, 756 pp., 52 pls.

WARMKE, GERMAINE L. 1958. *Radula and Operculum of Vasum capitellum.* Nautilus, vol. 72, no. 1, pp. 29-30, pl. 4, figs. 1-6.

WARMKE, GERMAINE L. 1960. *Seven Puerto Rico Cones: Notes and Radulae.* Nautilus, vol. 73, no. 4, pp. 119-124, figs. 1-7.

WARMKE, G. L. and R. T. ABBOTT. 1953. *The Gross Anatomy and Occurrence in Puerto Rico of the Pelecypod Yoldia perprotracta.* Jour. Wash. Acad. Sciences, vol. 43, no. 8, pp. 260-261.

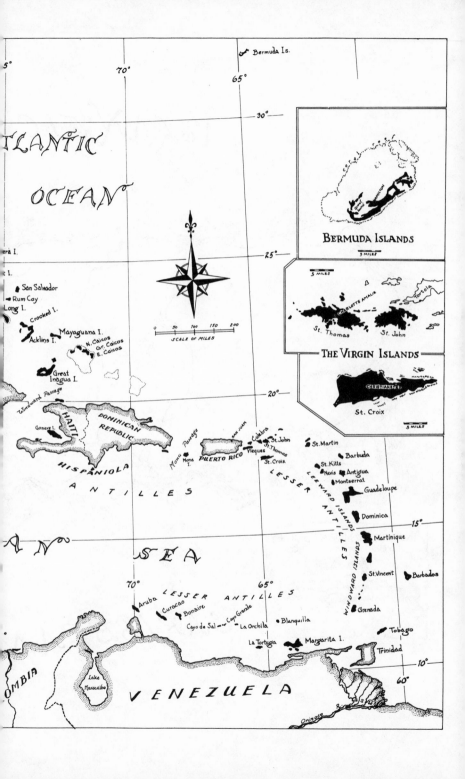

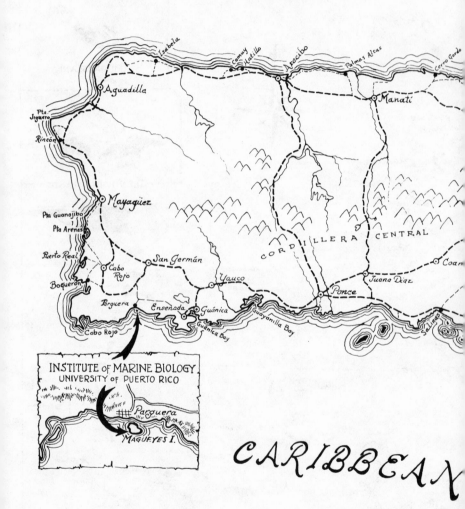

ATLANTIC

Isabela
Camuy
Hatillo
Arecibo
Palmas Altas
Cerro Gordo
Aguadilla
Manati
Pta Jiguero
Rincón
Mayagüez
Pta Guanajibo
Pta Arenas
Puerto Real
Cabo Rojo
San Germán
CORDILLERA CENTRAL
Coamo
Boquerón
Yauco
Juana Diaz
Parguera
Ensenada
Guánica
Ponce
Cabo Rojo
Guánica Bay
Guayanilla Bay
Salinas

INSTITUTE of MARINE BIOLOGY
UNIVERSITY of PUERTO RICO

Parguera
MAGUEYES I.

CARIBBEAN

OCEAN

San Juan

UNIVERSITY OF
PUERTO RICO

Rio Piedras

Rio Grande

Fajardo

Playa de Fajardo

CULEBRA

Culebra

Caguas

Pta Puerca

Humacao

Playa de Humacao

Isabel II

Cayey

VIEQUES

Yabucoa

Guayama

Arroyo

PUERTO RICO

SCALE OF MILES
0   5   10

SEA

TRITONS, CONCHS AND HELMET SHELLS

PLATE 2

HAIRY TRITONS, COWRIES AND MUREX SHELLS

a. ATLANTIC HAIRY TRITON, *Cymatium pileare* Linné, 1½ to 3 inches, p. 100.

b. DOG-HEAD TRITON, *Cymatium caribbaeum* Clench and Turner, 2 inches, p. 100.

c. ANGULAR TRITON, *Cymatium femorale* Linné, 3 to 7 inches, p. 102.

d. TRUE TULIP, *Fasciolaria tulipa* Linné, 3 to 5 inches, p. 119.

e. MEASLED COWRIE, *Cypraea zebra* Linné, 2 to 3½ inches, p. 91.

f. ATLANTIC PARTRIDGE TUN, *Tonna maculosa* Dillwyn, 2 to 5 inches, p. 104.

g. APPLE MUREX, *Murex pomum* Gmelin, 2 to 4½ inches, p. 104.

h. WEST INDIAN MUREX, *Murex brevifrons* Lamarck, 3½ to 6 inches, p. 105.

i. BROWN-LINED LATIRUS, *Latirus infundibulum* Gmelin, 2 to 3 inches, p. 119.

HAIRY TRITONS, COWRIES AND MUREX SHELLS

PLATE 3

SCOTCH BONNETS, MOONS, AUGERS AND OLIVES

a. SMOOTH SCOTCH BONNET, *Phalium cicatricosum* Gmelin, 1½ to 2 inches, p. 98.

b. SCOTCH BONNET, *Phalium granulatum* Born, 1½ to 4 inches, p. 98.

c. RETICULATED COWRIE-HELMET, *Cypraecassis testiculus* Linné, 1 to 3 inches, p. 99.

d. COLORFUL ATLANTIC NATICA, *Natica canrena* Linné, 1 to 2 inches, p. 96.

e. CAYENNE NATICA, *Natica cayennensis* Récluz, 1 inch, p. 96.

f. BROWN MOON-SHELL, *Polinices hepaticus* Röding, 1 to 2 inches, p. 95.

g. MOROCCO NATICA, *Natica marochiensis* Gmelin, ½ to 1 inch, p. 96.

h. COMMON PURPLE SEA-SNAIL, *Janthina janthina* Linné, 1 to 1½ inches, p. 77.

i. FLAME AUGER, *Terebra taurinus* Solander, 4 to 6 inches, p. 132.

j. NETTED OLIVE, *Oliva reticularis* Lamarck, ·1½ to 1¾ inches, p. 121.

k. CARIBBEAN OLIVE, *Oliva caribaeensis* Dall and Simpson, 1 to 2 inches, p. 122.

l. VARIEGATED TURRET SHELL, *Turritella variegata* Linné, 3½ to 4½ inches, p. 63.

SCOTCH BONNETS, MOONS, AUGERS AND OLIVES

PLATE 4

SCALLOPS, COCKLES, CLAMS AND TELLINS

a. Zigzag Scallop, *Pecten ziczac* Linné, (upper valve), 2 to 4 inches, p. 167.

b. Lion's Paw, *Lyropecten nodosus* Linné, (two color forms), 3 to 6 inches, p. 169.

c. Leafy Jewel Box, *Chama macerophylla* Gmelin, (two color forms), 1 to 3 inches, p. 179.

d. Prickly Cockle, *Trachycardium isocardia* Linné, 2 to 3 inches, p. 182.

e. Atlantic Thorny Oyster, *Spondylus americanus* Hermann, 3 to 4 inches, p. 170.

f. Cross-barred Venus, *Chione cancellata* Linné, 1 to 1¾ inches, p. 185.

g. Watermelon Tellin, *Tellina punicea* Born, 1 to 2¼ inches, p. 195.

h. Lightning Venus, *Pitar fulminata* Menke, 1 to 1½ inches, p. 188.

i. Sunrise Tellin, *Tellina radiata* Linné, 2 to 4 inches, p. 192.

j. Speckled Tellin, *Tellina listeri* Röding, 2 to 3½ inches, p. 192.

k. Atlantic Sanguin, *Sanguinolaria cruenta* Solander, 1½ to 2 inches, p. 202.

l. Common Caribbean Donax, *Donax denticulatus* Linné, (four valves), 1 inch, p. 201.

SCALLOPS, COCKLES, CLAMS AND TELLINS

PLATE 5

KEYHOLE LIMPETS

a. PYGMY EMARGINULA, *Emarginula pumila* A. Adams, 1/3 to 1/2 inch, p. 36.

b. EMARGINATE LIMPET, *Hemitoma emarginata* Blainville, 3/4 to 1 inch, p. 36.

c. RUFFLED RIMULA, *Emarginula phrixodes* Dall, 1/4 to 1/3 inch, p. 36.

d. VARIEGATED KEYHOLE LIMPET, *Diodora variegata* Sowerby, 1/2 inch, p. 38.

e. DYSON'S KEYHOLE LIMPET, *Diodora dysoni* Reeve, 1/2 to 3/4 inch, p. 37.

f. EIGHT-RIBBED LIMPET, *Hemitoma octoradiata* Gmelin, 3/4 to 1 inch, p. 36.

g. DWARF KEYHOLE LIMPET, *Diodora minuta* Lamarck, 1/2 inch, p. 38.

h. ARCUATE LIMPET, *Diodora arcuata* Sowerby, 3/8 inch, p. 38.

i. GREEN KEYHOLE LIMPET, *Diodora viridula* Lamarck, 1 inch, p. 38.

j. LISTER'S KEYHOLE LIMPET, *Diodora listeri* Orbigny, 1 1/4 to 1 3/4 inches, p. 37.

k. CAYENNE KEYHOLE LIMPET, *Diodora cayenensis* Lamarck, 1 to 2 inches, p. 37.

239

Plate 6

a. SOWERBY'S FLESHY LIMPET, *Lucapina sowerbii* Sowerby, ¾ inch, p. 39.

b. DWARF SUCK-ON LIMPET, *Acmaea leucopleura* Gmelin, ½ inch, p. 41.

c. SPOTTED LIMPET, *Acmaea pustulata* Helbling, ½ to 1 inch, p. 41.

d. FILE FLESHLY LIMPET, *Lucapinella limatula* Reeve, ¾ inch, p. 38.

e. ANTILLEAN LIMPET, *Acmaea antillarum* Sowerby, ¾ to 1 inch, p. 40.

f. CANCELLATE FLESHY LIMPET, *Lucapina suffusa* Reeve, 1 to 1½ inches, p. 39.

g. KNOBBY KEYHOLE LIMPET, *Fissurella nodosa* Born, 1 to 1½ inches, p. 39.

h. WOBBLY KEYHOLE LIMPET, *Fissurella fascicularis* Lamarck, ¾ to 1½ inches, p. 40.

i. HAMILLE'S LIMPET, *Phenacolepas hamillei* Fischer, ¼ inch, p. 52.

j. POINTED KEYHOLE LIMPET, *Fissurella angusta* Gmelin, ¾ to 1 inch, p. 40.

k. RAYED KEYHOLE LIMPET, *Fissurella nimbosa* Linné, 2 inches, p. 40.

l. BARBADOS KEYHOLE LIMPET, *Fissurella barbadensis* Gmelin, 1 to 1½ inches, p. 39.

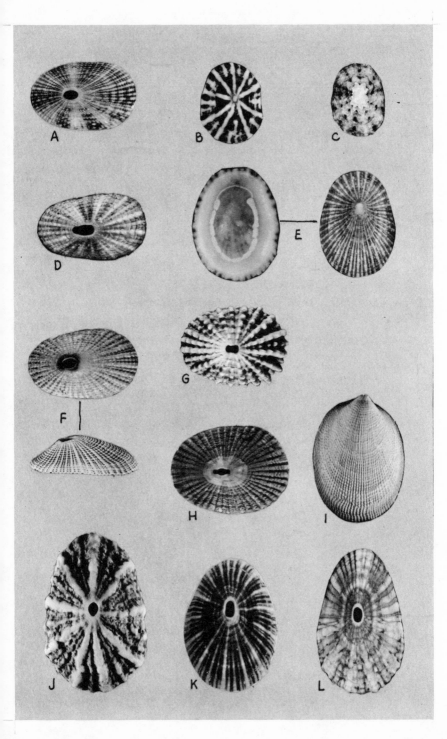

Plate 7

a. RED-SPOTTED EUCHELUS, *Euchelus guttarosea* Dall, 1/4 inch, p. 42.

b. PAINTED FALSE STOMATELLA, *Synaptocochlea picta* Orbigny, 1/8 to 1/4 inch, p. 43.

c. CANCELLATE CYCLOSTREME, *Cyclostrema cancellatum* Marryat, 1/2 inch, p. 46.

d. SMOOTH ATLANTIC TEGULA, *Tegula fasciata* Born, 1/2 to 3/4 inch, p. 44.

e. GREEN-BASE TEGULA, *Tegula excavata* Lamarck, 1/2 to 3/4 inch, p. 44.

f. WEST INDIAN TEGULA, *Tegula lividomaculata* C. B. Adams, 3/4 inch, p. 44.

g. JUJUBE TOP-SHELL, *Calliostoma jujubinum* Gmelin, 3/4 to 1 1/4 inches, p. 45.

h. SCARLET FALSE STOMATELLA, *Pseudostomatella coccinea* A. Adams, 1/8 inch, p. 43.

i. THREE-CORDED ARENE, *Arene tricarinata* Stearns, 1/8 inch, p. 45.

j. CHOCOLATE-LINED TOP-SHELL, *Calliostoma javanicum* Lamarck, 3/4 to 1 inch, p. 44.

k. CHESTNUT TURBAN, *Turbo castanea* Gmelin, 1 inch, p. 46.

l. DALL'S FALSE STOMATELLA, *Pseudostomatella erythrocoma* Dall, 4 to 6 mm., p. 43.

m. WEST INDIAN TOP-SHELL, *Cittarium pica* Linné, 2 to 4 inches, p. 43.

n. CHANNELED TURBAN, *Turbo canaliculatus* Hermann, 2 to 3 inches, p. 47.

Plate 8

a. POLKA-DOT PHEASANT, *Tricolia affinis* C. B. Adams, ¼ to ⅜ inch, p. 48.

b. CHECKERED PHEASANT, *Tricolia tessellata* Potiez and Michaud, ¼ inch, p. 49.

c. ADAMS' PHEASANT, *Tricolia adamsi* Philippi, 3/16 inch, p. 48.

d. THALASSIA PHEASANT, *Tricolia thalassicola* Robertson, ¼ inch, p. 48.

e. STAR ARENE, *Arene cruentata* Mühlfeld, ¼ to ½ inch, p. 45.

f. SHOULDERED PHEASANT, *Tricolia bella* M. Smith, ¼ inch, p. 49.

g. LONG-SPINED STAR-SHELL, *Astraea phoebia* Röding, 2 to 2½ inches, p. 47.

h. GREEN STAR-SHELL, *Astraea tuber* Linné, 1 to 2 inches, p. 47.

i. IMBRICATED STAR-SHELL, *Astraea tecta* Solander, 1 inch, p. 48.

j. CARVED STAR-SHELL, *Astraea caelata* Gmelin, 2 to 3 inches, p. 47.

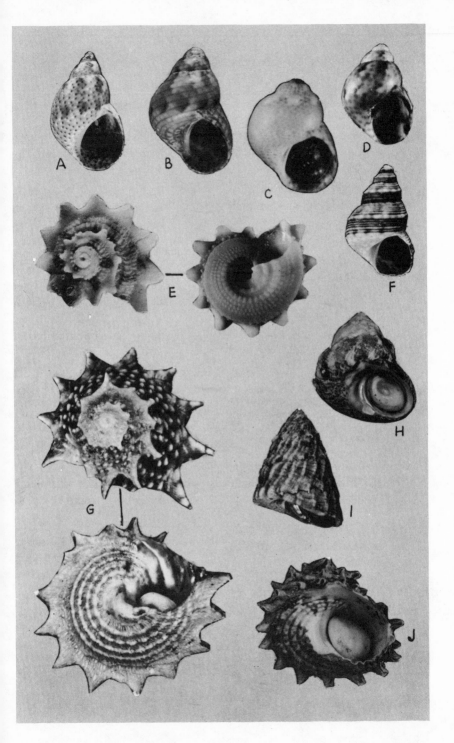

245

Plate 9

a. Zebra Nerite, *Puperita pupa* Linné, 1/3 to 1/2 inch, p. 50.

b. Netted Nerite, *Neritina piratica* Russell, 3/4 to 1 inch, p. 51.

c. Clench Nerite, *Neritina clenchi* Russell, 3/4 to 1 inch, p. 51.

d. Spotted Nerite, *Neritina punctulata* Lamarck, 3/4 to 1 inch, p. 51.

e. Emerald Nerite, *Smaragdia viridis viridemaris* Maury, 1/4 to 1/3 inch, p. 52.

f. Virgin Nerite, *Neritina virginea* Linné, 1/4 to 3/4 inch, p. 50.

g. Bleeding Tooth, *Nerita peloronta* Linné, 3/4 to 1 1/2 inches, p. 49.

h. Tessellated Nerite, *Nerita tessellata* Gmelin, 3/4 inch, p. 49.

i. Antillean Nerite, *Nerita fulgurans* Gmelin, 3/4 to 1 1/4 inches, p. 50.

j. Scaly Nerite, *Neritina meleagris* Lamarck, 1/2 inch, p. 50.

k. Four-toothed Nerite, *Nerita versicolor* Gmelin, 3/4 to 1 inch, p. 49.

l. Zebra Periwinkle, *Littorina ziczac* Gmelin, 1/2 to 1 inch, p. 52.

m. Dwarf Periwinkle, *Littorina mespillum* Mühlfeld, 1/4 inch, (specimens from St. Croix), p. 53.

n. Spotted Periwinkle, *Littorina meleagris* Potiez and Michaud, 1/8 to 1/4 inch, p. 53.

o. False Prickly-winkle, *Echininus nodulosus* Pfeiffer, 1/2 to 1 inch, p. 54.

p. Cloudy Periwinkle, *Littorina nebulosa* Lamarck, 1/2 to 3/4 inch, p. 53.

q. Beaded Periwinkle, *Tectarius muricatus* Linné, 1/2 to 1 inch, p. 54.

r. Common Prickly-winkle, *Nodilittorina tuberculata* Menke, 1/2 to 3/4 inch, p. 54.

s. Angulate Periwinkle, *Littorina angulifera* Lamarck, 1 to 1 1/2 inches, p. 53.

Plate 10

a. DOUBLE-LIP TRUNCATELLA, *Truncatella pulchella bilabiata* Pfeiffer, 5 to 7 mm., p. 55.

b. BEAUTIFUL TRUNCATELLA, *Truncatella pulchella* Pfeiffer, 5 to 7.5 mm., p. 55.

c. SHOULDERED TRUNCATELLA, *Truncatella scalaris* Michaud, 4 to 5 mm., p. 55.

d. WEST INDIAN TRUNCATELLA, *Truncatella scalaris clathrus* Lowe, 4 to 5 mm., p. 56.

e. CARIBBEAN TRUNCATELLA, *Truncatella caribaeensis* Reeve, 7 to 9 mm., p. 55.

f. SMOOTH RISSO, *Zebina browniana* Orbigny, 4 to 5 mm., p. 58.

g. FLORIDA MICRODOCHUS, *Microdochus floridanus* Rehder, 2 mm., p. 58.

h. MANY-RIBBED RISSO, *Rissoina multicostata* C. B. Adams, 6 to 7 mm., p. 56.

i. STRIATE RISSO, *Rissoina striosa* C. B. Adams, 5 to 10 mm., p. 57.

j. CERITH-LIKE ALVANIA, *Alvania aberrans* C. B. Adams, 5 mm., p. 59.

k. WEST INDIAN ALVANIA, *Alvania auberiana* Orbigny, 2 mm., p. 58.

l. CANCELLATED RISSO, *Rissoina cancellata* Philippi, 8 mm., p. 57.

m. CARIBBEAN RISSO, *Rissoina bryerea* Montagu, 4 to 6 mm., p. 56.

n. FISCHER'S RISSO, *Rissoina fischeri* Desjardin, 4 to 6 mm., p. 56.

o. DECUSSATE RISSO, *Rissoina decussata* Montagu, 6 to 8 mm., p. 57.

249

Plate 11

a. CYLINDER SUNDIAL, *Heliacus cylindricus* Gmelin, ½ inch, p. 64.

b. BEAU'S VITRINELLA, *Cyclostremiscus beaui* Fischer, ⅓ to ½ inch, p. 60.

c. MINIATURE TURBO, *Parviturboides comptus* Woodring, 2 mm., p. 63.

d. CHANNELED SUNDIAL, *Heliacus infundibuliformis* Gmelin, ⅝ inch, p. 65.

e. KREBS' SUNDIAL, *Philippia krebsi* Mörch, ½ inch, p. 65.

f. ORBIGNY'S SUNDIAL, *Heliacus bisulcatus* Orbigny, ¼ to ½ inch, p. 65.

g. COMMON SUNDIAL, *Architectonica nobilis* Röding, 1 to 2 inches, p. 65.

h. VARIEGATED TURRET SHELL, *Turritella variegata* Linné, 3½ to 4½ inches, p. 63.

i. EASTERN TURRET SHELL, *Turritella exoleta* Linné, 2 inches, p. 63.

j. ATLANTIC MODULUS, *Modulus modulus* Linné, ½ inch, p. 70.

k. ANGLED MODULUS, *Modulus carchedonius* Lamarck, ½ inch, p. 71.

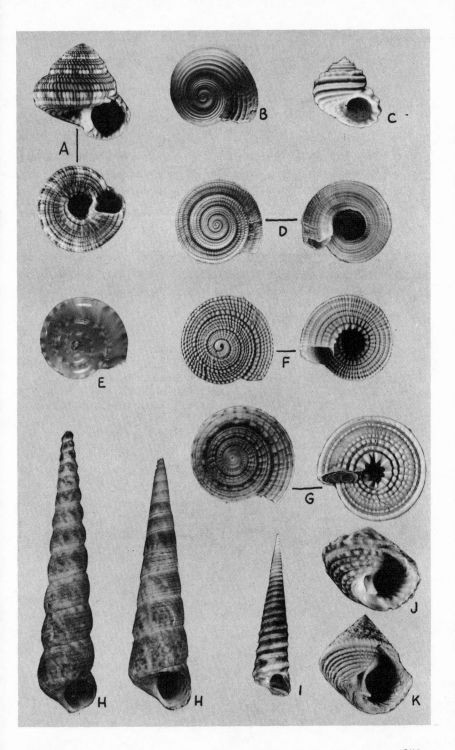

Plate 12

a. ERECT WORM SHELL, *Petaloconchus erectus* Dall, 1 to 2 inches, p. 66.

b. ATLANTIC CARRIER SHELL, *Xenophora conchyliophora* Born, 3 inches, p. 88.

c. KNORR'S WORM SHELL, *Vermicularia knorri* Deshayes, 2 to 4 inches, p. 64.

d. DECUSSATE WORM SHELL, *Serpulorbis decussata* Gmelin, 1 inch, p. 66.

e. MCGINTY'S WORM SHELL, *Petaloconchus mcgintyi* Olsson and Harbison, 2 inches, p. 66.

f. RIISE'S WORM SHELL, *Serpulorbis riisei* Mörch, 1 to 2 inches, p. 67.

g. SLIT WORM SHELL, *Siliquaria anguillae* Mörch, 1 inch, p. 67.

h. IRREGULAR WORM SHELL, *Petaloconchus irregularis* Orbigny, 1 to 2 inches, p. 65.

i. FLORIDA WORM SHELL, *Petaloconchus floridanus* Olsson and Harbison, 1 inch, p. 66.

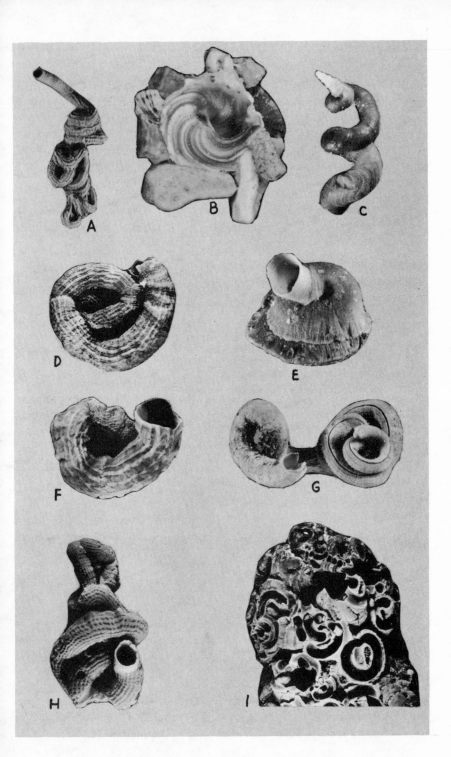

Plate 13

a. BLACK ATLANTIC PLANAXIS, *Planaxis nucleus* Bruguière, ½ inch, p. 70.

b. MINIATURE HORN SHELL, *Alabina cerithidioides* Dall, 2 to 4 mm., p. 73.

c. AWL MINIATURE CERITH, *Cerithiopsis emersoni* C. B. Adams, ½ to ¾ inch, p. 74.

d. BARBADOS MATHILDA, *Mathilda barbadensis* Dall, ¼ inch, p. 76.

e. LATUM MINIATURE CERITH, *Cerithiopsis latum* C. B. Adams, 3 mm., p. 75.

f. DWARF ATLANTIC PLANAXIS, *Planaxis lineatus* da Costa, ¼ inch, p. 70.

g. BROWN SARGASSUM SNAIL, *Litiopa melanostoma* Rang, ⅛ to ¼ inch, p. 74.

h. VARIABLE BITTIUM, *Bittium varium* Pfeiffer, ⅛ inch, p. 73.

i. ORNATE TRIFORA, *Triphora ornata* Deshayes, ¼ inch, p. 76.

j. THOMAS' TRIFORA, *Triphora turris-thomae* Holten, ¼ inch, p. 76.

k. BLACK-LINED TRIFORA, *Triphora nigrocincta* C. B. Adams, ⅛ to ¼ inch, p. 76.

l. BLACK-TIPPED TRIFORA, *Triphora melanura* C. B. Adams, ¼ to ⅜ inch, p. 76.

m. ADAMS' MINIATURE CERITH, *Seila adamsi*, H. C. Lea, ¼ to ½ inch, p. 75.

n. IVORY CERITH, *Cerithium eburneum* Bruguière, ¾ to 1 inch, p. 73.

o. STOCKY CERITH, *Cerithium litteratum* Born, 1 inch, p. 72.

p. MIDDLE-SPINED CERITH, *Cerithium algicola* C. B. Adams, 1 to 1½ inches, p. 73.

q. SCHWENGEL'S CERITH, *Cerithium auricoma* Schwengel, 1¾ inches, p. 73.

r. UNCERTAIN MINIATURE CERITH, *Alaba incerta* Orbigny ¼ inch, p. 74.

s. TURRET HORN SHELL, *Cerithidea costata* da Costa, ½ inch, p. 71.

t. BEADED HORN SHELL, *Cerithidea beattyi* Bequaert, ½ inch, p. 71.

u. PLICATE HORN SHELL, *Cerithidea pliculosa* Menke, 1 inch, p. 71.

v. FALSE CERITH, *Batillaria minima* Gmelin, ½ to ¾ inch, p. 72.

w. DWARF CERITH, *Cerithium variabile* C. B. Adams, ⅓ to ½ inch, p. 72.

Plate 14

a. FRIELE'S WENTLETRAP, *Epitonium frielei* Dall, 5/8 inch, p. 81.

b. CANDÉ'S WENTLETRAP, *Epitonium candeanum* Orbigny, 1/4 to 1/2 inch, p. 81.

c. RETICULATED WENTLETRAP, *Amaea retifera* Dall, 1 inch, p. 78.

d. TURRETED WENTLETRAP, *Epitonium turritellulum* Mörch, 1/8 to 1/4 inch, p. 81.

e. NEW ENGLAND WENTLETRAP, *Epitonium novangliae* Couthouy, 1/4 to 1/2 inches, p. 81.

f. CRENULATED WENTLETRAP, *Opalia crenata* Linné, 1 inch, p. 78.

g. PUMILIO WENTLETRAP, *Opalia pumilio* Mörch, 3/8 inch, p. 78.

h. DALL'S WENTLETRAP, *Cirsotrema dalli* Rehder, 1 1/2 inches, (beach worn specimen), p. 77.

i. WRINKLED-RIBBED WENTLETRAP, *Epitonium foliaceicostum* Orbigny, 1/2 to 3/4 inch, p. 79.

j. BROWN WENTLETRAP, *Depressiscala nautlae* Mörch, 5/8 inch, p. 82.

k. TIBURON WENTLETRAP, *Epitonium tiburonense* Clench and Turner, 1/4 to 3/8 inch, p. 81.

l. ONE-BANDED WENTLETRAP, *Epitonium unifasciatum* Sowerby, 1/2 inch, p. 80.

m. LAMELLOSE WENTLETRAP, *Epitonium lamellosum* Lamarck, 1 1/4 inch, p. 80.

n. BLADED WENTLETRAP, *Epitonium albidum* Orbigny, 1/2 to 3/4 inch, p. 79.

o. DENTATE WENTLETRAP, *Epitonium denticulatum* Sowerby, 5/8 inch, (specimen from St. Croix), p. 82.

p. WEST ATLANTIC WENTLETRAP, *Epitonium occidentale* Nyst, 3/4 to 1 inch, p. 79.

q. WIDELY-COILED WENTLETRAP, *Epitonium echinaticostum* Orbigny, 1/4 to 3/8 inch, p. 79.

r. KREBS' WENTLETRAP, *Epitonium krebsi* Mörch, 3/4 inch, p. 79.

257

Plate 15

a. SULCATE VANIKORO, *Vanikoro sulcata* Orbigny, ¼ to ⅜ inch, p. 85.

b. GLOBE PURPLE SEA-SNAIL, *Janthina globosa* Swainson, ½ to ¾ inch, p. 77.

c. COMMON PURPLE SEA-SNAIL, *Janthina janthina* Linné, 1 to 1½ inches, p. 77.

d. ORBIGNY'S FOSSARUS, *Fossarus orbignyi* Fischer, 2 to 3 mm., p. 85.

e. ANOMALOUS FOSSARUS, *Iselica anomala* C. B. Adams, 2 to 5 mm., p. 85.

f. INCURVED CAP-SHELL, *Capulus intortus* Lamarck, ¼ to ½ inch, p. 86.

g. ORANGE HOOF-SHELL, *Hipponix subrufus subrufus* Lamarck, ½ inch, p. 85.

h. WHITE HOOF-SHELL, *Hipponix antiquatus* Linné, ½ inch, p. 84.

i. SPINY SLIPPER-SHELL, *Crepidula aculeata* Gmelin, ½ to 1 inch, p. 86.

j. EASTERN WHITE SLIPPER-SHELL, *Crepidula plana* Say, 1 inch, p. 87.

k. CONVEX SLIPPER-SHELL, *Crepidula convexa* Say, ¼ to ½ inch, p. 87.

l. FADED SLIPPER-SHELL, *Crepidula glauca* Say, ½ inch, p. 87.

m. FALSE CUP-AND-SAUCER, *Cheilea equestris* Linné, ½ to 1¼ inches, p. 84.

n. WEST INDIAN CUP-AND-SAUCER, *Crucibulum auricula* Gmelin, 1 inch, p. 86.

o. CIRCULAR CUP-AND-SAUCER, *Calyptraea centralis* Conrad, ¼ inch, p. 86.

259

Plate 16

a. SUFFUSE TRIVIA, *Trivia suffusa* Gray, ¼ to ⅓ inch, p. 90.

b. WHITE GLOBE TRIVIA, *Trivia nix* Schilder, ⅜ inch, p. 91.

c. LITTLE WHITE TRIVIA, *Trivia leucosphaera* Schilder, ⅛ to ¼ inch, p. 91.

d. FOUR-SPOTTED TRIVIA, *Trivia quadripunctata* Gray, ¼ inch, p. 90.

e. ANTILLEAN TRIVIA, *Trivia antillarum* Schilder, ⅛ to ¼ inch, p. 90.

f. COFFEE BEAN TRIVIA, *Trivia pediculus* Linné, ½ inch, p. 90.

g. FINGERPRINT CYPHOMA, *Cyphoma signatum* Pilsbry and McGinty, ¾ to 1 inch, (live specimen found by Ted and Lois Arnow), p. 93.

h. ATLANTIC GRAY COWRIE, *Cypraea cinerea* Gmelin, ¾ to 1½ inches, p. 92.

i. ATLANTIC YELLOW COWRIE, *Cypraea spurca acicularis,* Gmelin, ½ to 1¼ inches, p. 92.

j. WEAK-RIDGED CYPHOMA, *Cyphoma intermedium* Sowerby, about 1½ inches, p. 93.

k. FLAMINGO TONGUE, *Cyphoma gibbosum* Linné, ¾ to 1 inch (left: shell only; right: mantle extended over shell), p. 93.

l. COMMON WEST INDIAN SIMNIA, *Neosimnia acicularis* Lamarck, ½ inch, p. 92.

m. SINGLE-TOOTHED SIMNIA, *Neosimnia uniplicata* Sowerby, ½ to ¾ inch, p. 92.

n. MEASLED COWRIE, *Cypraea zebra* Linné, 2 to 3½ inches, young shell at left, p. 91.

Plate 17

a. MILK MOON-SHELL, *Polinices lacteus* Guilding, ¾ to 1½ inches, p. 94.

b. RANG'S LAMELLARIA, *Lamellaria rangi* Bergh, ¼ inch, p. 89.

c. MENKE'S NATICA, *Natica menkeana* Philippi, ½ inch, p. 96.

d. MINIATURE NATICA, *Tectonatica pusilla* Say, ¼ to ⅓ inch, p. 97.

e. SULCATE NATICA, *Stigmaulax sulcata* Born, ½ to ¾ inch, p. 97.

f. CAYENNE NATICA, *Natica cayennensis* Récluz, 1 inch, p. 96.

g. COLORFUL ATLANTIC NATICA, *Natica canrena* Linné, 1 to 2 inches, p. 96.

h. MACULATED BABY'S EAR, *Sinum maculatum* Say, 1 to 2 inches, p. 95.

i. BROWN MOON-SHELL, *Polinices hepaticus* Röding, 1 to 2 inches, p. 95.

j. LIVID NATICA, *Natica livida* Pfeiffer, ½ inch, p. 95.

k. COMMON BABY'S EAR, *Sinum perspectivum* Say, 1 to 2 inches, p. 95.

Plate 18

a. Lip Triton, *Cymatium labiosum* Wood, ¾ inch, p. 100.

b. Dwarf Hairy Triton, *Cymatium vespaceum* Lamarck; 1 to 1½ inches, p. 101.

c. McGinty's Distorsio, *Distorsio mcgintyi* Emerson a n d Puffer, 1 to 1¾ inches, p. 103.

d. Atlantic Distorsio, *Distorsio clathrata* Lamarck, ¾ to 3 inches, p. 102.

e. Poulsen's Triton, *Cymatium poulseni* Mörch, 2 to 3 inches, p. 100.

f. von Salis' Triton, *Cymatium parthenopeum* von Salis, 5¾ inches, (young shell) p. 101.

g. Gold-mouthed Triton, *Cymatium nicobaricum* Röding, 1 to 2½ inches, p. 100.

h. Knobby Triton, *Cymatium muricinum* Röding, 1 to 2 inches, p. 101.

i. Granular Frog-shell, *Bursa cubaniana* Orbigny, ¾ to 2 inches, p. 103.

j. St. Thomas Frog-shell, *Bursa thomae* Orbigny, ½ to 1 inch, p. 103.

k. Dog-head Triton, *Cymatium caribbaeum* Clench and Turner, 1½ to 2½ inches, p. 100.

l. Chestnut Frog-shell, *B u r s a spadicea* Montfort, 1 to 2 inches, p. 103.

m. Gaudy Frog-shell, *Bursa corrugata* Perry, 2 to 3 inches, p. 103.

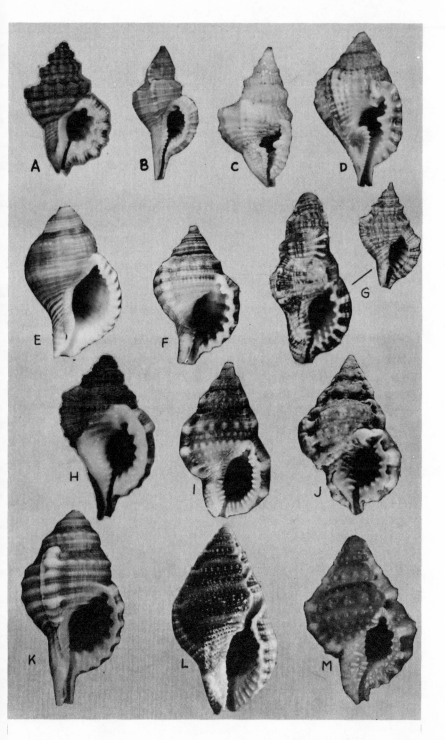

265

Plate 19

a. BLACKBERRY DRUPE, *Drupa nodulosa* C. B. Adams, ½ to 1 inch, p. 106.

b. PINK DRUPE, *Risomurex roseus* Reeve, ½ inch, p. 106.

c. TWO-SIDED ASPELLA, *Aspella anceps* Lamarck, ½ inch, p. 108.

d. LITTLE ASPELLA, *Aspella paupercula* C. B. Adams, ¾ inch, p. 108.

e. HEXAGONAL MUREX, *Muricopsis oxytatus* M. Smith, 1 to 1½ inches, p. 106.

f. PITTED MUREX, *Murex cellulosus* Conrad, 1 inch, p. 106.

g. GLOBULAR PITTED MUREX, *Murex cellulosus nuceus* Mörch, 1 inch, p. 106.

h. BROWNISH PITTED MUREX, *Murex cellulosus leviculus* Dall, 1 inch, p. 106.

i. FRILLY DWARF TRITON, *Ocenebra intermedia* C. B. Adams, 1 inch, 108.

j. FLORIDA ROCK SHELL, *Thais haemastoma floridana* Conrad, 2 to 3 inches, p. 107.

k. RUSTIC ROCK SHELL, *Thais rustica* Lamarck, 1½ inches, p. 107.

l. DELTOID ROCK SHELL, *Thais deltoidea* Lamarck, 1 to 2 inches, p. 108.

m. WOODRING'S MUREX, *Murex woodringi* Clench and Pérez Farfante, 2 to 2¾ inches, p. 105.

n. ROSE MUREX, *Murex recurvirostris rubidus*, F. C. Baker, 1 to 2 inches, p. 105.

o. WIDE-MOUTHED PURPURA, *Purpura patula* Linné, 2 to 3½ inches, p. 107.

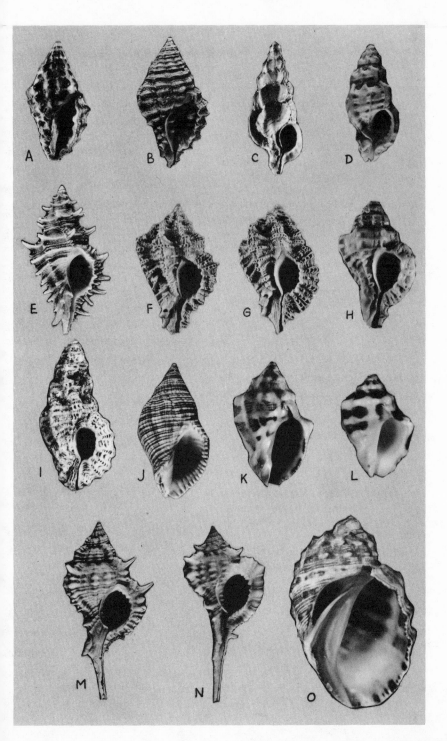

267

Plate 20

a. COMMON DOVE-SHELL, *Columbella mercatoria* Linné, ½ to ¾ inch, p. 110.

b. CARIBBEAN CORAL-SHELL, *Coralliophila caribaea* Abbott, ½ to 1 inch, p. 109.

c. SHORT CORAL-SHELL, *Coralliophila abbreviata* Lamarck, 1 inch, p. 109.

d. PAGODA CORAL-SHELL, *Coralliophila scalariformis* Lamarck, 1 inch, p. 110.

e. GLOBULAR CORAL-SHELL, *Coralliophila aberrans* C. B. Adams, ½ inch, p. 109.

f. SHINY DOVE-SHELL, *Mitrella nitens* C. B. Adams, ½ inch, p. 113.

g. BEAUTIFUL DOVE-SHELL, *Anachis pulchella* Sowerby, ¼ to ⅜ inch, p. 111.

h. THICK-LIP DOVE-SHELL, *Anachis crassilabris* Reeve, 3/16 to ¼ inch, p. 112.

i. LUNAR DOVE-SHELL, *Mitrella lunata* Say, 3/16 inch, p. 113.

j. WHITE-SPOTTED DOVE-SHELL, *Nitidella ocellata* Gmelin, ¼ to ½ inch, p. 112.

k. TWO-COLORED DOVE-SHELL, *Nitidella dichroa* Sowerby, ¼ to ½ inch, p. 112.

l. FENESTRATE DOVE-SHELL, *Mitrella fenestrata* C. B. Adams, ¼ inch, p. 113.

m. MANY-SPOTTED DOVE-SHELL, *Psarostola monilifera* Sowerby, 3/16 inch, p. 114.

n. BANDED DOVE-SHELL, *Psarostola minor* C. B. Adams, ¼ inch, p. 114.

o. MANGELIA-LIKE DOVE-SHELL, *Anachis mangelioides* Reeve, 5/16 inch, p. 111.

p. GLOSSY DOVE-SHELL, *Nitidella nitida* Lamarck, ½ inch, p. 112.

q. FAT DOVE-SHELL, *Anachis obesa* C. B. Adams, 3/16 to ¼ inch, p. 111.

r. CHAIN DOVE-SHELL, *Anachis catenata* Sowerby, ¼ inch, p. 110.

s. SPRINKLED DOVE-SHELL, *Anachis sparsa* Reeve, ¼ to ⅜ inch, p. 111.

t. OVATE DOVE-SHELL, *Pyrene ovulata* Lamarck, ½ to ¾ inch, p. 110.

u. SMOOTH DOVE-SHELL, *Nitidella laevigata* Linné, ½ to ¾ inch, p. 113.

Plate 21

a. WEST INDIAN BAILY-SHELL, *Bailya parva* C. B. Adams, ¾ inch, p. 114.

b. INTRICATE BAILY-SHELL, *Bailya intricata* Dall, ½ inch, p. 115.

c. GAUDY CANTHARUS, *Cantharus lautus* Reeve, ¾ inch, p. 118.

d. WHITE-SPOTTED ENGINA, *Engina turbinellas* K i e n e r, ½ inch, p. 116.

e. MINIATURE TRITON TRUMPET, *Pisania pusio* Linné, 1 to 1¾ inches, p. 117.

f. GUADELOUPE PHOS, *Engoniophos guadelupensis* Petit, 1 inch, p. 115.

g. PUERTO RICAN PHOS, *Antillophos oxyglyptus* Dall and Simpson, ⅝ inch, p. 115.

h. BEADED PHOS, *Antillophos candei* Orbigny, 1 to 1¼ inches, p. 115.

i. SWIFT'S DWARF TRITON, *Colubraria swifti* Tryon, ¾ inch, p. 117.

j. LINED PHOS, *Engoniophos unicintus* Say, 1 inch, p. 116.

k. TINTED CANTHARUS, *Cantharus tinctus* Conrad, ¾ to 1¼ inches, p. 117.

l. COMMON CANTHARUS, *Cantharus auritulus* Link, ¾ to 1¼ inches, p. 117.

m. ARROW DWARF TRITON, *Colubraria lanceolata* Menke, ¾ inch, p. 116.

n. DWARF NASSA, *Nassarius nanus* Usticke, ¼ to ½ inch, p. 118.

o. VARIABLE NASSA, *Nassarius albus* Say, ½ inch, p. 118.

p. COMMON EASTERN NASSA, *Nassarius vibex* Say, ⅜ inch, p. 118.

q. LEANING DWARF TRITON, *Colubraria obscura* Reeve, 1 to 2 inches, p. 116.

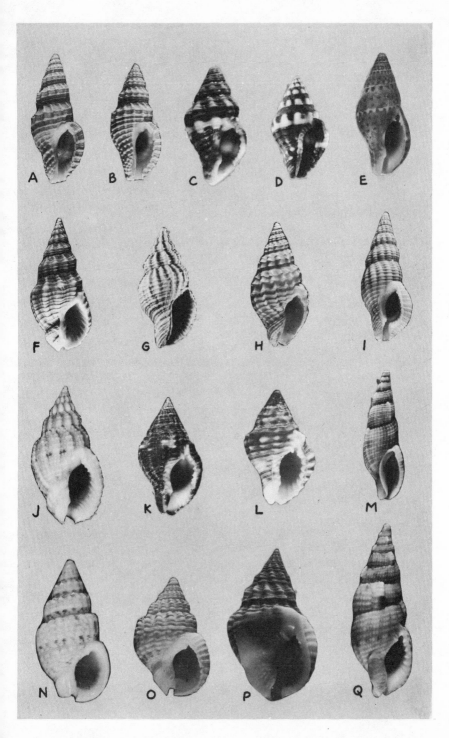

Plate 22

a. LITTLE GEM MITER, *Pusia gemmata* Sowerby, ¼ inch, p. 125.

b. HANLEY'S MITER, *Pusia hanleyi* Dohrn, ¼ inch, p. 125.

c. WHITE-LINED MITER, *Pusia albocincta* C. B. Adams, 1 inch, p. 125.

d. GULF STREAM MITER, *Mitra fluviimaris* Pilsbry and McGinty, 1 inch, p. 124.

e. BEAUTIFUL MITER, *Pusia pulchella* Reeve, ½ inch, p. 125.

f. GIRL MITER, *Pusia puella* Reeve, ¼ to ½ inch, p. 125.

g. RUGOSE NUTMEG, *Trigonostoma rugosum* Lam. 1¼ inch (specimen from St. Croix), p. 126.

h. COMMON NUTMEG, *Cancellaria reticulata* Linné, 1 to 1¾ inches, p. 126.

i. PAINTED MITER, *Pusia histrio* Reeve, ½ inch, p. 126.

j. BEADED MITER, *Mitra nodulosa* Gmelin, ¾ to 1 inch, p. 124.

k. WHITE-SPOTTED LATIRUS, *Leucozonia ocellata* Gmelin, 1 inch, p. 121.

l. SHORT-TAILED LATIRUS, *Latirus brevicaudatus* Reeve, 1 to 2½ inches, p. 120

m. CHESTNUT LATIRUS, *Leucozonia nassa* Gmelin, 1½ to 2 inches, p. 120.

n. VIRGIN ISLAND LATIRUS, *Latirus virginensis* Abbott, 1 to 1½ inches, p. 120.

o. BARBADOS MITER, *Mitra barbadensis* Gmelin, 1 to 1½ inches, p. 124.

p. CARIBBEAN VASE, *Vasum muricatum* Born, 2½ inches, p. 121.

q. SPINY VASE, *Vasum capitellus* Linné, 2 to 3 inches, p. 121.

r. MUSIC VOLUTE, *Voluta musica* Linné, 2 to 2½ inches, p. 126.

Plate 23

a. TAN MARGINELLA, *Marginella denticulata* Conrad, ⅛ to ⅜ inch, p. 127.

b. CARMINE MARGINELLA, *Marginella haematita* Kiener, ¼ to ½ inch, p. 127.

c. MAUGER'S ERATO, *Erato maugeriae* Gray, ¼ inch, p. 90.

d. SNOWFLAKE MARGINELLA, *Persicula lavalleeana* Orbigny, ⅛ inch, p. 128.

e. TEARDROP MARGINELLA, *Bullata ovuliformis* Orbigny, ⅛ inch, p. 128.

f. PALE MARGINELLA, *Hyalina tenuilabra* Tomlin, ½ to ¾ inch, p. 129.

g. GRACEFUL MARGINELLA, *Marginella gracilis* C. B. Adams, ¼ inch, p. 127.

h. ORANGE-BANDED MARGINELLA, *Hyalina avena* Kiener, ¼ to ½ inch, p. 129.

i. WHITE-LINED MARGINELLA, *Hyalina albolineata* Orbigny, ¼ inch, p. 129.

j. WHITE MARGINELLA, *Marginella lactea* Kiener, ¼ inch, p. 127.

k. TINY DWARF OLIVE, *Olivella perplexa* Olsson, 5 mm., p. 123.

l. OLSSON'S DWARF OLIVE, *Olivella acteocina* Olsson, 4 mm., p. 123.

m. WHITE DWARF OLIVE, *Olivella dealbata* Reeve, ¼ inch, p. 122.

n. WEST INDIAN DWARF OLIVE, *Olivella nivea* Gmelin, ½ to 1 inch. p. 122.

o. DECORATED MARGINELLA, *Persicula pulcherrima* Gaskoin, ¼ inch, p. 128.

p. CARIBBEAN DWARF OLIVE, *Olivella petiolita* Duclos, ½ to ¾ inch, p. 122.

q. JASPER DWARF OLIVE, *Jaspidella jaspidea* Gmelin, ½ to ¾ inch, p. 124.

r. ATLANTIC WOOD-LOUSE, *Morum oniscus* Linné, ¾ to 1 inch, p. 97.

s. NETTED OLIVE, *Oliva reticularis* Lamarck, 1½ to 1¾ inches, p. 121.

t. CARIBBEAN OLIVE, *Oliva caribaeensis* Dall and Simpson, 1 to 2 inches, p. 122.

u. MINUTE DWARF OLIVE, *Olivella minuta* Link, ¼ to ½ inch, p. 123.

v. VERREAU'S DWARF OLIVE, *Olivella verreauxi* Ducros, ¼ to ½ inch, p. 123.

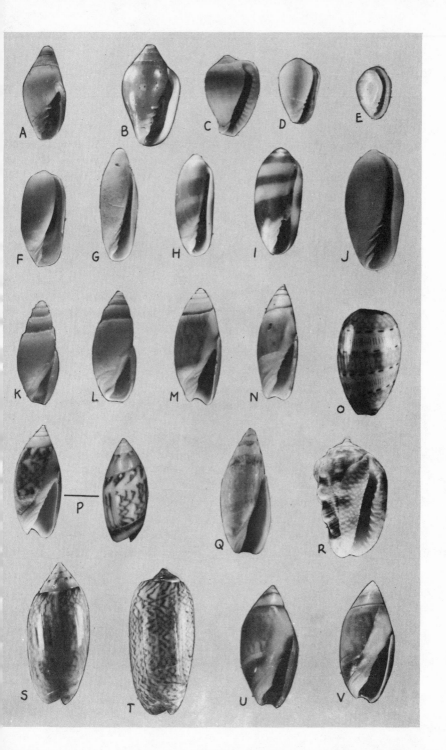

275

Plate 24

a. WEST INDIAN FIGHTING CONCH, *Strombus pugilis* Linné (juvenile shell, 1½ inches), p. 88.

b. QUEEN CONCH, *Strombus gigas* Linné, (juvenile shell, 3 inches), p. 88.

c. HAWK WING CONCH, *Strombus raninus Gmelin,* (juvenile shell, 1½ inches), p. 89.

d. JULIA'S CONE, *Conus juliae* Clench, 1½ to 2 inches, p. 131.

e. WARTY CONE, *Conus verrucosus* Hwass, ¾ to 1¼ inches, p. 130.

f. JASPER CONE, *Conus jaspideus* Gmelin, ½ to ¾ inch, p. 130.

g. GLORY OF THE ATLANTIC CONE, *Conus granulatus* Linné 1 to 1¾ inches, (specimen from Mona Island), p. 132.

h. WEST INDIAN ALPHABET CONE, *Conus spurius* Gmelin, 1½ to 2½ inches, p. 130.

i. CROWN CONE, *Conus regius* Gmelin, 2 to 3 inches, p. 129.

j. CENTURION CONE, *Conus centurio* Born, 1½ to 2 inches, p. 131.

k. MOUSE CONE, *Conus mus* Hwass, 1 to 1½ inches, p. 130.

l. CARROT CONE, *Conus daucus* Hwass, 1 to 2 inches, p. 131.

m. CENTURION CONE, *Conus centurio* Born, 1½ to 2 inches, p. 131.

n. ATLANTIC AGATE CONE, *Conus ranunculus* Hwass, 1½ to 2¾ inches, p. 131.

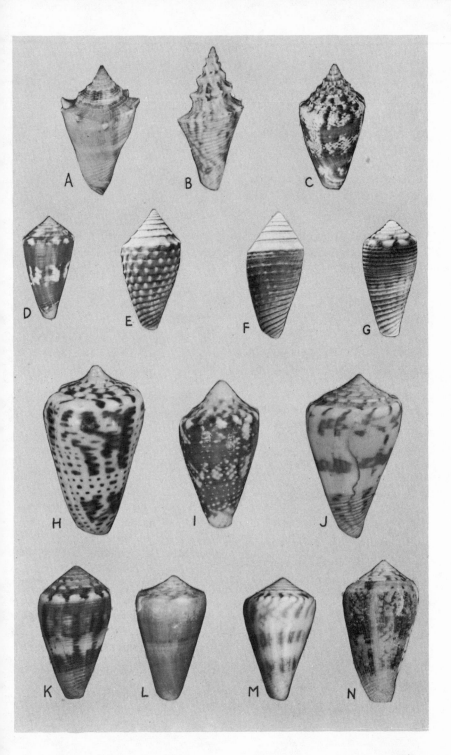

277

Plate 25

a. SHINY ATLANTIC AUGER, *Terebra hastata* Gmelin, 1¼ to 1½ inches, p. 132.

b. GRAY AUGER, *Terebra cinerea* Born, 1 to 2 inches, p. 133.

c. FINE-RIBBED AUGER, *Terebra protexta* Conrad ¾ to 1 inch, p. 133.

d. ATLANTIC AUGER, *Terebra dislocata* Say, 1½ to 2 inches, p. 132.

e. BROWN MANGELIA, *Mangelia fusca* C. B. Adams, ¼ inch, p. 137.

f. BARTLETT'S MANGELIA, *Mangelia bartletti* Dall, ¼ inch, p. 137.

g. JANET'S TURRET, *Fenimorea janetae* Bartsch, 1½ inches, p. 139.

h. SCARLET-STAINED DRILLIA, *Drillia coccinata* Reeve, ½ inch, p. 135.

i. THEA DRILLIA, *Drillia thea* Dall, ⅓ inch, p. 140.

j. SPLENDID TURRET, *Leptadrillia splendida* Bartsch, ⅜ inch, p. 136.

k. DOUBLE-CROWNED MANGELIA, *Mangelia biconica* C. B. Adams, ¼ inch, p. 137.

l. THREE-LINED MANGELIA, *Mangelia trilineata* C. B. Adams, ¼ inch, p. 137.

m. BLACK TURRET, *Crassispira nigrescens* C. B. Adams, ¼ inch, p. 135.

n. WHITE-NODED TURRET, *Drillia albinodata* Reeve, ⅓ inch, p. 140.

o. MELONESE TURRET, *Clathrodrillia melonesiana* Dall and Simpson, ¼ to ½ inch, p. 135.

p. INTERPLEURA DRILLIA, *Drillia interpleura* Dall and Simpson, ⅓ inch, p. 140.

q. WHITE-KNOBBED TURRET, *Crassispira leucocyma* Dall, ⅓ inch, p. 135.

r. BROWN-STAINED MANGELIA, *Mangelia melanitica* Dall, ⅛ to ¼ inch, p. 136.

s. CYDIA DRILLIA, *Drillia cydia* Bartsch, ¾ inch, p. 136.

t. COX'S TURRET, *Pyrgocythara coxi* Fargo, ¼ inch, p. 138.

u. METRIA TURRET, *Vitricythara metria* Dall, ¼ inch, p. 138.

v. FOUR-LINED MANGELIA, *Mangelia quadrilineata* C. B. Adams, ¼ inch, p. 137.

w. EBONY TURRET, *Crassispira fuscescens* Reeve, ¾ inch, p. 134.

279

Plate 26

a. INTERRUPTED TURBONILLA, *Turbonilla interrupta* Totten, 5 to 6 mm., p. 149.

b. ELEGANT TURBONILLA, *Turbonilla elegans* Orbigny, 3 to 4 mm., p. 148.

c. ABRUPT TURBONILLA, *Turbonilla abrupta* Bush, 4 mm., p.149.

d. FAT TURBONILLA, *Turbonilla pupoides* Orbigny, 3 mm., p. 148.

e. HALF-SMOOTH ODOSTOME, *Odostomia seminuda* C. B. Adams, 3 to 4 mm., p. 148.

f. NODULOSE ODOSTOME, *Odostomia gemmulosa* C. B. Adams, 3/16 inch, p. 148.

g. HAYCOCK'S TURBONILLA, *Turbonilla haycocki* D. and B., 4 mm., p. 149

h. CUCUMBER MELANELLA, *Balcis intermedia* Cantraine, ¼ to ½ inch, p. 83.

i. DOUBLE-BANDED EULIMA, *Eulima bifasciata* Orbigny, ¼ inch, p. 83.

j. SINGLE-BANDED EULIMA, *Eulima auricincta* Abbott, ⅛ to ¼ inch, p. 83.

k. SMOOTH ODOSTOME, *Odostomia laevigata* Orbigny, 3 to 5 mm., p. 147.

l. CHANNELED ODOSTOME, *Odostomia canaliculata* C. B. Adams, 3 mm., p. 148.

m. BROWN PYRAM, *Pyramidella fusca* C. B. Adams, ¼ inch, p. 147.

n. SOLID ODOSTOME, *Odostomia solidula* C. B. Adams, 5 to 8 mm., p. 147.

o. SINGLE-BANDED EULIMA, *Eulima auricincta* Abbott, ¼ inch, p. 83.

p. CONICAL MELANFLLA, *Balcis conoidea* Kurtz and Stimpson, ¼ inch, p. 83.

q. COMMON STAR TURRET, *Ancistrosyrinx radiata* Dall, ½ inch, p. 134.

r. SPEAR TURRET, *Ithycythara lanceolata* C. B. Adams, ¼ to ½ inch, p. 137.

s. PARKER'S TURRET, *Ithycythara parkeri* Abbott, ¼ inch, p. 138.

t. STEGER'S TURRET, *Daphnella stegeri* McGinty, ½ inch, p. 140.

u. WHITE GIANT TURRET, *Polystira albida* Perry, 3 to 4 inches, p. 134.

v. PUERTO RICAN TURRET, *Carinodrillia liella* Corea, ½ inch, p. 136.

w. FROSTED TURRET, *Glyphoturris quadrata rugirima* Dall, ¼ inch, p. 138.

x. FLORENCE'S TURRET, *Polystira florencae* Bartsch, 1¼ inch, p. 134.

y. VOLUTE TURRET, *Daphnella lymneiformis* Kiener, ½ to ¾ inch, p. 139.

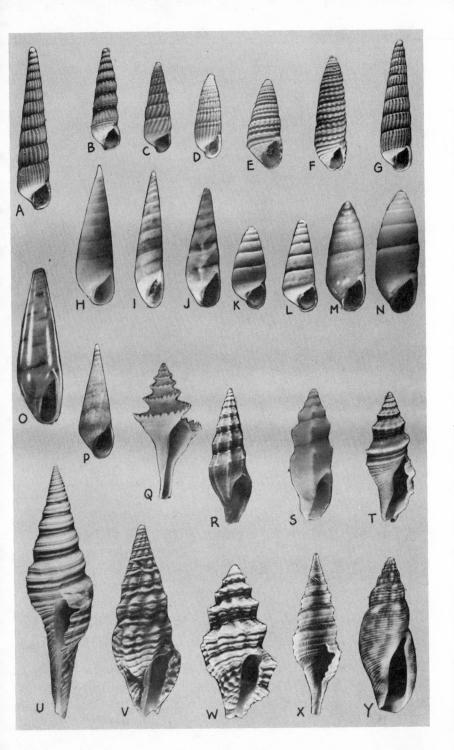

Plate 27

a. BROWN-LINED PAPER-BUBBLE, *Hydatina vesicaria* Solander, 1 to 1½ inch, p. 141.

b. KREBS' BARREL-BUBBLE, *Cylichna krebsi* Mörch, 2 to 3 mm., p. 144.

c. ORBIGNY'S BARREL-BUBBLE, *Cylichna bidentata* Orbigny, 3 mm., p. 144.

d. SOUTHERN SPINDLE-BUBBLE, *Rhizorus oxytatus* Bush, 3 to 4 mm., p. 144.

e. STRIATED BUBBLE, *Bulla striata* Bruguière, ¾ to 1½ inches, p. 141.

f. STRIATE BARREL-BUBBLE, *Retusa bullata* Kiener, 5 to 8 mm., p. 143.

g. CHANNELED BARREL-BUBBLE, *Retusa candei* Orbigny, 3 to 5 mm., p. 143.

h. CRENULATED PAPER-BUBBLE, *Philine sagra* Orbigny, ⅛ to ¼ inch, p. 145.

i. RIISE'S PAPER-BUBBLE, *Atys riiseana* Mörch, ¼ to ½ inch, p. 142.

j. LINED PAPER-BUBBLE, *Atys lineata* Usticke, ¼ inch, p. 143.

k. GUILDING'S PAPER-BUBBLE, *Atys guildingi* Sowerby, ¼ to ½ inch, p. 142.

l. MINIATURE MELO, *Micromelo undata* Bruguière, ¼ to ½ inch, p. 141.

m. ELEGANT PAPER-BUBBLE, *Haminoea elegans* Gray, ½ to ¾ inch, p. 141.

n. CONRAD'S PAPER-BUBBLE, *Haminoea succinea* Conrad, ½ inch, p. 142.

o. ANTILLEAN PAPER-BUBBLE, *Haminoea antillarum* Orbigny, ½ to ¾ inch, p. 142.

p. PETIT'S PAPER-BUBBLE, *Haminoea petiti* Orbigny, ¼ to ½ inch, p. 142.

q. CARIBBEAN PAPER-BUBBLE, *Atys caribaea* Orbigny, ¼ inch, p. 143.

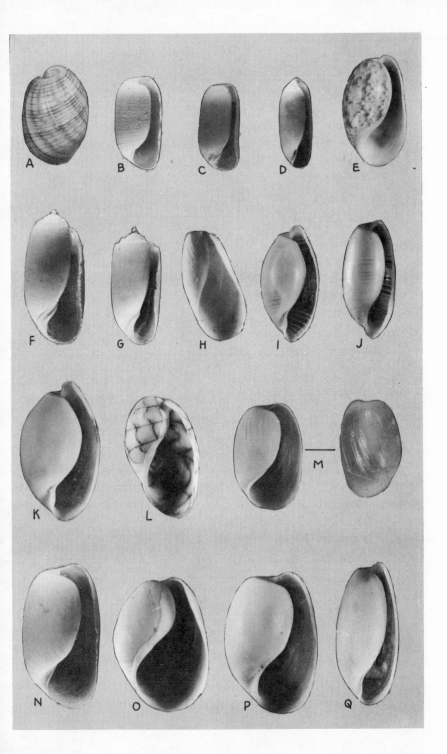

283

Plate 28

a. SOUVERBIE'S LOBIGER, *Lobiger souverbii* Fischer, 10 mm., p. 150.

b. ADAM'S BABY-BUBBLE, *Acteon punctostriatus* C. B. Adams, 3 to 6 mm., p. 140.

c. GIANT ATLANTIC PYRAM, *Pyramidella dolabrata* Linné, ¾ to 1¼ inches, p. 146.

d. BRILLIANT PYRAM, *Pyramidella candida* Mörch, ½ inch, p. 147.

e. THREE-CORDED PYRAM, *Triptychus niveus* Mörch, ¼ inch, p. 147.

f. KREBS' FALSE LIMPET, *Williamia krebsi* Mörch, ¼ inch, p. 154.

g. ROYAL BONNET, *Sconsia striata* Lamarck, 1½ to 2½ inches, p. 97.

h. COMMON SPIRULA, *Spirula spirula* Linné, 1 inch, p. 213.

i. GOES' FALSE LIMPET, *Trimusculus goesi* Hubendick, ¼ to ½ inch, p. 153.

j. STEPPING SHELL, *Pedipes mirabilis* Mühlfeld, 3 mm., p. 152.

k. PERON'S ATLANTA, *Atlanta peroni* Lesueur, ½ inch, p. 93.

l. PUERTO RICAN NISO, *Niso portoricensis* Dall and Simpson, ¼ to ½ inch, p. 84.

m. EGG TRALIA, *Tralia ovula* Bruguière, ½ inch, p. 153.

n. YELLOWISH MELAMPUS, *Melampus monile* Bruguière, ½ to ¾ inch, p. 153.

o. BULLA MELAMPUS, *Detracia bullaoides* Montagu, ½ inch, p. 153.

p. COFFEE MELAMPUS, *Melampus coffeus* Linné, ½ to ¾ inch, p. 153.

Plate 29

a. INSULAR GOULD CLAM, *Gouldia insularis* Dall and Simpson, ¼ inch, p. 189.

b. PUERTO RICAN TRANSENNELLA, *Transennella culebrana* Dall and Simpson, ⅜ inch, p. 187.

c. LAMELLATED LUCINA, *Myrtea pristiphora* Dall and Simpson, left valve, ½ inch, p. 177.

d. ROMBERG'S STRIGILLA, *Strigilla rombergi* Mörch, ¾ to 1 inch, p. 197.

e. PINK MICROCOCKLE, *Microcardium tinctum* Dall, ¼ to ⅝ inch, p. 184 (also see pl. 38f).

f. LARGE STRIGILLA, *Strigilla carnaria* Linné, ¾ to 1 inch, p. 197.

g. PUERTO RICAN TELLIN, *Tellina persica* Dall and Simpson, ¾ inch, p. 195.

h. PUERTO RICO MACOMA, *Macoma pseudomera* Dall and Simpson, ½ to ¾ inch, p. 198.

i. PUERTO RICAN TURBONILLA, *Turbonilla portoricana* Dall and Simpson, ¼ inch, p. 149.

j. ASARCA MANGELIA, *"Mangelia" asarca* Dall and Simpson, ¼ inch, p. 140.

k. HALF-SCRATCHED RINGICULA, *Ringicula semistriata* Orbigny, 2 mm., p. 141.

l. LARGE-MOUTHED MELANELLA, *Eulima patula* Dall and Simpson, ¼ inch, p. 83.

m. PUERTO RICAN ALVANIA, *Alvania portoricana* Dall Simpson, ⅛ inch, p. 59.

n. FILE AUGER, *Terebra limatula* var. *acrior* Dall, ¾ inch, p. 133.

o. AGUADILLE MANGELIA, *Glyphostoma aguadillana* Dall and Simpson, ⅝ inch, p. 140.

p. BROWN-STRIPED NASSARINA, *Nassarina metabrunnea* Dall and Simpson, ⅜ inch, p. 114.

q. ROSE DWARF TRITON, *Ocenebra minirosea* Abbott, ¼ inch, p. 109.

r. SAN JUAN AUGER, *Terebra juanica* Dall and Simpson, ¼ inch, p. 133.

s. ISLAND TURBONILLA, *Turbonilla insularis* Dall and Simpson, ⅜ inch, p. 150.

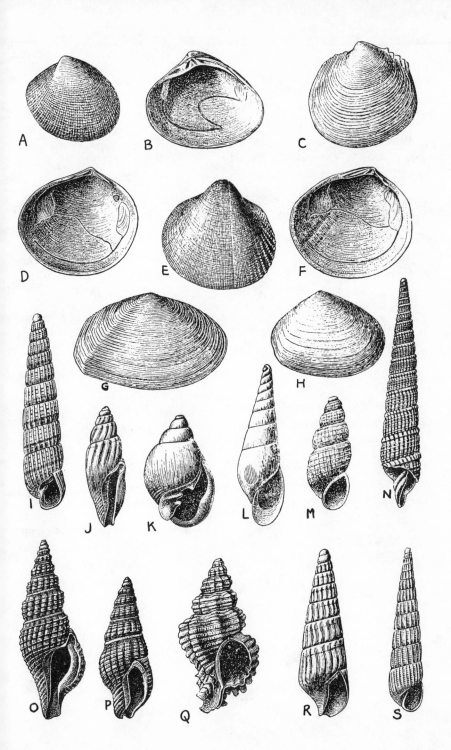

Plate 30

a. POINTED NUT CLAM, *Nuculana acuta* Conrad, ¼ to ⅜ inch, p. 156.

b. WEST INDIAN AWNING CLAM, *Solemya occidentalis* Deshayes, ¼ inch, p. 155.

c. LONG YOLDIA, *Yoldia perprotracta* Dall, 1 inch, p. 156.

d. WHITE RETICULATED ARK, *Barbatia domingensis* Lamarck, ½ to ¾ inch, p. 158.

e. MOSSY ARK, *Arca imbricata* Bruguière, 1 to 2½ inches, p. 158.

f. ADAMS' MINIATURE ARK, *Arcopsis adamsi* Dall, ¼ to ⅓ inch, p. 159.

g. DOC BALES' ARK, *Barbatia tenera* C. B. Adams, 1 to 1½ inches, p. 158.

h. EARED ARK, *Anadara notabilis* Röding, 1½ to 3½ inches, p. 159.

i. WHITE BEARDED ARK, *Barbatia candida* Helbling, 1 to 2 inches, p. 158.

j. RED-BROWN ARK, *Barbatia cancellaria* Lamarck, 1 to 1½ inches, p. 158.

k. CUT-RIBBED ARK, *Anadara lienosa floridana* Conrad, 2½ to 5 inches, p. 159.

l. TURKEY WING, *Arca zebra* Swainson, 2 to 3 inches, p. 157.

m. BLOOD ARK, *Anadara ovalis* Bruguière, 1½ to 2 inches p. 159.

n. INCONGRUOUS ARK, *Anadara brasiliana* Lamarck, 1 to 2½ inches, p. 160.

o. CHEMNITZ'S ARK, *Anadara chemnitzi* Philippi, 1 inch or less, p. 160.

Plate 31

a. COMB BITTERSWEET, *Glycymeris pectinata* Gmelin, ½ to 1 inch, p. 161.

b. DECUSSATE BITTERSWEET, *Glycymeris decussata* Linné, 2 inches, p. 160.

c. LATERAL MUSCULUS, *Musculus lateralis* Say, ⅜ inch, p. 163.

d. CINNAMON CHESTNUT MUSSEL, *Botula fusca* Gmelin, ¾ inch, p. 163.

e. YELLOW MUSSEL, *Brachidontes citrinus* Röding, 1 to 1½ inches, yellow, p. 162.

f. SCORCHED MUSSEL, *Brachidontes exustus* Linné, ¾ inch, brown, p. 162.

g. HOOKED MUSSEL, *Brachidontes recurvus* Rafinesque, 1 to 2 inches, p. 162.

h. SAY'S CHESTNUT MUSSEL, *Lioberus castaneus* Say, ½ to 1 inch, brown, p. 163.

i. ATLANTIC WING OYSTER, *Pteria colymbus* Röding, 1½ to 3 inches, p. 165.

j. MAHOGANY DATE MUSSEL, *Lithophaga bisulcata* Orbigny, 1 to 1½ inches, p. 164.

k. TULIP MUSSEL, *Modiolus americanus* Leach, 1 to 4 inches, p. 162.

l. RIDGED MUSSEL, *Gregariella coralliophaga* Gmelin, ¾ inch, p. 164.

m. BLACK DATE MUSSEL, *Lithophaga nigra* Orbigny, 1 to 2 inches, p. 163.

n. PAPER MUSSEL, *Amygdalum dendriticum* Mühlfeld, 1 to 1¼ inches, p. 163.

Plate 32

a. LISTER'S TREE OYSTER, *Isognomon radiatus* Anton, 1 to 2 inches, p. 165.

b. ATLANTIC PEARL OYSTER, *Pinctada radiata* Leach, 1½ to 3 inches, p. 166.

c. FLAT TREE OYSTER, *Isognomon alatus* Gmelin, 2 to 3 inches, p. 165.

d. LAURENT'S SCALLOP, *Pecten laurenti* Gmelin, left valve, 2½ to 3½ inches, p. 167.

e. CHAZALIE SCALLOP, *Pecten chazaliei* Dautzenberg, 1 inch, right valve, p. 168.

f. RAVENEL'S SCALLOP, *Pecten raveneli* Dall, 1 to 2 inches, p. 167.

g. LAURENT'S SCALLOP, *Pecten laurenti* Gmelin, right valve, 2½ to 3½ inches, p. 167.

h. ZIGZAG SCALLOP, *Pecten ziczac* Linné, 2 to 4 inches, p. 167.

Plate 33

a. ORNATE SCALLOP, *Chlamys ornata* Lamarck, 1 to 1¼ inch, p. 168.

b. BENEDICT'S SCALLOP, *Chlamys benedicti* V e r r i l l and Bush, ½ inch, p. 168.

c. SENTIS SCALLOP, *Chlamys sentis* Reeve, 1 to 1½ inches, p. 168.

d. BAVAY'S SCALLOP, *Leptopecten bavayi* Dautzenberg, ½ inch, p. 169.

e. ROUGH SCALLOP, *Aequipecten muscosus* Wood, ¾ to1¼ inches, p. 170.

f. ANTILLEAN SCALLOP, *Lyropecten antillarum* Récluz, ½ to ¾ inch, p. 169.

g. LION'S PAW, *Lyropecten nodosus* Linné, 3 to 6 inches, p. 169.

h. WAVY-LINED SCALLOP, *Aequipecten lineolaris* Lamarck, 1 inch, p. 170.

i. CALICO SCALLOP, *Aequipecten gibbus* Linné, 1 to 2 inches, p. 170.

j. LITTLE KNOBBY SCALLOP, *Chlamys imbricata* Gmelin, 1 to 1¾ inches, p. 168.

Plate 34

a. Atlantic Thorny Oyster, *S p o n d y l u s americanus* Hermann, 3 to 4 inches, p. 170.

b. Atlantic Thorny Oyster, *S p o n d y l u s americanus* Hermann, young, p. 170.

c. Rough Lima, *Lima scabra* Born, 1 to 3 inches, p. 171.

d. Rough Lima, *Lima scabra* form *tenera* Sowerby, 1 to 3 inches, p. 171.

e. Antillean Lima, *Lima pellucida* C. B. Adams, ¾ to 1 inch, p. 171.

f. Spiny Lima, *Lima lima* Linné, 1 to 1½ inches, p. 171.

g. Kitten's Paw, *Plicatula gibbosa* Lamarck, 1 inch, p. 167.

h. Common Jingle Shell, *Anomia simplex* Orbigny, 1 to 2 inches, p. 172.

i. Amber Pen Shell, *Pinna carnea* Gmelin, 4 to 9 inches, p. 166.

j. False Jingle Shell, *Pododesmus rudis* Broderip, 1 to 4 inches, p. 172.

k. Spiny Pen Shell, *Atrina seminuda* Lamarck, 5 to 9 inches, p. 166.

297

Plate 35

a. FALSE MUSSEL, *Mytilopsis domingensis* Récluz, ¾ to 1¼ inches, p. 174.

b. CARIBBEAN OYSTER, *Crassostrea rhizophorae* Guilding, 2 to 6 inches, p. 173.

c. CRESTED OYSTER, *Ostrea equestris* Say, 1 to 2 inches, p. 172.

d. WEST INDIAN CARDITA, *Cardita gracilis* Shuttleworth, 1 to 1½ inches, p. 174.

e. 'COON OYSTER, *Ostrea frons* Linné, 1 to 2 inches, p. 173.

f. FLATTENED DIPLODON, *Diplodonta notata* Dall & Simpson. ¼ to ½ inch, p. 175.

g. CORAL CLAM, *Coralliophaga coralliophaga* Gmelin, ½ to 1⅓ inches, p. 174.

h. and i. COMMON ATLANTIC DIPLODON, *Diplodonta punctata* Say, ½ to ¾ inch (h, interior; i, exterior), p. 175.

j. WAGNER'S DIPLODON, *Diplodonta nucleiformis* Wagner, ½ inch, p. 175.

k. LUNATE CRASSINELLA, *Crassinella lunulata* Conrad, ¼ to ⅓ inch, p. 173.

l. PIMPLED DIPLODON, *Diplodonta semiaspera* Philippi, ½ inch, p. 175.

m. GUADELOUPE CRASSINELLA, *Crassinella guadalupensis* Orbigny, ¼ inch, p. 174.

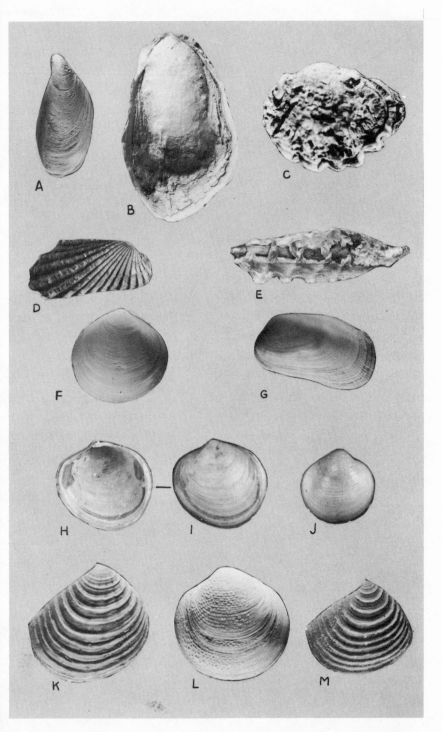

Plate 36

a. PENNSYLVANIA LUCINA, *Lucina pensylvanica* Linné, 1 to 2 inches, p. 176.

b. THICK LUCINA, *Phacoides pectinatus* Gmelin, 1 to 2½ inches, p. 177.

c. TINY LUCINA, *Codakia pectinella* C. B. Adams, ¼ inch, p. 179.

d. THREE-RIDGED LUCINA, *Lucina blanda* Dall and Simpson, ¼ to ½ inch, p. 176.

e. BUTTERCUP LUCINA, *Anodontia alba* Link, 1½ to 2 inches, p. 177.

f. ATLANTIC CLEFT CLAM, *Thyasira trisinuata* Orbigny, ¼ to ½ inch, p. 176.

g. TIGER LUCINA, *Codakia orbicularis* Linné, 2½ to 3½ inches, p. 178.

h. DWARF TIGER LUCINA, *Codakia orbiculata* Montagu, 1 inch, p. 178.

i. SPINOSE LUCINA, *Phacoides muricatus* Spengler, ½ inch, p. 177.

j. DOSINIA-LIKE LUCINA, *Phacoides radians* Conrad, ¾ inch, p. 177.

k. COSTATE LUCINA, *Codakia costata* Orbigny, ½ inch, p. 178.

l. CROSS-HATCHED LUCINA, *Divaricella quadrisulcata* Orbigny ½ to 1 inch, p. 179.

Plate 37

a. TRUE SPINY JEWEL BOX, *Echinochama arcinella* Linné, (worn and fresh, spiny specimen), 1 to 1½ inch, p. 180.

b. LEAFY JEWEL BOX, *Chama macerophylla* Gmelin, 1 to 3 inches, p. 179.

c. ATLANTIC LEFT-HANDED JEWEL BOX, *Pseudochama radians* Lamarck, 1 to 3 inches, p. 180.

d. RED JEWEL BOX, *Chama sarda* Reeve, 1 inch, p. 179.

e. FLORIDA JEWEL BOX, *Chama florida* Lamarck, 1 inch, p. 180.

f. INEQUILATERAL ERYCINA, *Erycina periscopiana* Dall, ¼ inch, p. 181.

g. LITTLE CORRUGATED JEWEL BOX, *Chama congregata* Conrad, ½ to 1½ inches, p. 179.

h. FRILLED PAPER COCKLE, *Papyridea semisulcata* G r a y, less than ½ inch, p. 183.

i. EMMONS' ERYCINA, *Erycina emmonsi* Dall, ⅓ inch, p. 181.

j. SPINY PAPER COCKLE, *Papyridea soleniformis* Bruguière, 1 to 1¾ inches, p. 182.

k. MAGNUM COCKLE, *Trachycardium magnum* Linné, 2 to 3½ inch, p. 182.

l. PRICKLY COCKLE, *Trachycardium isocardia* Linné, 2 to 3 inches, p. 182.

m. YELLOW COCKLE, *Trachycardium muricatum* Linné, 2 inches, p. 182.

Plate 38

a. GUPPY'S STRAWBERRY COCKLE, *Americardia guppyi* Thiele, 1/4 to 1/2 inch, p. 183.

b. ATLANTIC STRAWBERRY COCKLE, *Americardia media* Linné, 1 to 2 inches, p. 183.

c. ANTILLEAN STRAWBERRY COCKLE, *Trigoniocardia antillarum* Orbigny, 1/4 to 3/8 inch, p. 183.

d. DALL'S EGG COCKLE, *Laevicardium sybariticum* Dall, 1/2 to 1 inch, p. 184.

e. COMMON EGG COCKLE, *Laevicardium laevigatum* Linné, 1 to 2 inches, p. 184.

f. PINK MICRO-COCKLE, *Microcardium tinctum* Dall, 1/4 to 5/8 inch, p. 184. (also see pl. 29e).

g. WEST INDIAN POINTED VENUS, *Anomalocardia brasiliana* Gmelin, 3/4 to 1 1/2 inches, p. 187.

h. KING VENUS, *Chione paphia* Linné, 3/4 to 1 1/2 inches, p. 186.

i. BEADED VENUS, *Chione granulata* Gmelin, 3/4 to 1 1/4 inches, p. 186.

j. WHITE PYGMY VENUS, *Chione pygmaea* Lamarck, 1/4 to 1/2 inch, p. 186.

k. WAXY GOULD CLAM, *Gouldia cerina* C. B. Adams, 1/3 inch, p. 189.

l. PRINCESS VENUS, *Antigona listeri* Gray, 2 to 4 inches, p. 185.

m. RIGID VENUS, *Antigona rigida* Dillwyn, 1 1/2 to 2 1/2 inches, p. 185.

n. LADY-IN-WAITING VENUS, *Chione intapurpurea* Conrad, 1 to 1 1/2 inches, p. 186.

o. CROSS-BARRED VENUS, *Chione cancellata* Linné, 1 to 1 3/4 inches, p. 185.

305

Plate 39

a. STIMPSON'S TRANSENNELLA, *Transennella stimpsoni* Dall, ¼ to ½ inch, p. 187.

b. ATLANTIC CYCLINELLA, *Cyclinella tenuis* Récluz, 1 to 2 inches, p. 190.

c. LIGHTNING VENUS, *Pitar fulminata* Menke, 1 to 1½ inches, p. 188 (also see pl. 4h).

d. CUBAN TRANSENNELLA, *Transennella cubaniana* Orbigny, ⅜ inch, p. 187.

e. TRIGONAL TIVELA, *Tivela mactroides* Born, 1½ inches, p. 188.

f. CALICO CLAM, *Macrocallista maculata* Linné, 1½ to 2½ inches, p. 189.

g. CONRAD'S TRANSENNELLA, *Transennella conradina* Dall, ⅝ inch, p. 187.

h. ABACO TIVELA, *Tivela abaconis* Dall, ½ inch, p. 188.

i. SOUTHERN DOSINIA, *Dosinia concentrica* Born, 2 to 3 inches, p. 190.

j. PURPLE VENUS, *Pitar circinata* Born, 1 to 1¾ inches, p. 189.

k. ROYAL COMB VENUS, *Pitar dione* Linné, 1 to 1¾ inches, p. 189.

l. BROWN GEM CLAM, *Parastarte triquetra* Conrad, ⅛ inch, p. 190.

m. WEST INDIAN VENUS, *Pitar aresta* Dall and Simpson, 2 inches, p. 188.

n. WHITE VENUS, *Pitar albida* Gmelin, 1 to 2 inches, p. 188.

o. AMETHYST GEM CLAM, *Gemma purpurea* Lea, ⅛ inch, p. 190.

Plate 40

a. GEORGIA TELLIN, *Tellina georgiana* Dall, 1 inch, p. 195.

b. CRYSTAL TELLIN, *Tellina cristallina* Spengler, 1 inch, p. 196.

c. MERA TELLIN, *Tellina mera* Say, ½ to ¾ inch, p. 193.

d. WATERMELON TELLIN, *Tellina punicea* Born, 1 to 2¼ inches, p. 195.

e. DALL'S DWARF TELLIN, *Tellina sybaritica* Dall, ¼ to ⅓ inch, p. 193.

f. STRIATED TELLIN, *Tellina aequistriata* Say, ⅜ to ¾ inch, p. 196.

g. PINK THIN TELLIN, *Tellina exilis* Lamarck, ½ to ¾ inch, p. 193.

h. ALTERNATE TELLIN, *Tellina alternata* Say, 2 to 3 inches, p. 195.

i. MARTINIQUE TELLIN, *Tellina martinicensis* Orbigny, ⅜ inch, p. 196.

j. WEDGE TELLIN, *Tellina candeana* Orbigny, 5/16 inch, p. 193.

k. SPECKLED TELLIN, *Tellina listeri* Röding, 2 to 3 inches, p. 192.

l. ROSE PETAL TELLIN, *Tellina lineata* Turton, 1 to 1½ inches, p. 195.

m. CARIBBEAN TELLIN, *Tellina caribaea* Orbigny, 1 inch, p. 193.

n. CANDY STICK TELLIN, *Tellina similis* Sowerby, 1 inch, p. 192.

o. SMOOTH TELLIN, *Tellina laevigata* Linné, 2 to 3 inches, from St. Croix, Hayes Collection), p. 192.

p. SUNRISE TELLIN, *Tellina radiata* Linné, 2 to 4 inches, p. 192 (also see pl. 4i).

Plate 41

a. HANLEY'S MACOMA, *Macoma aurora* Hanley, ½ to ¾ inch, p. 199.

b. ATLANTIC UNDULATED MACOMA, *Macoma orientalis hendersoni* Rehder, ¼ to ⅜ inch, p. 199.

c. TENTA MACOMA, *Macoma tenta* Say, ½ to 1 inch, p. 199.

d. LARGE STRIGILLA, *Strigilla carnaria* Linné ¾ to 1 inch, p. 197 (also see pl. 29f).

e. PEA STRIGILLA, *Strigilla pisiformis* Linné, ⅓ to ½ inch, p. 197.

f. PUERTO RICO MACOMA, *Macoma pseudomera* Dall & Simpson, ½ to ¾ inch, p. 198.

g. ATLANTIC GROOVED MACOMA, *Apolymetis intastriata* Say, 2 to 3 inches, p. 199.

h. SHORT MACOMA, *Macoma brevifrons* Say, 1½ inches, p. 199.

i. TAGELUS-LIKE MACOMA, *Macoma tageliformis* Dall, 1 to 2 inches, p. 198.

j. LINTEA TELLIN, *Quadrans lintea* Conrad, ¾ to 1 inch, p. 198.

k. CONSTRICTED MACOMA, *Macoma constricta* Bruguière, 1 to 2½ inches, p. 198.

l. FAUST TELLIN, *Arcopagia fausta* Pulteney, 2 to 4 inches, p. 197.

Plate 42

a. CANCELLATE SEMELE, *Semele bellastriata* Conrad, ½ to ¾ inch, p. 200.

b. TINY SEMELE, *Semele nuculoides* Conrad, ¼ inch, p. 200.

c. PURPLISH SEMELE, *Semele purpurascens* Gmelin, 1 to 1½ inches, p. 200.

d. COMMON CARIBBEAN DONAX, *Donax denticulatus* Linné, 1 inch, p. 201.

e. WHITE ATLANTIC SEMELE, *Semele proficua* Pulteney, ½ to 1½ inches, p. 200.

f. FAT LITTLE DONAX, *Donax tumidus* Philippi, ⅓ to ½ inch, p. 201.

g. ATLANTIC SANGUIN, *Sanguinolaria cruenta* Solander, 1½ to 2 inches, p. 202.

h. STRIATE DONAX, *Donax striatus* Linné, 1 inch, p. 202.

i. COMMON ATLANTIC ABRA, *Abra aequalis* Say, ¼ inch, p. 201.

j. SMALL FALSE DONAX, *Heterodonax bimaculatus* Linné, ½ to 1 inch, p. 203.

k. GAUDY ASAPHIS, *Asaphis deflorata* Linné, 1½ to 2½ inches, p. 202.

l. PURPLISH TAGELUS, *Tagelus divisus* Spengler, 1 to 1½ inches, p. 202.

m. GIANT FALSE DONAX, *Iphigenia brasiliensis* Lamarck, 2 to 2½ inches, p. 202.

n. STOUT TAGELUS, *Tagelus plebeius* Solander, 2 to 3⅓ inches, p. 203.

Plate 43

a. CONTRACTED CORBULA, *Corbula contracta* Say, ¼ to ½ inch, p. 207.

b. COMMON ERVILIA, *Ervilia nitens* Montagu, ¼ inch, p. 205.

c. CARIBBEAN CORBULA, *Corbula caribaea* Orbigny, ½ to ⅝ inch, p. 207.

d. PUERTO RICAN SURF CLAM, *Mulinia portoricensis* Shuttleworth, 1 to 1½ inches, p. 204.

e. ANTILLEAN SPHENIA, *Sphenia antillensis* Dall & Simpson, ⅛ to ¼ inch, p. 205.

f. ST. MARTHA'S RAZOR CLAM, *Solecurtus sanctaemarthae* Orbigny, ½ inch, p. 204.

g. FRAGILE ATLANTIC MACTRA, *Mactra fragilis* Gmelin, 2 to 3 inches, p. 204.

h. CORRUGATED RAZOR CLAM, *Solecurtus cumingianus* Dunker, 1 to 2 inches, p. 203.

i. ANTILLEAN JACKKNIFE CLAM, *Solen obliquus* Spengler, 4 to 6 inches, p. 203.

j. SMOOTH DUCK CLAM, *Labiosa anatina* Spengler, 2 to 3 inches, p. 204.

k. WINGED MACTRA, *Mactra alata* Spengler, 2 to 4 inches, p. 204.

Plate 44

a. SOUTHERN PANDORA, *Pandora bushiana* Dall, ½ inch, p. 210.

b. ATLANTIC RUPELLARIA, *Rupellaria typica* Jonas, 1 inch, p. 191.

c. PEARLY LYONSIA, *Lyonsia beana* Orbigny, ½ to 1¼ inches, p. 209.

d. WEST INDIAN CUSPIDARIA, *Cardiomya perrostrata* Dall, ¼ to ⅜ inch, p. 211.

e. BORING PETRICOLA, *Petricola lapicida* Gmelin, ½ to 1 inch, p. 191.

f. FLORIDA GLASSY LYONSIA, *Lyonsia hyalina floridana* Conrad, ¼ to ½ inch, p. 210.

g. SPENGLER CLAM, *Spengleria rostrata* Spengler, 1 inch, p. 208.

h. WAVY CARIBBEAN THRACIA, *Cyathodonta semirugosa* Reeve, ¾ to 1 inch, p. 210.

i. ORNATE VERTICORD, *Verticordia ornata* Orbigny, ¼ inch, p. 210.

j. STRIATE MARTESIA, *Martesia striata* Linné, ¾ to 1¼ inches, p. 209.

k. ATLANTIC GASTROCHAENA, *Gastrochaena hians* Gmelin, ½ to ¾ inch, p. 208.

l. WEDGE-SHAPED MARTESIA, *Martesia cuneiformis* Say, ½ to ¾ inch, p. 209.

m. ANGEL WING, *Cyrtopleura costata* Linné, 4 to 8 inches, p. 208.

Distribution Maps

The warm, tropical waters of the Caribbean are a special subdivision of the Western Atlantic. Fairly uniform conditions permit many species to exist throughout the province. Within the Caribbean area, however, are many species which have very restricted ranges. These distribution maps indicate the known ranges of many of the more common Caribbean seashells. It should be borne in mind that species having special habitats such as mangroves, rocks or mud bottoms will have discontinuous distributions because of the varied environmental conditions throughout this vast area. These distributions are based upon specimens existing in the Academy of Natural Sciences of Philadelphia, the U. S. National Museum and the Museum of Comparative Zoölogy at Harvard College.

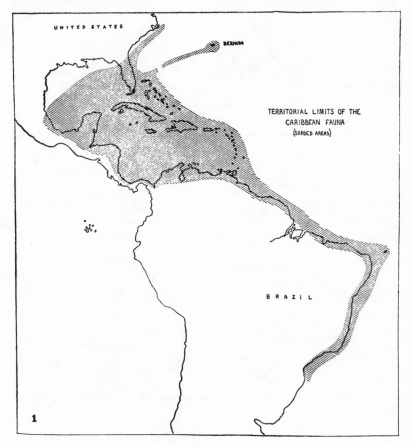

TERRITORIAL LIMITS OF THE
CARIBBEAN FAUNA
(SHADED AREAS)

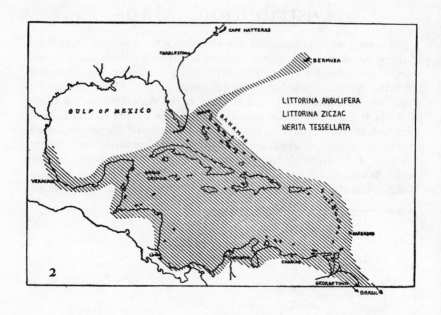

LITTORINA ANGULIFERA
LITTORINA ZICZAC
NERITA TESSELLATA

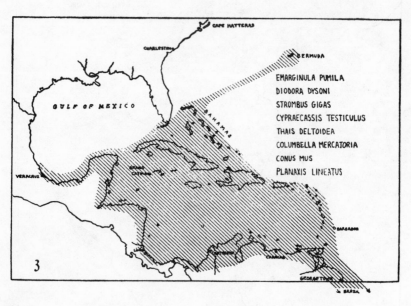

EMARGINULA PUMILA
DIODORA DYSONI
STROMBUS GIGAS
CYPRAECASSIS TESTICULUS
THAIS DELTOIDEA
COLUMBELLA MERCATORIA
CONUS MUS
PLANAXIS LINEATUS

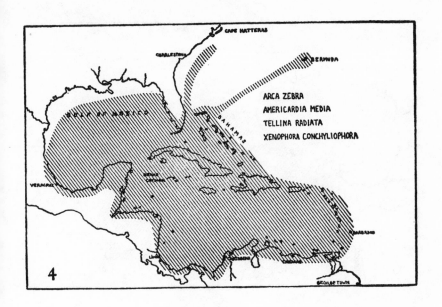

ARCA ZEBRA
AMERICARDIA MEDIA
TELLINA RADIATA
XENOPHORA CONCHYLIOPHORA

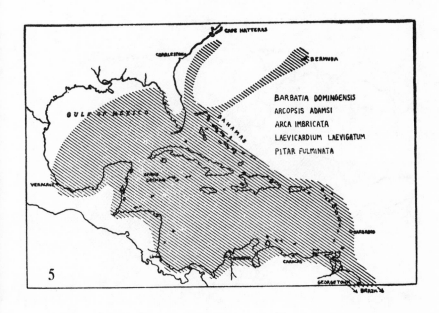

BARBATIA DOMINGENSIS
ARCOPSIS ADAMSI
ARCA IMBRICATA
LAEVICARDIUM LAEVIGATUM
PITAR FULMINATA

321

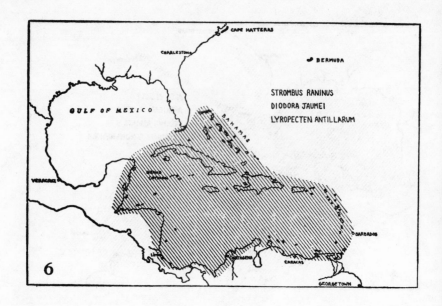

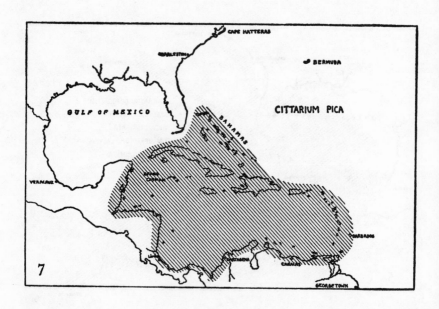

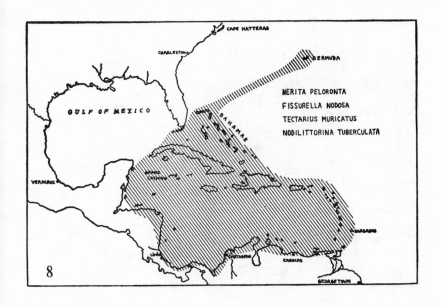

NERITA PELORONTA
FISSURELLA NODOSA
TECTARIUS MURICATUS
NODILITTORINA TUBERCULATA

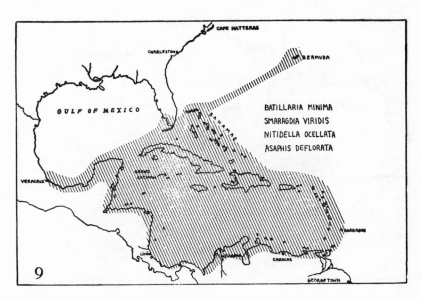

BATILLARIA MINIMA
SMARAGDIA VIRIDIS
NITIDELLA OCELLATA
ASAPHIS DEFLORATA

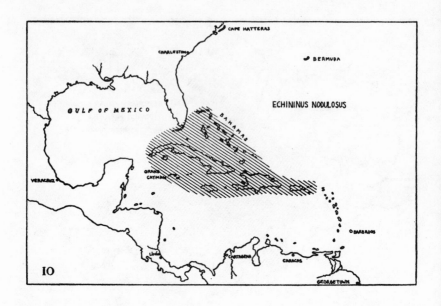

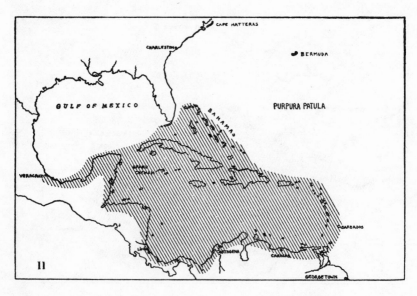

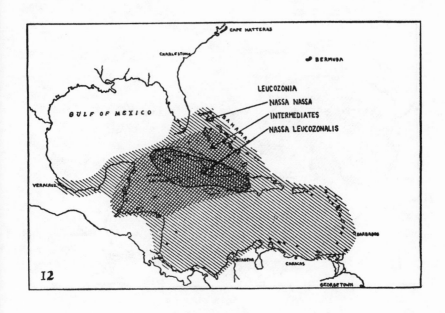

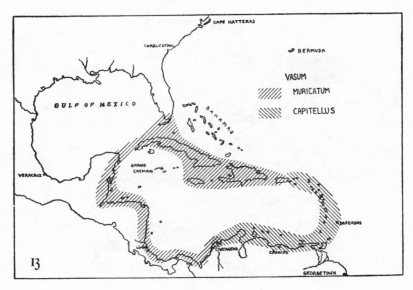

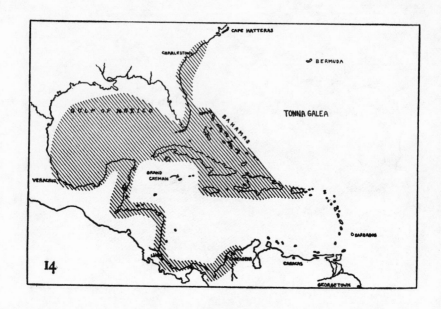

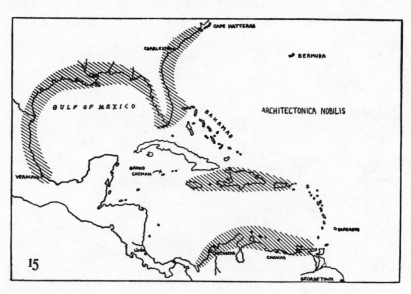

326

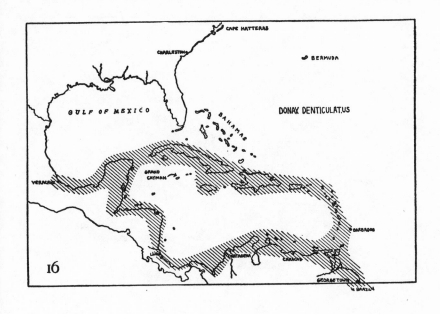

DONAX DENTICULATUS

16

MELONGENA MELONGENA
MODULUS CARCHEDONIUS
LITTORINA NEBULOSA

17

327

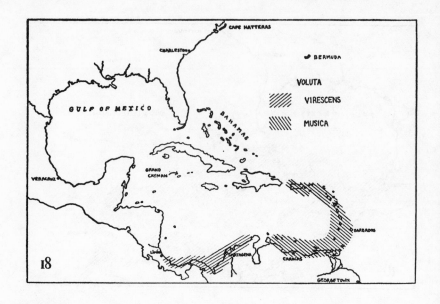

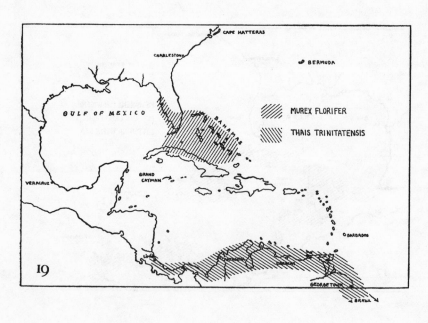

328

INDEX

To Popular Scientific Names and Subject matter

INDEX

To Popular Scientific Names and Subject matter

331

A CATALOGUE OF SELECTED DOVER BOOKS
IN ALL FIELDS OF INTEREST

A CATALOGUE OF SELECTED DOVER BOOKS IN ALL FIELDS OF INTEREST

CELESTIAL OBJECTS FOR COMMON TELESCOPES, T. W. Webb. The most used book in amateur astronomy: inestimable aid for locating and identifying nearly 4,000 celestial objects. Edited, updated by Margaret W. Mayall. 77 illustrations. Total of 645pp. 5⅜ x 8½.
20917-2, 20918-0 Pa., Two-vol. set $9.00

HISTORICAL STUDIES IN THE LANGUAGE OF CHEMISTRY, M. P. Crosland. The important part language has played in the development of chemistry from the symbolism of alchemy to the adoption of systematic nomenclature in 1892. ". . . wholeheartedly recommended,"—Science. 15 illustrations. 416pp. of text. 5⅝ x 8¼. 63702-6 Pa. $6.00

BURNHAM'S CELESTIAL HANDBOOK, Robert Burnham, Jr. Thorough, readable guide to the stars beyond our solar system. Exhaustive treatment, fully illustrated. Breakdown is alphabetical by constellation: Andromeda to Cetus in Vol. 1; Chamaeleon to Orion in Vol. 2; and Pavo to Vulpecula in Vol. 3. Hundreds of illustrations. Total of about 2000pp. 6⅛ x 9¼.
23567-X, 23568-8, 23673-0 Pa., Three-vol. set $26.85

THEORY OF WING SECTIONS: INCLUDING A SUMMARY OF AIRFOIL DATA, Ira H. Abbott and A. E. von Doenhoff. Concise compilation of subatomic aerodynamic characteristics of modern NASA wing sections, plus description of theory. 350pp. of tables. 693pp. 5⅜ x 8½.
60586-8 Pa. $7.00

DE RE METALLICA, Georgius Agricola. Translated by Herbert C. Hoover and Lou H. Hoover. The famous Hoover translation of greatest treatise on technological chemistry, engineering, geology, mining of early modern times (1556). All 289 original woodcuts. 638pp. 6¾ x 11.
60006-8 Clothbd. $17.95

THE ORIGIN OF CONTINENTS AND OCEANS, Alfred Wegener. One of the most influential, most controversial books in science, the classic statement for continental drift. Full 1966 translation of Wegener's final (1929) version. 64 illustrations. 246pp. 5⅜ x 8½. 61708-4 Pa. $4.50

THE PRINCIPLES OF PSYCHOLOGY, William James. Famous long course complete, unabridged. Stream of thought, time perception, memory, experimental methods; great work decades ahead of its time. Still valid, useful; read in many classes. 94 figures. Total of 1391pp. 5⅜ x 8½.
20381-6, 20382-4 Pa., Two-vol. set $13.00

THE SENSE OF BEAUTY, George Santayana. Masterfully written discussion of nature of beauty, materials of beauty, form, expression; art, literature, social sciences all involved. 168pp. 5⅜ x 8½. 20238-0 Pa. $3.00

ON THE IMPROVEMENT OF THE UNDERSTANDING, Benedict Spinoza. Also contains *Ethics, Correspondence,* all in excellent R. Elwes translation. Basic works on entry to philosophy, pantheism, exchange of ideas with great contemporaries. 402pp. 5⅜ x 8½. 20250-X Pa. $4.50

THE TRAGIC SENSE OF LIFE, Miguel de Unamuno. Acknowledged masterpiece of existential literature, one of most important books of 20th century. Introduction by Madariaga. 367pp. 5⅜ x 8½.
20257-7 Pa. $4.50

THE GUIDE FOR THE PERPLEXED, Moses Maimonides. Great classic of medieval Judaism attempts to reconcile revealed religion (Pentateuch, commentaries) with Aristotelian philosophy. Important historically, still relevant in problems. Unabridged Friedlander translation. Total of 473pp. 5⅜ x 8½. 20351-4 Pa. $6.00

THE I CHING (THE BOOK OF CHANGES), translated by James Legge. Complete translation of basic text plus appendices by Confucius, and Chinese commentary of most penetrating divination manual ever prepared. Indispensable to study of early Oriental civilizations, to modern inquiring reader. 448pp. 5⅜ x 8½. 21062-6 Pa. $5.00

THE EGYPTIAN BOOK OF THE DEAD, E. A. Wallis Budge. Complete reproduction of Ani's papyrus, finest ever found. Full hieroglyphic text, interlinear transliteration, word for word translation, smooth translation. Basic work, for Egyptology, for modern study of psychic matters. Total of 533pp. 6½ x 9¼. (Available in U.S. only) 21866-X Pa. $5.95

THE GODS OF THE EGYPTIANS, E. A. Wallis Budge. Never excelled for richness, fullness: all gods, goddesses, demons, mythical figures of Ancient Egypt; their legends, rites, incarnations, variations, powers, etc. Many hieroglyphic texts cited. Over 225 illustrations, plus 6 color plates. Total of 988pp. 6⅛ x 9¼. (Available in U.S. only)
22055-9, 22056-7 Pa., Two-vol. set $16.00

THE STANDARD BOOK OF QUILT MAKING AND COLLECTING, Marguerite Ickis. Full information, full-sized patterns for making 46 traditional quilts, also 150 other patterns. Quilted cloths, lame, satin quilts, etc. 483 illustrations. 273pp. 6⅞ x 9⅝. 20582-7 Pa. $4.95

CORAL GARDENS AND THEIR MAGIC, Bronsilaw Malinowski. Classic study of the methods of tilling the soil and of agricultural rites in the Trobriand Islands of Melanesia. Author is one of the most important figures in the field of modern social anthropology. 143 illustrations. Indexes. Total of 911pp. of text. 5⅝ x 8¼. (Available in U.S. only)
23597-1 Pa. $12.95

DRAWINGS OF WILLIAM BLAKE, William Blake. 92 plates from Book of Job, *Divine Comedy, Paradise Lost,* visionary heads, mythological figures, Laocoon, etc. Selection, introduction, commentary by Sir Geoffrey Keynes. 178pp. 8⅛ x 11.   22303-5 Pa. $4.00

ENGRAVINGS OF HOGARTH, William Hogarth. 101 of Hogarth's greatest works: *Rake's Progress, Harlot's Progress, Illustrations for Hudibras, Before and After, Beer Street and Gin Lane,* many more. Full commentary. 256pp. 11 x 13¾.   22479-1 Pa. $7.95

DAUMIER: 120 GREAT LITHOGRAPHS, Honore Daumier. Wide-ranging collection of lithographs by the greatest caricaturist of the 19th century. Concentrates on eternally popular series on lawyers, on married life, on liberated women, etc. Selection, introduction, and notes on plates by Charles F. Ramus. Total of 158pp. 9⅜ x 12¼.   23512-2 Pa. $5.50

DRAWINGS OF MUCHA, Alphonse Maria Mucha. Work reveals drafts-man of highest caliber: studies for famous posters and paintings, render-ings for book illustrations and ads, etc. 70 works, 9 in color; including 6 items not drawings. Introduction. List of illustrations. 72pp. 9⅜ x 12¼. (Available in U.S. only)   23672-2 Pa. $4.00

GIOVANNI BATTISTA PIRANESI: DRAWINGS IN THE PIERPONT MORGAN LIBRARY, Giovanni Battista Piranesi. For first time ever all of Morgan Library's collection, world's largest. 167 illustrations of rare Piranesi drawings—archeological, architectural, decorative and visionary. Essay, detailed list of drawings, chronology, captions. Edited by Felice Stampfle. 144pp. 9⅜ x 12¼.   23714-1 Pa. $7.50

NEW YORK ETCHINGS (1905-1949), John Sloan. All of important American artist's N.Y. life etchings. 67 works include some of his best art; also lively historical record—Greenwich Village, tenement scenes. Edited by Sloan's widow. Introduction and captions. 79pp. 8⅜ x 11¼.
                                                23651-X Pa. $4.00

CHINESE PAINTING AND CALLIGRAPHY: A PICTORIAL SURVEY, Wan-go Weng. 69 fine examples from John M. Crawford's matchless private collection: landscapes, birds, flowers, human figures, etc., plus calligraphy. Every basic form included: hanging scrolls, handscrolls, album leaves, fans, etc. 109 illustrations. Introduction. Captions. 192pp. 8⅞ x 11¾.
                                                23707-9 Pa. $7.95

DRAWINGS OF REMBRANDT, edited by Seymour Slive. Updated Lipp-mann, Hofstede de Groot edition, with definitive scholarly apparatus. All portraits, biblical sketches, landscapes, nudes, Oriental figures, classical studies, together with selection of work by followers. 550 illustrations. Total of 630pp. 9⅛ x 12¼.   21485-0, 21486-9 Pa., Two-vol. set $15.00

THE DISASTERS OF WAR, Francisco Goya. 83 etchings record horrors of Napoleonic wars in Spain and war in general. Reprint of 1st edition, plus 3 additional plates. Introduction by Philip Hofer. 97pp. 9⅜ x 8¼.
                                                21872-4 Pa. $3.75

THE PHILOSOPHY OF HISTORY, Georg W. Hegel. Great classic of Western thought develops concept that history is not chance but a rational process, the evolution of freedom. 457pp. 5⅜ x 8½.   20112-0 Pa. $4.50

LANGUAGE, TRUTH AND LOGIC, Alfred J. Ayer. Famous, clear introduction to Vienna, Cambridge schools of Logical Positivism. Role of philosophy, elimination of metaphysics, nature of analysis, etc. 160pp. 5⅜ x 8½. (Available in U.S. only)   20010-8 Pa. $2.00

A PREFACE TO LOGIC, Morris R. Cohen. Great City College teacher in renowned, easily followed exposition of formal logic, probability, values, logic and world order and similar topics; no previous background needed. 209pp. 5⅜ x 8½.   23517-3 Pa. $3.50

REASON AND NATURE, Morris R. Cohen. Brilliant analysis of reason and its multitudinous ramifications by charismatic teacher. Interdisciplinary, synthesizing work widely praised when it first appeared in 1931. Second (1953) edition. Indexes. 496pp. 5⅜ x 8½.   23633-1 Pa. $6.50

AN ESSAY CONCERNING HUMAN UNDERSTANDING, John Locke. The only complete edition of enormously important classic, with authoritative editorial material by A. C. Fraser. Total of 1176pp. 5⅜ x 8½.
20530-4, 20531-2 Pa., Two-vol. set $16.00

HANDBOOK OF MATHEMATICAL FUNCTIONS WITH FORMULAS, GRAPHS, AND MATHEMATICAL TABLES, edited by Milton Abramowitz and Irene A. Stegun. Vast compendium: 29 sets of tables, some to as high as 20 places. 1,046pp. 8 x 10½.   61272-4 Pa. $14.95

MATHEMATICS FOR THE PHYSICAL SCIENCES, Herbert S. Wilf. Highly acclaimed work offers clear presentations of vector spaces and matrices, orthogonal functions, roots of polynomial equations, conformal mapping, calculus of variations, etc. Knowledge of theory of functions of real and complex variables is assumed. Exercises and solutions. Index. 284pp. 5⅝ x 8¼.   63635-6 Pa. $5.00

THE PRINCIPLE OF RELATIVITY, Albert Einstein et al. Eleven most important original papers on special and general theories. Seven by Einstein, two by Lorentz, one each by Minkowski and Weyl. All translated, unabridged. 216pp. 5⅜ x 8½.   60081-5 Pa. $3.50

THERMODYNAMICS, Enrico Fermi. A classic of modern science. Clear, organized treatment of systems, first and second laws, entropy, thermodynamic potentials, gaseous reactions, dilute solutions, entropy constant. No math beyond calculus required. Problems. 160pp. 5⅜ x 8½.
60361-X Pa. $3.00

ELEMENTARY MECHANICS OF FLUIDS, Hunter Rouse. Classic undergraduate text widely considered to be far better than many later books. Ranges from fluid velocity and acceleration to role of compressibility in fluid motion. Numerous examples, questions, problems. 224 illustrations. 376pp. 5⅝ x 8¼.   63699-2 Pa. $5.00

THE COMPLETE BOOK OF DOLL MAKING AND COLLECTING, Catherine Christopher. Instructions, patterns for dozens of dolls, from rag doll on up to elaborate, historically accurate figures. Mould faces, sew clothing, make doll houses, etc. Also collecting information. Many illustrations. 288pp. 6 x 9. 22066-4 Pa. $4.50

THE DAGUERREOTYPE IN AMERICA, Beaumont Newhall. Wonderful portraits, 1850's townscapes, landscapes; full text plus 104 photographs. The basic book. Enlarged 1976 edition. 272pp. 8¼ x 11¼. 23322-7 Pa. $7.95

CRAFTSMAN HOMES, Gustav Stickley. 296 architectural drawings, floor plans, and photographs illustrate 40 different kinds of "Mission-style" homes from The Craftsman (1901-16), voice of American style of simplicity and organic harmony. Thorough coverage of Craftsman idea in text and picture, now collector's item. 224pp. 8⅛ x 11. 23791-5 Pa. $6.00

PEWTER-WORKING: INSTRUCTIONS AND PROJECTS, Burl N. Osborn. & Gordon O. Wilber. Introduction to pewter-working for amateur craftsman. History and characteristics of pewter; tools, materials, step-by-step instructions. Photos, line drawings, diagrams. Total of 160pp. 7⅞ x 10¾. 23786-9 Pa. $3.50

THE GREAT CHICAGO FIRE, edited by David Lowe. 10 dramatic, eyewitness accounts of the 1871 disaster, including one of the aftermath and rebuilding, plus 70 contemporary photographs and illustrations of the ruins—courthouse, Palmer House, Great Central Depot, etc. Introduction by David Lowe. 87pp. 8¼ x 11. 23771-0 Pa. $4.00

SILHOUETTES: A PICTORIAL ARCHIVE OF VARIED ILLUSTRATIONS, edited by Carol Belanger Grafton. Over 600 silhouettes from the 18th to 20th centuries include profiles and full figures of men and women, children, birds and animals, groups and scenes, nature, ships, an alphabet. Dozens of uses for commercial artists and craftspeople. 144pp. 8⅜ x 11¼. 23781-8 Pa. $4.00

ANIMALS: 1,419 COPYRIGHT-FREE ILLUSTRATIONS OF MAMMALS, BIRDS, FISH, INSECTS, ETC., edited by Jim Harter. Clear wood engravings present, in extremely lifelike poses, over 1,000 species of animals. One of the most extensive copyright-free pictorial sourcebooks of its kind. Captions. Index. 284pp. 9 x 12. 23766-4 Pa. $7.95

INDIAN DESIGNS FROM ANCIENT ECUADOR, Frederick W. Shaffer. 282 original designs by pre-Columbian Indians of Ecuador (500-1500 A.D.). Designs include people, mammals, birds, reptiles, fish, plants, heads, geometric designs. Use as is or alter for advertising, textiles, leathercraft, etc. Introduction. 95pp. 8¾ x 11¼. 23764-8 Pa. $3.50

SZIGETI ON THE VIOLIN, Joseph Szigeti. Genial, loosely structured tour by premier violinist, featuring a pleasant mixture of reminiscenes, insights into great music and musicians, innumerable tips for practicing violinists. 385 musical passages. 256pp. 5⅝ x 8¼. 23763-X Pa. $3.50

TONE POEMS, SERIES II: TILL EULENSPIEGELS LUSTIGE STREICHE, ALSO SPRACH ZARATHUSTRA, AND EIN HELDEN-LEBEN, Richard Strauss. Three important orchestral works, including very popular *Till Eulenspiegel's Marry Pranks,* reproduced in full score from original editions. Study score. 315pp. 9⅜ x 12¼. (Available in U.S. only)
23755-9 Pa. $8.95

TONE POEMS, SERIES I: DON JUAN, TOD UND VERKLARUNG AND DON QUIXOTE, Richard Strauss. Three of the most often performed and recorded works in entire orchestral repertoire, reproduced in full score from original editions. Study score. 286pp. 9⅜ x 12¼. (Available in U.S. only)
23754-0 Pa. $7.50

11 LATE STRING QUARTETS, Franz Joseph Haydn. The form which Haydn defined and "brought to perfection." *(Grove's).* 11 string quartets in complete score, his last and his best. The first in a projected series of the complete Haydn string quartets. Reliable modern Eulenberg edition, otherwise difficult to obtain. 320pp. 8⅜ x 11¼. (Available in U.S. only)
23753-2 Pa. $7.50

FOURTH, FIFTH AND SIXTH SYMPHONIES IN FULL SCORE, Peter Ilyitch Tchaikovsky. Complete orchestral scores of Symphony No. 4 in F Minor, Op. 36; Symphony No. 5 in E Minor, Op. 64; Symphony No. 6 in B Minor, "Pathetique," Op. 74. Bretikopf & Hartel eds. Study score. 480pp. 9⅜ x 12¼.
23861-X Pa. $10.95

THE MARRIAGE OF FIGARO: COMPLETE SCORE, Wolfgang A. Mozart. Finest comic opera ever written. Full score, not to be confused with piano renderings. Peters edition. Study score. 448pp. 9⅜ x 12¼. (Available in U.S. only)
23751-6 Pa. $11.95

"IMAGE" ON THE ART AND EVOLUTION OF THE FILM, edited by Marshall Deutelbaum. Pioneering book brings together for first time 38 groundbreaking articles on early silent films from *Image* and 263 illustrations newly shot from rare prints in the collection of the International Museum of Photography. A landmark work. Index. 256pp. 8¼ x 11.
23777-X Pa. $8.95

AROUND-THE-WORLD COOKY BOOK, Lois Lintner Sumption and Marguerite Lintner Ashbrook. 373 cooky and frosting recipes from 28 countries (America, Austria, China, Russia, Italy, etc.) include Viennese kisses, rice wafers, London strips, lady fingers, hony, sugar spice, maple cookies, etc. Clear instructions. All tested. 38 drawings. 182pp. 5⅜ x 8.
23802-4 Pa. $2.50

THE ART NOUVEAU STYLE, edited by Roberta Waddell. 579 rare photographs, not available elsewhere, of works in jewelry, metalwork, glass, ceramics, textiles, architecture and furniture by 175 artists—Mucha, Seguy, Lalique, Tiffany, Gaudin, Hohlwein, Saarinen, and many others. 288pp. 8⅜ x 11¼.
23515-7 Pa. $6.95

THE AMERICAN SENATOR, Anthony Trollope. Little known, long unavailable Trollope novel on a grand scale. Here are humorous comment on American vs. English culture, and stunning portrayal of a heroine/villainess. Superb evocation of Victorian village life. 561pp. 5⅜ x 8½.
23801-6 Pa. $6.00

WAS IT MURDER? James Hilton. The author of *Lost Horizon* and *Goodbye, Mr. Chips* wrote one detective novel (under a pen-name) which was quickly forgotten and virtually lost, even at the height of Hilton's fame. This edition brings it back—a finely crafted public school puzzle resplendent with Hilton's stylish atmosphere. A thoroughly English thriller by the creator of Shangri-la. 252pp. 5⅜ x 8. (Available in U.S. only)
23774-5 Pa. $3.00

CENTRAL PARK: A PHOTOGRAPHIC GUIDE, Victor Laredo and Henry Hope Reed. 121 superb photographs show dramatic views of Central Park: Bethesda Fountain, Cleopatra's Needle, Sheep Meadow, the Blockhouse, plus people engaged in many park activities: ice skating, bike riding, etc. Captions by former Curator of Central Park, Henry Hope Reed, provide historical view, changes, etc. Also photos of N.Y. landmarks on park's periphery. 96pp. 8½ x 11. 23750-8 Pa. $4.50

NANTUCKET IN THE NINETEENTH CENTURY, Clay Lancaster. 180 rare photographs, stereographs, maps, drawings and floor plans recreate unique American island society. Authentic scenes of shipwreck, lighthouses, streets, homes are arranged in geographic sequence to provide walking-tour guide to old Nantucket existing today. Introduction, captions. 160pp. 8⅞ x 11¾. 23747-8 Pa. $6.95

STONE AND MAN: A PHOTOGRAPHIC EXPLORATION, Andreas Feininger. 106 photographs by *Life* photographer Feininger portray man's deep passion for stone through the ages. Stonehenge-like megaliths, fortified towns, sculpted marble and crumbling tenements show textures, beauties, fascination. 128pp. 9¼ x 10¾. 23756-7 Pa. $5.95

CIRCLES, A MATHEMATICAL VIEW, D. Pedoe. Fundamental aspects of college geometry, non-Euclidean geometry, and other branches of mathematics: representing circle by point. Poincare model, isoperimetric property, etc. Stimulating recreational reading. 66 figures. 96pp. 5⅝ x 8¼.
63698-4 Pa. $2.75

THE DISCOVERY OF NEPTUNE, Morton Grosser. Dramatic scientific history of the investigations leading up to the actual discovery of the eighth planet of our solar system. Lucid, well-researched book by well-known historian of science. 172pp. 5⅜ x 8½. 23726-5 Pa. $3.00

THE DEVIL'S DICTIONARY. Ambrose Bierce. Barbed, bitter, brilliant witticisms in the form of a dictionary. Best, most ferocious satire America has produced. 145pp. 5⅜ x 8½. 20487-1 Pa. $2.00

HISTORY OF BACTERIOLOGY, William Bulloch. The only comprehensive history of bacteriology from the beginnings through the 19th century. Special emphasis is given to biography-Leeuwenhoek, etc. Brief accounts of 350 bacteriologists form a separate section. No clearer, fuller study, suitable to scientists and general readers, has yet been written. 52 illustrations. 448pp. 5⅝ x 8¼.   23761-3 Pa. $6.50

THE COMPLETE NONSENSE OF EDWARD LEAR, Edward Lear. All nonsense limericks, zany alphabets, Owl and Pussycat, songs, nonsense botany, etc., illustrated by Lear. Total of 321pp. 5⅜ x 8½. (Available in U.S. only)   20167-8 Pa. $3.00

INGENIOUS MATHEMATICAL PROBLEMS AND METHODS, Louis A. Graham. Sophisticated material from Graham Dial, applied and pure; stresses solution methods. Logic, number theory, networks, inversions, etc. 237pp. 5⅜ x 8½.   20545-2 Pa. $3.50

BEST MATHEMATICAL PUZZLES OF SAM LOYD, edited by Martin Gardner. Bizarre, original, whimsical puzzles by America's greatest puzzler. From fabulously rare Cyclopedia, including famous 14-15 puzzles, the Horse of a Different Color, 115 more. Elementary math. 150 illustrations. 167pp. 5⅜ x 8½.   20498-7 Pa. $2.75

THE BASIS OF COMBINATION IN CHESS, J. du Mont. Easy-to-follow, instructive book on elements of combination play, with chapters on each piece and every powerful combination team—two knights, bishop and knight, rook and bishop, etc. 250 diagrams. 218pp. 5⅜ x 8½. (Available in U.S. only)   23644-7 Pa. $3.50

MODERN CHESS STRATEGY, Ludek Pachman. The use of the queen, the active king, exchanges, pawn play, the center, weak squares, etc. Section on rook alone worth price of the book. Stress on the moderns. Often considered the most important book on strategy. 314pp. 5⅜ x 8½.
                                                    20290-9 Pa. $4.50

LASKER'S MANUAL OF CHESS, Dr. Emanuel Lasker. Great world champion offers very thorough coverage of all aspects of chess. Combinations, position play, openings, end game, aesthetics of chess, philosophy of struggle, much more. Filled with analyzed games. 390pp. 5⅜ x 8½.
                                                    20640-8 Pa. $5.00

500 MASTER GAMES OF CHESS, S. Tartakower, J. du Mont. Vast collection of great chess games from 1798-1938, with much material nowhere else readily available. Fully annotated, arranged by opening for easier study. 664pp. 5⅜ x 8½.   23208-5 Pa. $7.50

A GUIDE TO CHESS ENDINGS, Dr. Max Euwe, David Hooper. One of the finest modern works on chess endings. Thorough analysis of the most frequently encountered endings by former world champion. 331 examples, each with diagram. 248pp. 5⅜ x 8½.   23332-4 Pa. $3.50

"OSCAR" OF THE WALDORF'S COOKBOOK, Oscar Tschirky. Famous American chef reveals 3455 recipes that made Waldorf great; cream of French, German, American cooking, in all categories. Full instructions, easy home use. 1896 edition. 907pp. 6⅝ x 9⅜.   20790-0 Clothbd. $15.00

COOKING WITH BEER, Carole Fahy. Beer has as superb an effect on food as wine, and at fraction of cost. Over 250 recipes for appetizers, soups, main dishes, desserts, breads, etc. Index. 144pp. 5⅜ x 8½. (Available in U.S. only)   23661-7 Pa. $2.50

STEWS AND RAGOUTS, Kay Shaw Nelson. This international cookbook offers wide range of 108 recipes perfect for everyday, special occasions, meals-in-themselves, main dishes. Economical, nutritious, easy-to-prepare: goulash, Irish stew, boeuf bourguignon, etc. Index. 134pp. 5⅜ x 8½.
23662-5 Pa. $2.50

DELICIOUS MAIN COURSE DISHES, Marian Tracy. Main courses are the most important part of any meal. These 200 nutritious, economical recipes from around the world make every meal a delight. "I . . . have found it so useful in my own household,"—*N.Y. Times*. Index. 219pp. 5⅜ x 8½.   23664-1 Pa. $3.00

FIVE ACRES AND INDEPENDENCE, Maurice G. Kains. Great back-to-the-land classic explains basics of self-sufficient farming: economics, plants, crops, animals, orchards, soils, land selection, host of other necessary things. Do not confuse with skimpy faddist literature; Kains was one of America's greatest agriculturalists. 95 illustrations. 397pp. 5⅜ x 8½.
20974-1 Pa. $3.95

A PRACTICAL GUIDE FOR THE BEGINNING FARMER, Herbert Jacobs. Basic, extremely useful first book for anyone thinking about moving to the country and starting a farm. Simpler than Kains, with greater emphasis on country living in general. 246pp. 5⅜ x 8½.
23675-7 Pa. $3.50

A GARDEN OF PLEASANT FLOWERS (PARADISI IN SOLE: PARADISUS TERRESTRIS), John Parkinson. Complete, unabridged reprint of first (1629) edition of earliest great English book on gardens and gardening. More than 1000 plants & flowers of Elizabethan, Jacobean garden fully described, most with woodcut illustrations. Botanically very reliable, a "speaking garden" of exceeding charm. 812 illustrations. 628pp. 8½ x 12¼.   23392-8 Clothbd. $25.00

ACKERMANN'S COSTUME PLATES, Rudolph Ackermann. Selection of 96 plates from the *Repository of Arts,* best published source of costume for English fashion during the early 19th century. 12 plates also in color. Captions, glossary and introduction by editor Stella Blum. Total of 120pp. 8⅜ x 11¼.   23690-0 Pa. $4.50

THE CURVES OF LIFE, Theodore A. Cook. Examination of shells, leaves, horns, human body, art, etc., in *"the* classic reference on how the golden ratio applies to spirals and helices in nature . . . . "—Martin Gardner. 426 illustrations. Total of 512pp. 5⅜ x 8½.   23701-X Pa. $5.95

AN ILLUSTRATED FLORA OF THE NORTHERN UNITED STATES AND CANADA, Nathaniel L. Britton, Addison Brown. Encyclopedic work covers 4666 species, ferns on up. Everything. Full botanical information, illustration for each. This earlier edition is preferred by many to more recent revisions. 1913 edition. Over 4000 illustrations, total of 2087pp. 6⅛ x 9¼.   22642-5, 22643-3, 22644-1 Pa., Three-vol. set $25.50

MANUAL OF THE GRASSES OF THE UNITED STATES, A. S. Hitchcock, U.S. Dept. of Agriculture. The basic study of American grasses, both indigenous and escapes, cultivated and wild. Over 1400 species. Full descriptions, information. Over 1100 maps, illustrations. Total of 1051pp. 5⅜ x 8½.   22717-0, 22718-9 Pa., Two-vol. set $15.00

THE CACTACEAE,, Nathaniel L. Britton, John N. Rose. Exhaustive, definitive. Every cactus in the world. Full botanical descriptions. Thorough statement of nomenclatures, habitat, detailed finding keys. The one book needed by every cactus enthusiast. Over 1275 illustrations. Total of 1080pp. 8 x 10¼.   21191-6, 21192-4 Clothbd., Two-vol. set $35.00

AMERICAN MEDICINAL PLANTS, Charles F. Millspaugh. Full descriptions, 180 plants covered: history; physical description; methods of preparation with all chemical constituents extracted; all claimed curative or adverse effects. 180 full-page plates. Classification table. 804pp. 6½ x 9¼.   23034-1 Pa. $12.95

A MODERN HERBAL, Margaret Grieve. Much the fullest, most exact, most useful compilation of herbal material. Gigantic alphabetical encyclopedia, from aconite to zedoary, gives botanical information, medical properties, folklore, economic uses, and much else. Indispensable to serious reader. 161 illustrations. 888pp. 6½ x 9¼. (Available in U.S. only)   22798-7, 22799-5 Pa., Two-vol. set $13.00

THE HERBAL or GENERAL HISTORY OF PLANTS, John Gerard. The 1633 edition revised and enlarged by Thomas Johnson. Containing almost 2850 plant descriptions and 2705 superb illustrations, Gerard's *Herbal* is a monumental work, the book all modern English herbals are derived from, the one herbal every serious enthusiast should have in its entirety. Original editions are worth perhaps $750. 1678pp. 8½ x 12¼.   23147-X Clothbd. $50.00

MANUAL OF THE TREES OF NORTH AMERICA, Charles S. Sargent. The basic survey of every native tree and tree-like shrub, 717 species in all. Extremely full descriptions, information on habitat, growth, locales, economics, etc. Necessary to every serious tree lover. Over 100 finding keys. 783 illustrations. Total of 986pp. 5⅜ x 8½.   20277-1, 20278-X Pa., Two-vol. set $11.00

AMERICAN BIRD ENGRAVINGS, Alexander Wilson et al. All 76 plates. from Wilson's *American Ornithology* (1808-14), most important ornithological work before Audubon, plus 27 plates from the supplement (1825-33) by Charles Bonaparte. Over 250 birds portrayed. 8 plates also reproduced in full color. 111pp. 9⅜ x 12½. 23195-X Pa. $6.00

CRUICKSHANK'S PHOTOGRAPHS OF BIRDS OF AMERICA, Allan D. Cruickshank. Great ornithologist, photographer presents 177 closeups, groupings, panoramas, flightings, etc., of about 150 different birds. Expanded *Wings in the Wilderness*. Introduction by Helen G. Cruickshank. 191pp. 8¼ x 11. 23497-5 Pa. $6.00

AMERICAN WILDLIFE AND PLANTS, A. C. Martin, et al. Describes food habits of more than 1000 species of mammals, birds, fish. Special treatment of important food plants. Over 300 illustrations. 500pp. 5⅜ x 8½. 20793-5 Pa. $4.95

THE PEOPLE CALLED SHAKERS, Edward D. Andrews. Lifetime of research, definitive study of Shakers: origins, beliefs, practices, dances, social organization, furniture and crafts, impact on 19th-century USA, present heritage. Indispensable to student of American history, collector. 33 illustrations. 351pp. 5⅜ x 8½. 21081-2 Pa. $4.50

OLD NEW YORK IN EARLY PHOTOGRAPHS, Mary Black. New York City as it was in 1853-1901, through 196 wonderful photographs from N.-Y. Historical Society. Great Blizzard, Lincoln's funeral procession, great buildings. 228pp. 9 x 12. 22907-6 Pa. $8.95

MR. LINCOLN'S CAMERA MAN: MATHEW BRADY, Roy Meredith. Over 300 Brady photos reproduced directly from original negatives, photos. Jackson, Webster, Grant, Lee, Carnegie, Barnum; Lincoln; Battle Smoke, Death of Rebel Sniper, Atlanta Just After Capture. Lively commentary. 368pp. 8⅜ x 11¼. 23021-X Pa. $8.95

TRAVELS OF WILLIAM BARTRAM, William Bartram. From 1773-8, Bartram explored Northern Florida, Georgia, Carolinas, and reported on wild life, plants, Indians, early settlers. Basic account for period, entertaining reading. Edited by Mark Van Doren. 13 illustrations. 141pp. 5⅜ x 8½. 20013-2 Pa. $5.00

THE GENTLEMAN AND CABINET MAKER'S DIRECTOR, Thomas Chippendale. Full reprint, 1762 style book, most influential of all time; chairs, tables, sofas, mirrors, cabinets, etc. 200 plates, plus 24 photographs of surviving pieces. 249pp. 9⅞ x 12¾. 21601-2 Pa. $7.95

AMERICAN CARRIAGES, SLEIGHS, SULKIES AND CARTS, edited by Don H. Berkebile. 168 Victorian illustrations from catalogues, trade journals, fully captioned. Useful for artists. Author is Assoc. Curator, Div. of Transportation of Smithsonian Institution. 168pp. 8½ x 9½.
23328-6 Pa. $5.00

YUCATAN BEFORE AND AFTER THE CONQUEST, Diego de Landa. First English translation of basic book in Maya studies, the only significant account of Yucatan written in the early post-Conquest era. Translated by distinguished Maya scholar William Gates. Appendices, introduction, 4 maps and over 120 illustrations added by translator. 162pp. 5⅜ x 8½.
23622-6 Pa. $3.00

THE MALAY ARCHIPELAGO, Alfred R. Wallace. Spirited travel account by one of founders of modern biology. Touches on zoology, botany, ethnography, geography, and geology. 62 illustrations, maps. 515pp. 5⅜ x 8½.
20187-2 Pa. $6.95

THE DISCOVERY OF THE TOMB OF TUTANKHAMEN, Howard Carter, A. C. Mace. Accompany Carter in the thrill of discovery, as ruined passage suddenly reveals unique, untouched, fabulously rich tomb. Fascinating account, with 106 illustrations. New introduction by J. M. White. Total of 382pp. 5⅜ x 8½. (Available in U.S. only) 23500-9 Pa. $4.00

THE WORLD'S GREATEST SPEECHES, edited by Lewis Copeland and Lawrence W. Lamm. Vast collection of 278 speeches from Greeks up to present. Powerful and effective models; unique look at history. Revised to 1970. Indices. 842pp. 5⅜ x 8½.
20468-5 Pa. $8.95

THE 100 GREATEST ADVERTISEMENTS, Julian Watkins. The priceless ingredient; His master's voice; 99 44/100% pure; over 100 others. How they were written, their impact, etc. Remarkable record. 130 illustrations. 233pp. 7⅞ x 10 3/5.
20540-1 Pa. $5.00

CRUICKSHANK PRINTS FOR HAND COLORING, George Cruickshank. 18 illustrations, one side of a page, on fine-quality paper suitable for watercolors. Caricatures of people in society (c. 1820) full of trenchant wit. Very large format. 32pp. 11 x 16.
23684-6 Pa. $5.00

THIRTY-TWO COLOR POSTCARDS OF TWENTIETH-CENTURY AMERICAN ART, Whitney Museum of American Art. Reproduced in full color in postcard form are 31 art works and one shot of the museum. Calder, Hopper, Rauschenberg, others. Detachable. 16pp. 8¼ x 11.
23629-3 Pa. $2.50

MUSIC OF THE SPHERES: THE MATERIAL UNIVERSE FROM ATOM TO QUASAR SIMPLY EXPLAINED, Guy Murchie. Planets, stars, geology, atoms, radiation, relativity, quantum theory, light, antimatter, similar topics. 319 figures. 664pp. 5⅜ x 8½.
21809-0, 21810-4 Pa., Two-vol. set $10.00

EINSTEIN'S THEORY OF RELATIVITY, Max Born. Finest semi-technical account; covers Einstein, Lorentz, Minkowski, and others, with much detail, much explanation of ideas and math not readily available elsewhere on this level. For student, non-specialist. 376pp. 5⅜ x 8½.
60769-0 Pa. $4.50

THE EARLY WORK OF AUBREY BEARDSLEY, Aubrey Beardsley. 157 plates, 2 in color: *Manon Lescaut, Madame Bovary, Morte Darthur, Salome,* other. Introduction by H. Marillier. 182pp. 8⅛ x 11. 21816-3 Pa. $4.50

THE LATER WORK OF AUBREY BEARDSLEY, Aubrey Beardsley. Exotic masterpieces of full maturity: *Venus and Tannhauser, Lysistrata, Rape of the Lock, Volpone,* Savoy material, etc. 174 plates, 2 in color. 186pp. 8⅛ x 11. 21817-1 Pa. $5.95

THOMAS NAST'S CHRISTMAS DRAWINGS, Thomas Nast. Almost all Christmas drawings by creator of image of Santa Claus as we know it, and one of America's foremost illustrators and political cartoonists. 66 illustrations. 3 illustrations in color on covers. 96pp. 8⅜ x 11¼. 23660-9 Pa. $3.50

THE DORÉ ILLUSTRATIONS FOR DANTE'S DIVINE COMEDY, Gustave Doré. All 135 plates from Inferno, Purgatory, Paradise; fantastic tortures, infernal landscapes, celestial wonders. Each plate with appropriate (translated) verses. 141pp. 9 x 12. 23231-X Pa. $4.50

DORÉ'S ILLUSTRATIONS FOR RABELAIS, Gustave Doré. 252 striking illustrations of *Gargantua and Pantagruel* books by foremost 19th-century illustrator. Including 60 plates, 192 delightful smaller illustrations. 153pp. 9 x 12. 23656-0 Pa. $5.00

LONDON: A PILGRIMAGE, Gustave Doré, Blanchard Jerrold. Squalor, riches, misery, beauty of mid-Victorian metropolis; 55 wonderful plates, 125 other illustrations, full social, cultural text by Jerrold. 191pp. of text. 9⅜ x 12¼. 22306-X Pa. $7.00

THE RIME OF THE ANCIENT MARINER, Gustave Doré, S. T. Coleridge. Dore's finest work, 34 plates capture moods, subtleties of poem. Full text. Introduction by Millicent Rose. 77pp. 9¼ x 12. 22305-1 Pa. $3.50

THE DORE BIBLE ILLUSTRATIONS, Gustave Doré. All wonderful, detailed plates: Adam and Eve, Flood, Babylon, Life of Jesus, etc. Brief King James text with each plate. Introduction by Millicent Rose. 241 plates. 241pp. 9 x 12. 23004-X Pa. $6.00

THE COMPLETE ENGRAVINGS, ETCHINGS AND DRYPOINTS OF ALBRECHT DURER. "Knight, Death and Devil"; "Melencolia," and more—all Dürer's known works in all three media, including 6 works formerly attributed to him. 120 plates. 235pp. 8⅜ x 11¼. 22851-7 Pa. $6.50

MECHANICK EXERCISES ON THE WHOLE ART OF PRINTING, Joseph Moxon. First complete book (1683-4) ever written about typography, a compendium of everything known about printing at the latter part of 17th century. Reprint of 2nd (1962) Oxford Univ. Press edition. 74 illustrations. Total of 550pp. 6⅛ x 9¼. 23617-X Pa. $7.95

THE COMPLETE WOODCUTS OF ALBRECHT DURER, edited by Dr. W. Kurth. 346 in all: "Old Testament," "St. Jerome," "Passion," "Life of Virgin," "Apocalypse," many others. Introduction by Campbell Dodgson. 285pp. 8½ x 12¼. 21097-9 Pa. $7.50

DRAWINGS OF ALBRECHT DURER, edited by Heinrich Wolfflin. 81 plates show development from youth to full style. Many favorites; many new. Introduction by Alfred Werner. 96pp. 8⅛ x 11. 22352-3 Pa. $5.00

THE HUMAN FIGURE, Albrecht Dürer. Experiments in various techniques—stereometric, progressive proportional, and others. Also life studies that rank among finest ever done. Complete reprinting of *Dresden Sketchbook*. 170 plates. 355pp. 8⅜ x 11¼. 21042-1 Pa. $7.95

OF THE JUST SHAPING OF LETTERS, Albrecht Dürer. Renaissance artist explains design of Roman majuscules by geometry, also Gothic lower and capitals. Grolier Club edition. 43pp. 7⅞ x 10¾ 21306-4 Pa. $3.00

TEN BOOKS ON ARCHITECTURE, Vitruvius. The most important book ever written on architecture. Early Roman aesthetics, technology, classical orders, site selection, all other aspects. Stands behind everything since. Morgan translation. 331pp. 5⅜ x 8½. 20645-9 Pa. $4.50

THE FOUR BOOKS OF ARCHITECTURE, Andrea Palladio. 16th-century classic responsible for Palladian movement and style. Covers classical architectural remains, Renaissance revivals, classical orders, etc. 1738 Ware English edition. Introduction by A. Placzek. 216 plates. 110pp. of text. 9½ x 12¾. 21308-0 Pa. $10.00

HORIZONS, Norman Bel Geddes. Great industrialist stage designer, "father of streamlining," on application of aesthetics to transportation, amusement, architecture, etc. 1932 prophetic account; function, theory, specific projects. 222 illustrations. 312pp. 7⅞ x 10¾. 23514-9 Pa. $6.95

FRANK LLOYD WRIGHT'S FALLINGWATER, Donald Hoffmann. Full, illustrated story of conception and building of Wright's masterwork at Bear Run, Pa. 100 photographs of site, construction, and details of completed structure. 112pp. 9¼ x 10. 23671-4 Pa. $5.50

THE ELEMENTS OF DRAWING, John Ruskin. Timeless classic by great Viltorian; starts with basic ideas, works through more difficult. Many practical exercises. 48 illustrations. Introduction by Lawrence Campbell. 228pp. 5⅜ x 8½. 22730-8 Pa. $3.75

GIST OF ART, John Sloan. Greatest modern American teacher, Art Students League, offers innumerable hints, instructions, guided comments to help you in painting. Not a formal course. 46 illustrations. Introduction by Helen Sloan. 200pp. 5⅜ x 8½. 23435-5 Pa. $4.00

CATALOGUE OF DOVER BOOKS

THE ANATOMY OF THE HORSE, George Stubbs. Often considered the great masterpiece of animal anatomy. Full reproduction of 1766 edition, plus prospectus; original text and modernized text. 36 plates. Introduction by Eleanor Garvey. 121pp. 11 x 14¾. 23402-9 Pa. $6.00

BRIDGMAN'S LIFE DRAWING, George B. Bridgman. More than 500 illustrative drawings and text teach you to abstract the body into its major masses, use light and shade, proportion; as well as specific areas of anatomy, of which Bridgman is master. 192pp. 6½ x 9¼. (Available in U.S. only) 22710-3 Pa. $3.50

ART NOUVEAU DESIGNS IN COLOR, Alphonse Mucha, Maurice Verneuil, Georges Auriol. Full-color reproduction of *Combinaisons orne-mentales* (c. 1900) by Art Nouveau masters. Floral, animal, geometric, interlacings, swashes—borders, frames, spots—all incredibly beautiful. 60 plates, hundreds of designs. 9⅜ x 8-1/16. 22885-1 Pa. $4.00

FULL-COLOR FLORAL DESIGNS IN THE ART NOUVEAU STYLE, E. A. Seguy. 166 motifs, on 40 plates, from *Les fleurs et leurs applications decoratives* (1902): borders, circular designs, repeats, allovers, "spots." All in authentic Art Nouveau colors. 48pp. 9⅜ x 12¼. 23439-8 Pa. $5.00

A DIDEROT PICTORIAL ENCYCLOPEDIA OF TRADES AND IN-DUSTRY, edited by Charles C. Gillispie. 485 most interesting plates from the great French Encyclopedia of the 18th century show hundreds of working figures, artifacts, process, land and cityscapes; glassmaking, paper-making, metal extraction, construction, weaving, making furniture, clothing, wigs, dozens of other activities. Plates fully explained. 920pp. 9 x 12. 22284-5, 22285-3 Clothbd., Two-vol. set $40.00

HANDBOOK OF EARLY ADVERTISING ART, Clarence P. Hornung. Largest collection of copyright-free early and antique advertising art ever compiled. Over 6,000 illustrations, from Franklin's time to the 1890's for special effects, novelty. Valuable source, almost inexhaustible.
Pictorial Volume. Agriculture, the zodiac, animals, autos, birds, Christmas, fire engines, flowers, trees, musical instruments, ships, games and sports, much more. Arranged by subject matter and use. 237 plates. 288pp. 9 x 12. 20122-8 Clothbd. $14..50

Typographical Volume. Roman and Gothic faces ranging from 10 point to 300 point, "Barnum," German and Old English faces, script, logotypes, scrolls and flourishes, 1115 ornamental initials, 67 complete alphabets, more. 310 plates. 320pp. 9 x 12. 20123-6 Clothbd. $15.00

CALLIGRAPHY (CALLIGRAPHIA LATINA), J. G. Schwandner. High point of 18th-century ornamental calligraphy. Very ornate initials, scrolls, borders, cherubs, birds, lettered examples. 172pp. 9 x 13. 20475-8 Pa. $7.00

GEOMETRY, RELATIVITY AND THE FOURTH DIMENSION, Rudolf Rucker. Exposition of fourth dimension, means of visualization, concepts of relativity as Flatland characters continue adventures. Popular, easily followed yet accurate, profound. 141 illustrations. 133pp. 5⅜ x 8½.
23400-2 Pa. $2.75

THE ORIGIN OF LIFE, A. I. Oparin. Modern classic in biochemistry, the first rigorous examination of possible evolution of life from nitrocarbon compounds. Non-technical, easily followed. Total of 295pp. 5⅜ x 8½.
60213-3 Pa. $4.00

PLANETS, STARS AND GALAXIES, A. E. Fanning. Comprehensive introductory survey: the sun, solar system, stars, galaxies, universe, cosmology; quasars, radio stars, etc. 24pp. of photographs. 189pp. 5⅜ x 8½. (Available in U.S. only)
21680-2 Pa. $3.75

THE THIRTEEN BOOKS OF EUCLID'S ELEMENTS, translated with introduction and commentary by Sir Thomas L. Heath. Definitive edition. Textual and linguistic notes, mathematical analysis, 2500 years of critical commentary. Do not confuse with abridged school editions. Total of 1414pp. 5⅜ x 8½.   60088-2, 60089-0, 60090-4 Pa., Three-vol. set $18.50

Prices subject to change without notice.

Available at your book dealer or write for free catalogue to Dept. GI, Dover Publications, Inc., 180 Varick St., N.Y., N.Y. 10014. Dover publishes more than 175 books each year on science, elementary and advanced mathematics, biology, music, art, literary history, social sciences and other areas.